Quantitative Methods for Business and Management

PEARSON

MyLab and Mastering from Pearson improve results for students and educators. Used by over ten million students, they effectively engage learners at every stage.

MyMathLab is a personalised online study and assessment system, which tailors to the unique learning needs of each student. Offering unlimited opportunities for practice and providing relevant and timely feedback, it helps students master key concepts, experience more 'I Get It' moments and ultimately achieve better results.

'MyMathLab was part of the key learning resources that I depend on for my maths module, since I can do my work at any time and anywhere.'
London Metropolitan University Student, UK

For students

- **Interactive Tutorial Exercises** – Homework and practice exercises are correlated to specific learning outcomes, and they regenerate algorithmically to give students unlimited opportunity for practice and mastery. Exercises include guided solutions, sample problems and learning aids for extra help at point-of-use, and they offer helpful feedback when students enter incorrect answers.

- **Study plan for Self-paced Learning** – A personalised Study Plan for each student based on his or her test results, and the Study Plan links directly to interactive tutorial exercises for topics the student hasn't yet mastered. Students can regenerate these exercises with new values for unlimited practice, and the exercises include guided solutions and multimedia learning aids to give students the extra help they need.

For educators

- **Powerful Homework and Test Manager** – Create, import, and manage online homework assignments, quizzes, and tests that are automatically graded, allowing you to spend less time grading and more time teaching. You can choose from a wide range of assignment options, including time limits, proctoring, and maximum number of attempts allowed.

- **Comprehensive Gradebook Tracking** – Tracks your students' results on tests, homework, and practice exercises and gives you control over managing results and calculating grades. The gradebook provides a number of flexible grading options (weighting, drops), including exporting grades to a spreadsheet program such as Microsoft Excel.

- **Blackboard Integration** – this integration allows for instructor and student to use a single sign-on to the MyMathLab course.

Use the power of MyMathLab to accelerate your learning. You need both an access card and a course ID to access MyMathLab:

1. Is your lecturer using MyMathLab? *Ask your lecturer* for your course ID.

2. Has an access card been included with the book? *Check the inside back cover of the book*.

3. If you have a course ID but no access card, go to: *http://www.mymathlab.com/* to buy access to this interactive study programme.

Quantitative Methods for Business and Management

An Entrepreneurial Perspective

Stuart Wall

Claire Coday

Chris Mitchell

PEARSON

Harlow, England • London • New York • Boston • San Francisco • Toronto • Sydney
Auckland • Singapore • Hong Kong • Tokyo • Seoul • Taipei • New Delhi
Cape Town • São Paulo • Mexico City • Madrid • Amsterdam • Munich • Paris • Milan

Pearson Education Limited
Edinburgh Gate
Harlow CM20 2JE
United Kingdom
Tel: +44 (0)1279 623623
Web: www.pearson.com/uk

First published 2014 (print and electronic)

The Financial Times. With a worldwide network of highly respected journalists, *The Financial Times* provides global business news, insightful opinion and expert analysis of business, finance and politics. With over 500 journalists reporting from 50 countries worldwide, our in-depth coverage of international news is objectively reported and analysed from an independent, global perspective. To find out more, visit **www.ft.com/pearsonoffer**.

ISBN: 978-0-273-77055-8 (print)
978-0-273-77061-9 (PDF)
978-0-273-78630-6 (eText)

British Library Cataloguing-in-Publication Data
A catalogue record for the print edition is available from the British Library

Library of Congress Cataloging-in-Publication Data
Wall, Stuart, 1946-
  Quantitative methods for business and management / Stuart Wall, Claire Coday, Chris Mitchell. – 1 Edition.
    pages cm
  Includes index.
  ISBN 978-0-273-77055-8 (pbk.)
  1. Industrial management–Statistical methods.   2. Commercial statistics.   I. Title.
  HD30.215.W36 2014
  658.5–dc23
                          2013050431
10 9 8 7 6 5 4 3 2 1
17 16 15 14

Print edition typeset in 9.5/12.5 pt Charter ITC Std by 71
Print edition printed and bound by Ashford Colour Press, Gosport

NOTE THAT ANY PAGE CROSS REFERENCES REFER TO THE PRINT EDITION

Brief contents

Preface xi
Guided tour xiii
Acknowledgements xv
Publisher's acknowledgements xvi

Part One
Introduction stage of product life cycle 1

1 Collecting and presenting data 3
2 Making sense of data: Central location and dispersion 35
3 Financial decision making: Project appraisal 66

Part Two
Growth stage of product life cycle 95

4 Regression, correlation and time series 97
5 Probability and probability distributions 135
6 Sampling and tests of hypotheses 176

Part Three
Maturity stage of product life cycle 219

7 Business modelling: Linear relationships 221
8 Business modelling: Non-linear relationships 252
9 Project management 286

Appendix 1 Review of basic mathematics 314
Appendix 2 Probabilities for the normal distribution 344
Appendix 3 Cumulative binomial probabilities 346
Appendix 4 Cumulative Poisson probabilities 347
Appendix 5 Student t critical values 348
Appendix 6 χ^2 critical values 350
Appendix 7 Table of random numbers 352
Index 353

Contents

Preface   xi
Guided tour   xiii
Acknowledgements   xv
Publisher's acknowledgements   xvi

Part One
Introduction stage of product life cycle   1

1 Collecting and presenting data   3
   Introduction   3
   Collection of data   5
   Presenting data using frequency tables   7
   Presenting data using bar charts and pie charts   10
   Presenting data using histograms   18
   Presenting data using frequency polygons and frequency curves   24
   Presenting data using the Lorenz curve   28
   Review questions   30

2 Making sense of data: Central location and dispersion   35
   Introduction   35
   Notation   37
   Measures of central location   39
   Normal and skewed distribution   46
   Measures of dispersion   52
   Coefficient of variation (C of V)   60
   Review questions   63

3 Financial decision making: Project appraisal   66
   Introduction   66
   Investment and financial decision making   68
   Interest rates and project appraisal   70
   Compound factors, discounting and present value   74
   Cash flow and financial decision making   78
   Investment appraisal: non-discounting techniques   79
   Investment appraisal: discounting techniques   82
   Review questions   91

Part Two
Growth stage of product life cycle — 95

4 Regression, correlation and time series — 97
Introduction — 97
Regression analysis — 98
Correlation — 108
Spearman's coefficient of rank correlation — 116
Time series and forecasting — 118
Review questions — 129

5 Probability and probability distributions — 135
Introduction — 135
Probability calculations — 137
Venn diagrams: events not mutually exclusive — 141
Independent events: AND rule — 142
Dependent events: conditional probability — 144
Game theory and expected value — 155
The normal distribution — 158
The binomial distribution — 165
The Poisson distribution — 170
Review questions — 173

6 Sampling and tests of hypotheses — 176
Introduction — 176
Types of sample — 178
Distribution of sample means — 185
Confidence intervals — 190
Tests of hypotheses: principles and practice — 196
Student t-distribution — 206
Chi-squared test — 210
Review questions — 217

Part Three
Maturity stage of product life cycle — 219

7 Business modelling: Linear relationships — 221
Introduction — 221
Break-even analysis — 222
Linear programming — 231

Solving the linear programme: maximisation 237

Solving the linear programme: minimisation 246

Review questions 249

8 Business modelling: Non-linear relationships 252

Introduction 252

Differentiation 253

Turning points 258

Rules of differentiation 260

Applications of differentiation 262

Partial differentiation 274

Integration 276

Review questions 284

9 Project management 286

Introduction 286

Defining projects 287

Planning a project 291

Network diagrams 295

Critical path analysis 298

Gantt charts 304

Taking account of uncertainty: PERT 306

Project costs and crashing 309

Review questions 311

Appendix 1 Review of basic mathematics 314

Introduction 314

Whole numbers, fractions and decimals 314

Rounding off 318

Percentages and ratios 319

Powers and roots 322

Simple algebra 325

Solving equations 329

Simultaneous equations 331

Inequalities 333

Graphs and functions 334

Progressions 338

Review questions 342

Contents

Appendix 2 Probabilities for the normal distribution   344
Appendix 3 Cumulative binomial probabilities   346
Appendix 4 Cumulative Poisson probabilities   347
Appendix 5 Student t critical values   348
Appendix 6 χ^2 critical values   350
Appendix 7 Table of random numbers   352
Index   353

Companion Website

For open-access **student resources** specifically written
to complement this textbook and support your learning,
please visit **www.pearsoned.co.uk/wall**

Lecturer Resources

For password-protected online resources tailored to support
the use of this textbook in teaching, please visit
www.pearsoned.co.uk/wall

Preface

Your ability to make sense of data is likely to play an important part in your future 'success' in business and management, whether in marketing, finance, HRM, strategy, logistics or even general management. The intention of this book is to equip you with the key quantitative skills you will need to analyse data yourself and to evaluate the data analysis and recommendations of others reporting to you.

The central theme throughout the text is enterprise and entrepreneurship, and the intention of this book is to develop and apply the various quantitative methods to real-life business decision making within the various stages of the *product life cycle*. While these stages, namely introduction, growth and maturity, invariably overlap, they nevertheless provide a useful focus for the three parts of the book, with the various quantitative techniques applied to the issues of particular concern to businesses taking decisions within that specific stage of their product life cycle.

In addition, each chapter focuses on a *particular sector* of economic activity, whether retail sales, clean technology, financial and educational services, tourism, computing and IT, music industry or pharmaceuticals, with the contexts, questions and activities clustered around that sector.

In Part One the emphasis is on the quantitative techniques that will be helpful to the business in the 'introduction stage' of the product life cycle. Whether large or small, the business will need to develop a 'business plan' and a 'cash flow forecast' for the product, whether to attract external funding (e.g. bank loans or investor support) or internal funding (e.g. allocation of funds from the finance department). Data collection, presentation and analysis will be important here, making use of a variety of graphs, tables and charts, as well as various descriptive statistics, including measures of central location and dispersion to capture market revenue and cost characteristics. Calculating the present value of future flows of revenue and cost will also be important, not least in selecting between alternative uses of scarce resources. In other words, measures involving the 'time value of money' play a significant role in the introduction phase for many product life cycles.

In Part Two the emphasis is on the quantitative techniques that will be most helpful to the business during the 'growth stage' of the product life cycle, in which the product (good or service) begins to gain market share and grow rapidly in terms of volume, sales revenue and often profit. Some more sophisticated quantitative techniques will often be required to evaluate the many decision-making opportunities encountered during this growth stage of the product life cycle. For example, regression analysis might be used to estimate whether, and to what extent, there is a linkage between the many variables influencing projected revenue, cost and profit streams. Forecasting various future scenarios in the growth phase can also be accomplished by using 'time series analysis', not least by estimating the trend line, and identifying the impact of seasonal factors on future revenue and expenditure.

Measures of probability and the use of probability distributions can also play a key role in the business decision making commonly conducted in the growth stage. Organisations will wish to use probabilities to estimate the 'expected values' of the many different decision paths available to them for further growing their business. They will rarely be able to check the data from all the items in the many variables affecting their revenue and cost base, so they must know how to design *samples* and to interpret the results from questionnaires, surveys and focus groups based on those samples.

A wide range of hypotheses will also need to be tested if the business is to be aware of, and responsive to, the internal and external environments in which it operates. For example, it can use appropriate probability distributions to assure the maintenance of quality controls on products and processes, bringing Z and t distributions into play, together with ideas of confidence intervals and critical values. Tests of hypotheses can also be applied to *whole distributions,* as in the use of chi square tests to identify unexpected differences in labour productivity, accidents, job satisfaction and so on at different times or among different categories of employee.

In Part Three the emphasis is on using various mathematical and statistical techniques to respond to issues that often occur in the 'maturity stage' of the product life cycle. These techniques will often be used to identify and develop new characteristics and competitive advantages in the design, production or distribution of various goods and services, thereby helping mature products continue to grow and to avoid a fourth, 'decline', stage in the product life cycle. A whole range of initiatives for identifying the level of output and appropriate prices for maximising revenue or profit, subject to various constraints, or for minimising costs, will be reviewed and evaluated. These will include optimisation techniques, both linear and non-linear, as well as various inventory, quality control and project planning techniques.

Guided tour

Part introductions divide the book into three parts, introduce the upcoming chapter topics and help you to navigate your way through the book

PART TWO

Growth stage of product life cycle

The emphasis in this part of the book is on the quantitative techniques most widely used when evaluating strategies for growing the revenue, profit or market share of a product that has already been introduced to the market. Even the global credit crunch since 2007 has not prevented the United Kingdom from nurturing some 4,000 fast-growing medium-sized firms, or 'gazelles', often identified as those growing revenues at more than 20% per annum.

The benefits of analysing data to better understand the current and future growth potential for a product or business has been usefully indicated by a recent film, *Moneyball*. If you ever thought business decision making had little to do with calculations and data analysis, then this film will have been something of an eye-opener! It tells the true story of how data analysis in baseball helps a previously little known team, Oakland A, to compete effectively and win against all the richer and better established US baseball teams. Billy Beane, the general manager of Oakland A, adopts the language and practices of Wall Street and uses computer simulations to transform the fortunes of the team. Beane's idea is to use extensive data on the performance of baseball players to find 'undervalued assets in an inefficient market' – that is, players who are far better in terms of the data on their actual achievements in key aspects of baseball than is reflected in their market valuation. Such 'undervalued assets' are then acquired at bargain prices by Oakland A on the transfer market, with immediate benefits to team performance.

Learning objectives enable you to see exactly where the chapter is going and to focus your reading

Learning objectives

When you have read this chapter you should be able to:

- find the least squares (regression) line to establish relationships between variables and forecast into the future;
- calculate various measures to establish the confidence you can have in forecasting from your regression line;
- use time series analysis to identify both the trend line and the seasonal variation around the line, and use these to forecast into the future;
- evaluate the factors influencing the reliability of such forecasts;
- apply all these techniques to forecast future outcomes for proposed M&A activities, and more generally.

Worked example 4.2

Here we apply our coding formula to the data on sales revenue (£bn) for a target acquisition already presented on p. 102. We used the data to find the least squares line, $\hat{Y} = 1.6X - 1$, but here we use the data to find R^2 and R. We reproduce our earlier workings below, noting that this time we need an extra column for y^2.

Solution

X	Y	$x(X-\bar{X})$	$y(Y-\bar{Y})$	$x\,y$	x^2	y^2
1	0.5	−1.5	−2.5	3.75	2.25	6.25
2	2	−0.5	−1	0.50	0.25	1
3	4.5	0.5	1.5	0.75	0.25	2.25
4	5	1.5	2	3.00	2.25	4
$\sum X = 10$	$\sum Y = 12$			$\sum xy = 8.00$	$\sum x^2 = 5.00$	$\sum y^2 = 13.50$

$$\bar{X} = \frac{\sum X}{4} = \frac{10}{4} = 2.5$$

$$\bar{Y} = \frac{\sum Y}{4} = \frac{12}{4} = 3$$

Worked examples break the concepts down into more manageable steps and illustrate key principles, guiding you step-by-step through the solution

Self-check questions encourage self-learning by reinforcing points made in the chapter

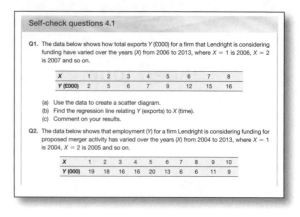

Self-check questions 4.1

Q1. The data below shows how total exports Y (£000) for a firm that Lendright is considering funding have varied over the years (X) from 2006 to 2013, where X = 1 is 2006, X = 2 is 2007 and so on.

X	1	2	3	4	5	6	7	8
Y (£000)	2	5	6	7	9	12	15	16

(a) Use the data to create a scatter diagram.
(b) Find the regression line relating Y (exports) to X (time).
(c) Comment on your results.

Q2. The data below shows that employment (Y) for a firm Lendright is considering funding for proposed merger activity has varied over the years (X) from 2004 to 2013, where X = 1 is 2004, X = 2 is 2005 and so on.

X	1	2	3	4	5	6	7	8	9	10
Y (000)	19	18	16	16	20	13	6	6	11	9

Did you know? boxed features provide topical real-life examples relevant to each chapter

Did you know?

The easiest way to interpret the meaning of a particular value of R, the Pearson coefficient of correlation, is to square it. For example, a value $R = +0.8$ means that $R^2 = (+0.8)^2 = 0.64$ that is, 64% of total variation can be 'explained' or accounted for by your regression line.

Pause for thought features help you reflect on what you have just read to check your understanding

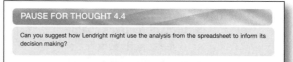

PAUSE FOR THOUGHT 4.4

Can you suggest how Lendright might use the analysis from the spreadsheet to inform its decision making?

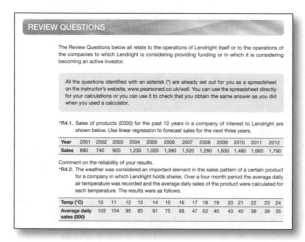

REVIEW QUESTIONS

The Review Questions below all relate to the operations of Lendright itself or to the operations of the companies to which Lendright is considering providing funding or in which it is considering becoming an active investor.

All the questions identified with an asterisk (*) are already set out for you as a spreadsheet on the instructor's website, www.pearsoned.co.uk/wall. You can use the spreadsheet directly for your calculations or you can use it to check that you obtain the same answer as you did when you used a calculator.

*R4.1. Sales of products (£000) for the past 12 years in a company of interest to Lendright are shown below. Use linear regression to forecast sales for the next three years.

Year	2001	2002	2003	2004	2005	2006	2007	2008	2009	2010	2011	2012
Sales	890	740	920	1,230	1,020	1,390	1,520	1,280	1,830	1,480	1,660	1,790

Comment on the reliability of your results.
*R4.2. The weather was considered an important element in the sales pattern of a certain product for a company in which Lendright holds shares. Over a four month period the average daily air temperature was recorded and the average daily sales of the product were calculated for each temperature. The results were as follows.

Temp (°C)	10	11	12	13	14	15	16	17	18	19	20	21	22	23	24
Average daily sales (000)	103	104	95	83	81	75	68	47	53	40	43	40	38	39	35

Review questions assess your knowledge and application of the principles and techniques covered in each chapter. Full solutions to the questions are provided on the instructor's website to allow you to self-assess your progress

Acknowledgements

We are grateful to Eleanor Wall for her extensive help in developing a wide range of web-related materials. We are also indebted to Naowarat Lewis for her expertise in creating video and other materials to bring the content alive and to support students in understanding the key concepts.

Publisher's acknowledgements

We are grateful to the following for permission to reproduce copyright material:

Figures

Figure 1.2B adapted from Eastern block: Overseas students opt for offshore platforms, *Times Higher Education*, 21/02/2013 (Gibney, E.) © Times Higher Education; Figure 1.3 from Coming up behind, *Financial Times* 04/12/2011 (Jacobs, M.), Financial Times © The Financial Times Limited. All Rights Reserved.; Figures 1.10, 2.1 and 4.11 adapted from *Quantitative Methods for Business and Economics*, 2 ed., Pearson Education (Burton, G., Carroll, G., and Wall, S.) © Pearson Education Limited; Figure 1.13 from *Applied Economics*, 12 ed., Pearson Education (Griffiths, A. and Wall, S 2012) © Pearson Education Limited; Figures 2.2, 2.3, 2.4, 3.2, 3.3, 3.4, 4.1, 4.2, 4.3, 4.4, 4.5, 4.7, 4.8, 4.9, 4.10, 4.11, 4.12, 4.13, 5.1, 5.2, 5.3, 5.4, 5.5, 5.6, 5.7, 5.8, 5.9, 5.10, 5.11, 5.12, 5.13, 6.1, 6.2, 6.3, 6.4, 6.5, 6.6, 6.7, 6.8, 6.9, 6.10, 6.11, 6.12, 6.13, 6.14, 6.15, 6.16, 6.17, 7.1, 7.2, 7.3, 7.4, 7.5, 7.6, 7.7, 7.9, 8.1, 8.2, 8.3, 8.4, 8.5, 8.6, 8.7, 8.8, 8.9, A.1, A.2, A.3, A.4, A.5, A.6, A.7, A.8, A.9, A.10 from *Quantitative Methods for Business and Economics*, 2 ed., Pearson (Burton, G., Carroll, G., and Wall, S.) © Pearson Education Limited; Figure 4.6 from Does high home ownership impair the labour market?, *Peterson Institute for International Economics, Working paper 3-13* (Blanchflower, D. and Oswald, A. 2013) © Blanchflower, D. and Oswald, A.

Screenshots

Screenshot 7.8 from *Quantitative Methods for Business and Economics*, 2 ed., Pearson (Burton, G., Carroll, G., and Wall, S.) © Pearson Education Limited.

Tables

Table R.1 adapted from Executive MBA Ranking 2011, *Financial Times* 24/11/2011, p. 24 (Jacobs, M.), Financial Times © The Financial Times Limited. All Rights Reserved.; Table R.2 adapted from Rankings, *Financial Times*, 05/12/2011, pp. 26–29 (Jacobs, M.), Financial Times, © The Financial Times Limited. All Rights Reserved.; Table R.3 adapted from Rankings, *Financial Times*, 05/12/2011, pp. 26–29 (Jacobs, M.), Financial Times, © The Financial Times Limited. All Rights Reserved.; Table R.4 adapted from Rankings, *Financial Times*, 05/12/2011, pp. 24–29 (Jacobs, M.), Financial Times, © The Financial Times Limited. All Rights Reserved.; Table R.5 adapted from Ranking: France loses stranglehold on the top, *Financial Times* 19/09/2011, p. 25 (Jacobs, M.), Financial Times, © The Financial Times Limited. All Rights Reserved.; Table R.6 adapted from Ranking: France loses stranglehold on the top, *Financial Times*, 19/09/2011 (Jacobs, M.), Financial Times, © The Financial Times Limited. All Rights Reserved.; Table 1.4 adapted from HM Treasury (2013) Public expenditure statistical analysis © Crown; Table 9.2 adapted from Insights and trends: Current programme and project management practices, PriceWaterhouseCoopers © PriceWaterhouse Coopers.

Text

Exhibit on page 36 from Intel and ARM Ltd. Intel, the Intel logo, Intel Atom, Intel Core, are trademarks of Intel Corporation in the U.S. and/or other countries. ARM is a registered trademark of ARM Limited (or its subsidiaries) in the EU and/or elsewhere. All rights reserved.; Exhibit on page 97 from Spending on M&A often wasteful, *Financial Times*, 13/04/2012 (Lucas, L.), Financial Times, © The Financial Times Limited. All Rights Reserved.; Case Study on page 221 from Ocado © Ocado; Exhibit on page 223 from Poundland © Poundland; Exhibit on page 230 adapted from Vouchers likely to remain on the menu, *The Financial Times*, 01/02/2013 (Thompson, C.), The Financial Times, © The Financial Times Limited. All Rights Reserved.; Exhibit on page 288 from Crossrail © Crossrail; Exhibit on page 289 from NHS project on critical list, *The Financial Times*, 19/08/2009 (Nicholas Timmins), © The Financial Times Limited. All Rights Reserved.; Exhibit on page 294 from EDF overruns at reactor may hit UK plans, *The Financial Times*, 03/12/2012 (Boxell, J.), Financial Times, © The Financial Times Limited. All Rights Reserved.; Exhibit on page 311 from Why do we need to pay billions of pounds for big projects?, *The Financial Times*, 21/08/2012 (Kay, J.), Financial Times, © The Financial Times Limited. All Rights Reserved.

In some instances we have been unable to trace the owners of copyright material, and we would appreciate any information that would enable us to do so.

PART ONE

Introduction stage of product life cycle

The emphasis in this part of the book is on the quantitative techniques most widely used when developing and introducing a new product to its intended market. Each of the 400,000 start-up businesses in the United States in 2013 was, by definition, involved in the introduction stage of the product life cycle as was each of the 48,000 start-up businesses in the United Kingdom. Of course the majority of *established* businesses will also be introducing one or more new products into their existing product portfolios each year, which means most of the 27 million businesses in the United States and most of the 5 million businesses in the United Kingdom.

Whether it is a business start-up or an established business that is introducing a new product, the collection of data and the use of various visual techniques to present that data will be expected by those who have command over scarce financial and other resources and who must decide whether or not to support any proposed new product. Indeed the importance of effective data analysis even *before* a product reaches the introduction stage of the product life cycle is all too clear when, for example, we discover that around 60% of all UK and US business start-ups fail within the first five years!

Chapter 1 presents a business start-up in international educational services to review the collection and presentation of data using tables, graphs and charts. These are used to identify various patterns and trends that are relevant to the new educational services it seeks to provide for international students.

Chapter 2 reviews the use of measures of central location ('average') and dispersion (variability around the 'average') to make sense of data from the IT sector of economic activity. The introduction stage for the business in this chapter involves the invention and patenting of a new type of data compression technology for mobile phones which allows faster access to the internet and at lower cost to the user.

Chapter 3 involves a more established business in the clean technology sector that has developed a 'cloud-based' web consultancy service to improve the efficiency of solar panel installation. We review various quantitative techniques that the business can use for project appraisal, taking into account the time periods over which revenue is received and costs incurred. These techniques will help the solar panel business evaluate which of the various possible projects it should pursue by allocating scarce resources during the introductory stage of its web-based consultancy services.

Chapter 1

Collecting and presenting data

Introduction

The higher education sector is the context for our study in this chapter and in particular the start-up activity of a small partnership specialising in the provision of pre-undergraduate and pre-masters courses in business and management in the United Kingdom and overseas. We review some approaches it can use to collect data and some simple, visual techniques to help identify patterns and trends relevant to the business decisions it must make.

Both opportunities and threats are facing the partnership as the UK higher education sector has moved from 2012 onwards to a system characterised by higher fees and more restrictive international student visa arrangements. In fact UK universities are now educating more than one-quarter more students than they did 10 years ago, and the number of full-time postgraduates has increased by three-quarters.

Tuition fees, capped at £3,375 until 2012, have been allowed to rise as high as £9,000, while teaching subsidies have been withdrawn for many subjects. New private providers are entering the higher education sector, which has become much more international, with the number of non-European Union (EU) students having more than doubled since 2001. China is the largest source for undergraduate and research degrees, while India provides the most students for taught postgraduate degrees. Tuition fees paid by non-EU students rose from £746 million in 2000–1 to over £25 billion in 2013.

As part of its initial business plan, the partnership is intending to run one- and two-semester programmes in major cities in the United Kingdom to prepare international students for university entry at both undergraduate and postgraduate level. Study skills and English language tuition will be provided alongside academic modules in business and management subjects. Progression Agreements with selected universities will reassure prospective students as regards both the quality of their educational experience during the programmes and their prospects of entering a major UK university on successful completion.

As noted above there are new opportunities for both established public sector universities and for new private sector entrants. However, there are also threats in terms of higher university fees and greater difficulties in obtaining student visas for study in the United Kingdom. With this in mind the partnership is also exploring the possibility of delivering its foundation programmes overseas, in a quality assured way, with carefully selected partners in key international locations.

In this chapter we will be reviewing how data can be collected and presented to show relevant patterns and trends to help the business decision making of the educational partnership across a wide range of pre-undergraduate and pre-masters programmes in business and management. However, the partnership is also paying particular attention to the possibilities of a pre-MBA 'flagship' programme, for reasons indicated in the 'Business Applications' box below. Review Question R1.1 at the end of the chapter will apply our various data collection and presentation techniques to the issues raised in the box below.

Business applications

Specialist pre-MBA programme

There is certainly good news for those who have taken their Master of Business Administration (MBA) or who are about to begin their MBA studies, as is clear from the results of a major survey by the *Financial Times* of the experiences of MBA graduates three years after completing their MBA studies (www.ft.com/businesseducation/mba2011).

Within three years of gaining your MBA you can, on average, expect the following.

- Your salary will be an average of 90% higher than your salary in the year *before* you took your MBA.

- You will have achieved the four most important reasons identified by MBA students for choosing this course, namely:
  - increased earnings;
  - enhanced management development skills;
  - a change of employer or of career focus;
  - improved networking.
- You will have gained higher status than you had before you started your MBA in terms of job title:
  - seven times as many MBA graduates had President/MD/CEO in their title;
  - eight times as many MBA graduates had Director/Vice President in their title;
  - three times as many MBA graduates had Department Head or Senior Executive in their title.

In this chapter we will see how some simple procedures of data collection, involving both original and already published data, can help analyse important patterns and trends relevant to the early business decisions of the higher education partnership. Presenting data in a more 'grouped' form using frequency tables can also help in identifying relevant patterns and trends, as can the use of diagrams such as bar charts, line graphs, pie charts, histograms, frequency curves and Lorenz curves.

Spreadsheets

The questions and activities in the Break-Out Boxes use spreadsheets which can be found on the student's website, www.pearsoned.co.uk/wall. Many of the Worked Examples, Self-Check Questions and Review Questions are set out for you as an Excel spreadsheet on the student's website and these questions are marked with an asterisk (*).

1.1 Collection of data

1.1.1 Types of data

It may be useful to identify the various types of data that might be collected by the educational partnership. Data is often put into one of two categories, namely primary data and secondary data.

Primary data

The educational partnership might collect its own data to inform its decision making, perhaps by using questionnaires and surveys of its students, parents and staff, and so on. Whenever the source of the data is original – that is, one in which the information or data first occurs – we say we are using *primary data*. In Chapter 6 we look more carefully at how to select samples for our surveys which will make the primary data we collect from these surveys more representative of the whole group.

Secondary data

The educational partnership can also use data that has been collected and published by others to inform its decision making. Vast amounts of such *secondary data* are collected routinely by government and non-government organisations and much of it is readily available in government reports, national and international journals, press articles and via many other sources, accessed online or on hard copy. Some key secondary sources providing data on education and on other sectors of economic activity are presented on the instructor's website for Chapter 1.

Did you know?

Future earnings from taking a degree, rather than leaving school at 18, are likely to be even higher than previously forecast. In a major report, 'First Steps to Wealth', published in January 2012 by investment managers Skandia, on average a graduate should earn £1,611,551 over their working life at today's prices, compared to £1,023,840 for those starting work at 18.

(continued)

This lifetime 'graduate premium' of around £600,000 is the equivalent of around £14,000 extra per year for the graduate over their working life compared to the non-graduate and is much higher than the earlier estimate of only £100,000 for the lifetime graduate premium recently reported by the UK universities minister.

Data is also often put into the categories 'discrete' or 'continuous'.

Discrete data

This is data that can only take on a *limited number* of values, namely whole number (integer) values. For example: the number of international students; the number of rooms in a student hall of residence; the number of computers used in a test.

Continuous data

This is data that can take on an *infinite* number of different values (at least in theory!). For example: the age of students; the time taken for staff to complete a task; the speed of travel. All these examples can take on any value, subject only to the minimum unit of measurement available and need not be integers (whole numbers); for example, 17.66 years, 4.03 seconds, 40.27 km per hour, and so on. Continuous data is often 'rounded off' to a certain number of decimal places even though still smaller measurements might theoretically be possible.

1.1.2 Surveys, tally charts and frequencies

As we see in Chapter 6, we often collect primary data using various types of survey, recording our results in tally charts and then converting these into frequency tables. Frequency is the number of times a certain event has happened, and is often found by means of a tally chart. For example, suppose you are in a major university city conducting a survey of the ages of international students involved in pre-undergraduate foundation programmes. Each student reply could be recorded in a tally chart, as shown in Table 1.1.

Each time an international student identifies themselves as being of a particular age, a vertical line is drawn, and should a fifth such line be needed a diagonal line is drawn through the previous four vertical lines. At the end of the data collection period the total number of

Table 1.1 Tally chart for ages of international students

Age in years	Tally	Frequency (*f*)
16 and under 18	IIII	4
18 and under 20	HHT HHT HHT HHT II	22
20 and under 22	HHT HHT HHT HHT HHT I	26
22 and under 24	HHT HHT HHT HHT IIII	24
24 and under 26	HHT HHT HHT I	16
26 and under 28	HHT I	6
28 and under 30	II	2
Total		100

tally marks is added for each age group and the total placed in the end column marked 'f' for frequency. The total frequency (100) is found by adding these individual (class) frequencies.

Did you know?

According to figures released by the Higher Education Statistics Agency around one in six of all the students enrolled in UK universities now study their entire programme overseas! These students are engaged in 'transnational education' and include those registered at overseas branch campuses run by UK universities, people studying for UK university awards at overseas higher education institutions, and those engaged in distance learning.

Self-check questions 1.1

Q1. Read the following passage and answer the questions that follow.

Universities eye tuition fee cuts

More than a fifth of English universities cut their tuition fees from the figure they originally intended to charge, which was £9,000, to a lower charge of £7,500 or below for 2012–13 in response to new government incentives that reward institutions offering undergraduate courses at low costs. This was in response to government plans that now allowed institutions with fees at £7,500 or below to bid for the right to offer more student places. A total of 20,000 places were eventually made available in 2012–13 for such a bidding system, which was intended to encourage competition between institutions.

(a) What type of data is involved in this comment on university fees?
(b) How might this data be useful to the educational partnership?

Q2. The educational partnership wished to find published (secondary) data to help identify the total number of students entering higher education in the United Kingdom and additional information on the country of origin of those students, the subjects studied and so on. Can you identify some actual sources that the educational partnership might use to find such information?

Note: Answers to Self-Check Questions can be found on the instrctor's website, www.pearsoned.co.uk/wall

---

1.2   Presenting data using frequency tables

Table 1.1 is essentially a *frequency table*, and it will be useful at the outset to define a number of terms often encountered when discussing such tables.

- *Class intervals*: these are the age groups into which we organise the data. There are seven class intervals in Table 1.1, the first being '16 and under 18'.
- *Class boundaries*: these are the values at which the different class intervals meet. For example, the second class interval has a lower class boundary (LCB) of 18 and an upper class boundary (UCB) of 20.
- *Class width (or size)*: this is the difference between the upper and lower class boundaries for each class interval. As we can see from Table 1.1 all the class intervals have a class width (or size) of 2 years.

- *Class frequency*: this is the number of observations found to occur in a particular class interval. For example, the class frequency is 22 for the '18 and under 20' class interval.

A frequency table is useful in giving an immediate impression of how the data is distributed. We can see from Table 1.1 that, although the relationship is not precise, most international students on pre-undergraduate programmes are aged between 18 and 24 years.

1.2.1 Constructing your own frequency table

The following steps may help when you try to construct your own frequency table from raw or untreated data.

Step 1. Determine the range of the data:

$$\text{Range} = \text{maximum value} - \text{minimum value}$$

Step 2. Determine the number of class intervals to be shown in the table. This is largely a matter of opinion – too many class intervals will confuse the data while too few class intervals will mean that you lose much of the information. Most published frequency tables use between 5 and 10 class intervals.

Step 3. Determine the width (size) of class intervals. As a general rule the width of each class interval should be approximately equal to the range of the data divided by the number of class intervals you intend to use.

Step 4. Determine the first lower class boundary (LCB).

Step 5. Construct the frequency table using a tally chart.

The Worked Example below will help clarify these steps.

Worked example 1.1

The percentage marks scored by 58 international students in their written English test were recorded as follows:

37	49	58	59	56	79
62	87	53	58	34	45
40	43	44	50	42	50
54	30	49	54	76	47
64	53	64	54	60	39
49	44	47	44	21	38
55	57	54	55	59	46
31	41	53	47	58	55
59	64	56	42	38	
33	33	47	50	37	

Construct a frequency table of the data, using class intervals with a class width (size) of 10 percentage marks.

Worked example 1.1 (cont'd)

Solution

Step 1. Determine the range of the data:

$$\text{Maximum} = 87; \text{minimum} = 21; \text{range} = 66$$

Step 2. Determine the number of class intervals.

Suppose you decide to use seven class intervals to cover the range of 66 percentage marks.

Step 3. Therefore 7 class intervals of 10 will be required to cover scores 20 to 90 (per cent) should we decide to set the first lower class boundary at 20, as in Step 4.

Step 4. First lower class boundary (LCB) = 20.

Class	Tally	Frequency
20–29	I	1
30–39	⊞⊞ ⊞⊞	10
40–49	⊞⊞ ⊞⊞ ⊞⊞ I I	17
50–59	⊞⊞ ⊞⊞ ⊞⊞ ⊞⊞ I I	22
60–69	⊞⊞	5
70–79	I I	2
80–89	I	1

Step 5. Construct the frequency table.

Note: Strictly speaking, each class interval starts at 0.5 (e.g. 29.5 to 39.5 for the second class interval); any mark of 0.5 or above is rounded up and any mark below 0.5 is rounded down.

We review primary data collection using samples in more detail in Chapter 6.

Did you know?

Not only does being a graduate add significantly to your lifetime income, as we noted earlier, but it also increases your chances of employment, particularly important at times of global economic uncertainty! Unemployment rates among university graduates across the OECD countries in 2012 averaged 4.4%, but for non-graduates average unemployment across the OECD countries was as high as 11.5%.

Self-check question 1.2

*A survey has been conducted on the distance travelled to the college by international students from their lodgings (accommodation), with the results shown below. Some students live in a different town or city and travel by train or car to the college.

(continued)

Distance travelled to college (in kilometres)

13	1	2	9	27
4	63	7	2	3
12	43	6	4	3
73	26	7	8	2
48	16	42	3	2
8	26	49	21	15
2	53	7	16	21
57	2	55	18	25
6	71	8	2	8
3	4	8	4	3

(a) Construct a frequency table of the data, using class intervals 0–9, 10–19 and so on.
(b) Construct a frequency table of the data using class intervals 0–4, 5–9, 10–14 and so on.
(c) What do your frequency tables suggest?

Note: Answers to Self-Check Questions can be found on the instructor's website, www.pearsoned.co.uk/wall

1.3 Presenting data using bar charts and pie charts

Throughout this section we focus on data relevant to the business decisions facing our higher education partnership.

It is often said that 'a picture tells a thousand words' and it is certainly true that the visual impacts of diagrams can often reveal important patterns and trends in the data.

1.3.1 Bar charts

There are three main types of bar chart: simple, component and multiple. While less accurate than table-based data, these charts give a useful visual impression of relative values, patterns and trends for the key variables.

Simple bar chart

This can be drawn in vertical (Figure 1.1A) or horizontal (Figure 1.1B) form. The height of the vertical bar or length of the horizontal bar gives a visual impression of volume or value for the variable in question.

The data displayed in Figure 1.1A informs the partnership of the rapid growth in projected tuition fee income in the United Kingdom from overseas students. This revenue stream is a core element in the business plan of the educational partnership and is expected to rise from some £2.5 billion in 2010 to £5.2 billion in 2025, despite the current difficulties in securing visas for overseas students entering the United Kingdom.

The data displayed in Figure 1.1B uses a snapshot of data in the most recent year available for each country on the number of internationally mobile students who are studying across the world, and in the six countries in which the partnership is considering running its programmes, thereby avoiding UK visa issues. The United Kingdom is shown as host to some 380,000 overseas students, second to the United States with some 690,000 students. Interestingly the total number of 'internationally mobile' students is projected to increase

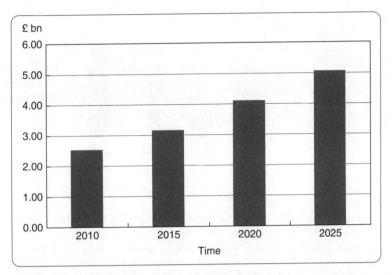

Figure 1.1A Tuition fee income (£bn) in the United Kingdom from overseas students

Source: Based on *Futures for Higher Education: Analysing Trends* (26 January, 2012); *Higher Education in Facts and Figures* (2011); *Driving Economic Growth* (1 December, 2011); *Parliamentary Briefing: Debate on the Importance of the Government's Growth Strategy for the United Kingdom Economy* (21 June, 2012) Universities UK.

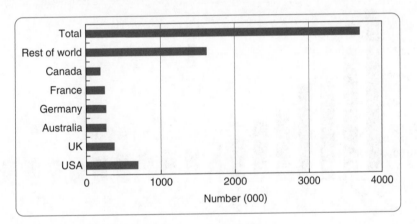

Figure 1.1B Number of internationally mobile students

Source: Based on *Futures for Higher Education: Analysing Trends* (26 January, 2012); *Higher Education in Facts and Figures* (2011); *Driving Economic Growth* (1 December, 2011); *Parliamentary Briefing: Debate on the Importance of the Government's Growth Strategy for the United Kingdom Economy* (21 June, 2012) Universities UK.

sharply from the current 3.7 million shown in the horizontal bar chart to over 7 million, making this option of overseas delivery still more attractive.

Component bar chart

This is useful for showing the components (or segments) that make up the total volume or value. The components can be arranged vertically or horizontally.

Figure 1.2A shows the overall contribution of overseas (non-EU) students to UK exports broken down into three components, namely expenditure by students on UK courses delivered overseas, off-campus expenditure in the United Kingdom by overseas students and tuition fees paid in the United Kingdom by overseas students. The diagram shows that all three

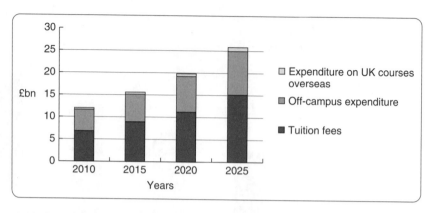

Figure 1.2A Contribution of overseas (non-EU) students to UK export earnings (£bn) at constant 2008–9 prices

Source: Based on *Futures for Higher Education: Analysing Trends* (26 January, 2012); *Higher Education in Facts and Figures* (2011); *Driving Economic Growth* (1 December, 2011); *Parliamentary Briefing: Debate on the Importance of the Government's Growth Strategy for the United Kingdom Economy* (21 June, 2012) Universities UK.

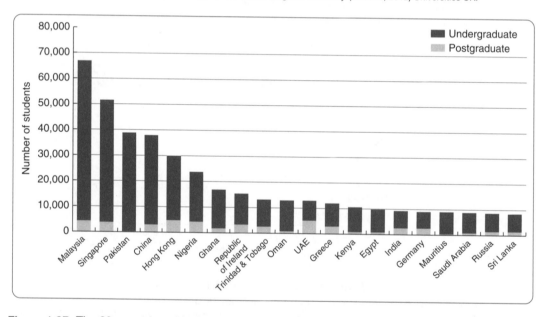

Figure 1.2B The 20 countries with the largest numbers of overseas students registered at UK institutions or studying for UK awards, 2011–12

components are projected to grow over time, including earnings from the study of UK courses delivered overseas. This might further increase the interest of the partnership in providing its foundation programmes overseas, perhaps as a collaborative venture with UK or overseas universities. However, the most significant projected growth in absolute terms is fees paid by overseas students in the United Kingdom, rising from £7.1 billion in 2010 to £14.9 billion in 2025. This market segment will therefore continue to be a major strategic focus for the educational partnership.

Figure 1.2B shows the total number of overseas higher education students from 20 different countries studying in the United Kingdom or in their own countries for UK awards.

The country totals are broken down into undergraduate and postgraduate components. We can immediately see that of the 570,000 higher education students from overseas, the largest number are from Malaysia (67,000), followed by Singapore (52,000), Pakistan (39,000), China (38,000) and Hong Kong (30,000). By far the largest component of higher education study from all countries involves undergraduate rather than postgraduate courses.

Multiple bar chart

A multiple bar chart uses a separate bar to represent each component of the total. These bars are joined together to form a set, as in Figure 1.3, which shows the percentage of female students on various European postgraduate programmes of interest to the partnership.

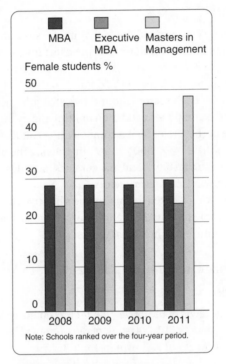

Figure 1.3 Women in European postgraduate business school programmes

Source: From Coming up behind, *Financial Times* 04/12/2011 (Jacobs, M.), Financial Times, © The Financial Times Limited. All Rights Reserved.

PAUSE FOR THOUGHT 1.1

How might the patterns and trends shown in the various bar charts of Figures 1.1, 1.2 and 1.3 be relevant to decision making for the educational partnership? You can also click on the three minute *FT* video (http://video.ft.com/v/1298242942001/The-Chinese-customer-is-king), which provides a useful example of how bar charts can be used by the media to give the 'audience' a visual impression of patterns and trends in data.

> ## BREAK-OUT BOX 1.1
>
> ### Bar charts and educational company performance
>
> #### Automatic example generator
>
> In the Excel sheet Chapter 1_Example_1 you will find an example generator that you can use to find data on the share price of three US educational companies. Such data might provide a useful reference point for our educational partnership, but in any case the data will give you the opportunity to develop (and continually update) your own simple bar chart to show the performance of the share price of each company over time.

1.3.2 Pie chart

Pie charts give an immediate visual impression of the relative contribution of particular components to the overall total. A pie chart involves a circle which is used to represent the whole data, with sectors of this circle ('pie') then used to represent the relative contribution of particular components of the data.

The size of each sector is found by calculating the proportion of the whole data represented by the component and then multiplying by 360° to obtain the angle of the sector from the centre of the circle. So if a component accounts for one quarter of the total, the angle of the sector will be $\frac{1}{4} \times 360° = 90°$. In drawing the pie chart it is helpful to draw the smallest sectors first, so that any small inaccuracies in angles will be visually less important when you come to drawing the larger sectors.

The following worked example shows how we can display data on 'internationally mobile' (i.e. overseas) students in the form of a pie chart showing the relative contribution of six selected countries to the global total.

*Worked example 1.2

Display the data shown in Table 1.2 in a pie chart.

Solution

To find the angle of the circle ('pie') represented by each country, we find the proportion of the whole data (3,701,000 students) represented by that country and then multiply by 360°.

The working out is shown in Table 1.3.

The pie chart is then drawn from this table using a protractor (angle measurer) or spreadsheet. The completed pie chart is shown in Figure 1.4A, displaying number, and Figure 1.4B, displaying angles (degrees).

Table 1.2 Numbers of internationally mobile students (000)

Country	Number (000)
US	691
UK	381
Australia	273
Germany	269
France	260
Canada	199
Rest of world	1,628
Total	3,701

Source: Based on Futures for Higher Education: Analysing Trends (26 January, 2012); Higher Education in Facts and Figures (2011); Driving Economic Growth (1 December, 2011); Parliamentary Briefing: Debate on the Importance of the Government's Growth Strategy for the United Kingdom Economy (21 June, 2012) Universities UK.

Worked
example
1.2
(cont'd)

We can see at a glance how the United States and the United Kingdom are the leading nations within the six countries identified as being of interest to the educational partnership in terms of their share of the total of internationally mobile students. Of course it may be useful to break down the large 'Rest of the world' segment into its component parts.

Table 1.3 Finding the sectors of the 'pie'

Country	Frequency	Angle*
US	691	$\dfrac{691}{3701} \times 360° = 67°$
UK	381	$\dfrac{381}{3701} \times 360° = 37°$
Australia	273	$\dfrac{273}{3701} \times 360° = 27°$
Germany	269	$\dfrac{269}{3701} \times 360° = 26°$
France	260	$\dfrac{260}{3701} \times 360° = 25°$
Canada	199	$\dfrac{199}{3701} \times 360° = 19°$
Rest of world	1,628	$\dfrac{1628}{3701} \times 360° = 158°$

* Because of rounding the total may differ slightly from 360°.

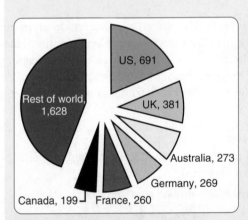

Figure 1.4A Pie chart for origins of internationally mobile students (000)

Source: Based on *Futures for Higher Education: Analysing Trends* (26 January, 2012); *Higher Education in Facts and Figures* (2011); *Driving Economic Growth* (1 December, 2011); *Parliamentary Briefing: Debate on the Importance of the Government's Growth Strategy for the United Kingdom Economy* (21 June, 2012) Universities UK.

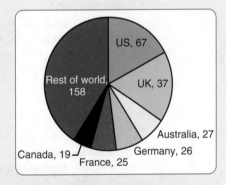

Figure 1.4B Pie chart for origins of internationally mobile students (degrees)

Source: Based on *Futures for Higher Education: Analysing Trends* (26 January, 2012); *Higher Education in Facts and Figures* (2011); *Driving Economic Growth* (1 December, 2011); *Parliamentary Briefing: Debate on the Importance of the Government's Growth Strategy for the United Kingdom Economy* (21 June, 2012) Universities UK.

PAUSE FOR THOUGHT 1.2

How might the detail of the pie chart be relevant to decision making by the educational partnership?

Did you know?

If you earn less than an average of £60,000 a year over a 30 year working life after graduation, you will not have to pay back the whole of your student loan! The Skandia consultancy report 'First Steps to Wealth', published in January 2012, estimates that in 30 years' time the UK government will have to write off as much as £8.7 billion a year (at today's prices), given that many current graduates will earn less than an average of £60,000 a year over their working lives.

1.3.3 Line graphs and scatter graphs

Line graphs can be useful in exploring patterns and trends, for example by using straight lines to connect various points on a diagram in which time is on the horizontal axis. The line graph in Figure 1.5 illustrates the increase in the percentage of UK students aged 18 to 19 years going on to higher education in the United Kingdom, which has risen sharply from around 3% in 1950 to around 35% in 2013.

Scatter graphs present the actual observations recorded (as co-ordinates) for the two variables shown on the graph. The scatter graph in Figure 1.6 plots the points for 10 countries using two variables, namely annual income per head ($000) and percentage of population in higher education.

The scatter graph can help suggest (not prove!) possible relationships between the two variables in question, in this case between the standard of living (national income per head) and the percentage of the population going into higher education. The scatter graph suggests that richer countries will tend to have a higher proportion of their population involved in higher education. We explore the meaning of such scatter graphs in more detail in Chapter 4.

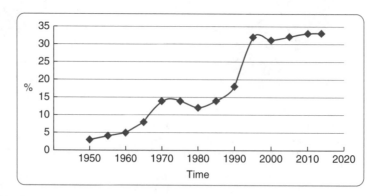

Figure 1.5 Percentage of 18–19 year olds going on to higher education in the United Kingdom

Source: Based on *Social Trends* (2011, 2012) Office for National Statistics; *Higher Education Statistics for the UK* (2011, 2012) Higher Education Statistics Agency.

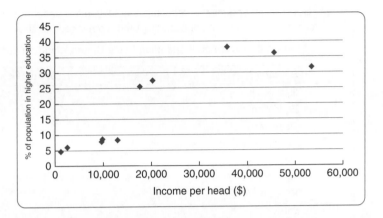

Figure 1.6 Income per head ($) and percentage of population in higher education
Source: Based on *Human Development Report* (2012), United Nations.

PAUSE FOR THOUGHT 1.3

How might the patterns and trends shown in the line graph (Figure 1.5) and scatter graph (Figure 1.6) influence the decision making of the educational partnership?

Self-check questions 1.3

*Q1 (a) Use an appropriate bar chart to display the following data on the income for a university from 'overseas students' and from 'all other sources' over the past 10 years.

(b) What do you notice?

Year	Overseas students income (£m)	All other sources of income (£m)
2002	2	6
2003	3	7
2004	3	7
2005	4	8
2006	5	8
2007	7	7
2008	8	8
2009	10	7
2010	12	7
2011	13	8

(continued)

*Q2. Government spending on education in 2013 in the United Kingdom was £97 billion, compared to government spending on the other sectors shown in Table 1.4.

Table 1.4 Government spending in the United Kingdom 2013–14 (£bn)

Sector	Government spending (£bn)
Healthcare	137
Education	97
Defence	40
Social protection and social services	251
Debt interest	51
Transport	21
Public order	31
Others	92
Total government spending	720

Construct a pie chart to show how the UK government spends its money on education compared to other sectors.

Note: Answers to Self-Check Questions can be found on the instructor's website, www.pearsoned.co.uk/wall

1.4   Presenting data using histograms

The histogram is often used to display data which has been arranged in the form of a frequency table. We start with the frequency table below, which uses published secondary data as its source. The data refers to the National Student Survey (NSS) which involved responses from over 13,000 full-time undergraduates in the United Kingdom in 2013 and is the most widely used data for assessing the student experience in UK universities. The partnership wishes to have a better idea as to how universities differ in the quality of the student experience they provide. In an era of high fees students will be increasingly aware of 'value for money' and the partnership is therefore keen to work with universities that have high published NSS scores.

Table 1.5 Frequency table for NSS scores in UK universities

NSS overall score (%)	Frequency (*f*)
60 and under 65	8
65 and under 70	14
70 and under 75	36
75 and under 80	41
80 and under 85	14
Total	113

Source: Based on data from National Student Survey.

Using published NSS data on 113 universities, the partnership has drawn up the frequency table (Table 1.5) for 'overall scores' in the NSS, which range from a maximum of 84.90% to a minimum of 60.35%.

Such frequency tables can be displayed visually using a histogram, which looks like a bar chart but with no gaps between the bars. Before constructing the histogram for Table 1.5 it will be useful to consider some of the features common to all histograms.

The histogram has a number of properties:

- It contains a set of rectangles, each of which represents the frequency of a particular class interval.
- Each rectangle is constructed so that its *area* is in proportion to the frequency of the class interval it represents.
- The base of each rectangle represents the width (or size) of the class interval and the height of each rectangle represents the frequency of the class interval.
- When all the class intervals have the same width (or size), then the vertical axis which represents the height of each rectangle is the class frequency.
- When the class intervals are of *unequal width* (or size), then the height of each rectangle must be adjusted where it differs from the 'standard' class width – that is, from the class width of the majority of class intervals. For example, if the width of a particular class interval *doubles* (and with it the base of the rectangle), then we must *halve* the height of the rectangle used to represent its class frequency. We must do this to keep the areas of the rectangles proportional to the class frequencies. The vertical axis is no longer the frequency of the class interval but the *frequency density*, as we shall see below.

1.4.1 Equal-width histograms

As can be seen in Table 1.5, each class interval has an equal width (or size) of 5 percentage points. This is sometimes called the standard class width. The equal-width histogram that represents this data is shown in Figure 1.7.

Note that the rectangles are connected together, that the base of each rectangle represents the standard class width (5 percentage points) and is the same throughout, and that the height of each rectangle represents the class frequency. As a result the *areas* of the rectangles are in proportion to the respective class frequencies, and so we can see at a glance that the bulk of the frequency distribution is in the rectangles of the histogram with base values 70–75% and 75–80%.

We gain an immediate visual impression from the histogram that there are relatively few poorly performing universities in terms of national student experience (NSS) and relatively few high performing universities.

1.4.2 Unequal-width histograms

Sometimes the data will be such that the class intervals are of different widths (or sizes). In the previous example of NSS scores, the width of each class interval was 5%. In the next example (Table 1.6), however, we have a frequency table in which the widths of the various class intervals vary, being either 5% or 10%.

Remembering that the areas of the rectangles must be in proportion to the class frequencies, we must adjust the height of any rectangle in line with any variations in the base of

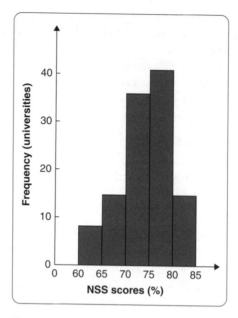

Figure 1.7 Equal-width histogram

Table 1.6 Frequency table for NSS scores

NSS overall score	Frequency (f)
60 and under 70	22
70 and under 75	36
75 and under 80	41
80 and under 85	14
Total	113

that rectangle. So if the base (class width) doubles in length we must halve the height (class frequency), and so on. The value on the vertical axis is no longer frequency, but *frequency density*. These adjustments are shown in Table 1.7.

Remembering that the class width is the difference between upper and lower class boundaries, we can see that the first class interval has a class width of 10%, and the other three class intervals have class widths of 5%. The adjusted frequency densities from Table 1.7 are shown in the unequal-width histogram (Figure 1.8).

The class width that appears most often in an unequal-width frequency table and histogram is often called the *standard class width*. In Table 1.7 the standard class width is 5%. We derive the frequency density by dividing the class frequency by the number of standard class widths in that class interval. So, for example, we divide the class frequency of 22 in the first class interval by two, to give a *frequency density* of 11.

This approach can be seen more clearly in the following worked example.

Table 1.7 Frequency density of NSS scores

NSS overall score	Frequency (f)	Number of standard class widths	Frequency density
60 and under 70	22	2	11
70 and under 75	36	1	36
75 and under 80	41	1	41
80 and under 85	14	1	14

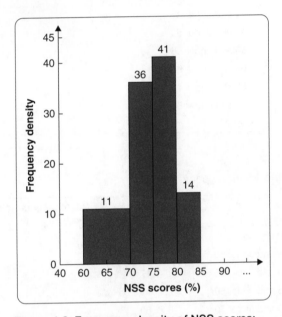

Figure 1.8 Frequency density of NSS scores: unequal-width histogram

The educational partnership has developed an application form for its programmes and wishes to review the length of time it takes students to complete the form. In its survey of 146 students, the following times (in minutes) were recorded.

From the data in Table 1.8 construct a histogram to represent the data.

What do you notice?

Solution

Step 1. From the frequency table decide on a standard class width = 5 minutes.

Step 2. Enlarge the original table, adding columns for number of standard class widths and frequency density (see Table 1.9).

Note that where the standard class width has doubled, as in the case of the last two class intervals, we must halve the height (frequency density) of the corresponding rectangles.

Step 3. Construct the histogram (see Figure 1.9).

Clearly most application forms take between 55 and 70 minutes to complete, with a small proportion being completed in less than 45 minutes and a small proportion over 70 minutes. The partnership will be interested in simplifying the application form, with a higher proportion taking less time to complete the form.

Table 1.8 Time taken (minutes) for completing the application form

Time to complete form (minutes)	Number of students (f)
40 and under 45	4
45 and under 50	13
50 and under 55	17
55 and under 60	44
60 and under 70	60
70 and under 80	8
Total	146

Table 1.9 Frequency density

Time	Frequency (f)	No. of standard class widths	Height (frequency density)
40 and under 45	4	1	4
45 and under 50	13	1	13
50 and under 55	17	1	17
55 and under 60	44	1	44
60 and under 70	60	2	(60 ÷ 2) = 30
70 and under 80	8	2	(8 ÷ 2) = 4
Total	146		

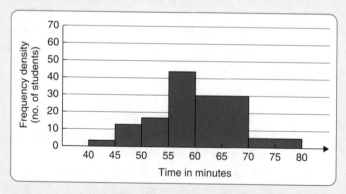

Figure 1.9 Histogram showing the time taken to complete the application form

Did you know?

Norway is highly unusual in providing free higher education, not just to its own nationals, or those from the EU, but to all students, whatever their country of origin. In 2012 over 16,500 non-EU students enrolled at Norwegian universities, with a growing range of undergraduate and postgraduate courses delivered in the English language. Students from any nationality can also receive Norwegian state loans of up to £10,000 per year.

Self-check questions 1.4

Q1. Education is big business all over the world. Education Management Corporation, a US stock market listed company (NASDAQ: EDMC) operates higher educational institutions, primarily in the United States. Over a year of trading their share price changes as good and bad news is released about recent contracts and targets. For example, the frequency distribution below shows their share price over a 250 trading day period (roughly one year).

Share price ($)	Number of days at share price
15–19	0
20–24	114
25–29	118
30–34	18
35 and over	0

Can you construct an equal-width histogram so that the distribution of share prices can be seen more clearly?

*Q2. The frequency table below shows the scores on a test of written English of 100 international students at the start of a pre-undergraduate foundation course (40% is the pass mark).

Scores in written English (%)	Frequency (f)
0–9	8
10–19	18
20–29	22
30–39	24
40–49	13
50–59	12
60–69	2
70–79	1

(a) Construct a histogram of the data.
(b) What does the histogram suggest?
(c) How might this information be useful to the educational partnership?

(continued)

*Q3. Here is the frequency table of the weekly expenditure on accommodation of 70 international students in a survey in a UK university city.

Weekly expenditure (£)	Frequency (f)
76–100	14
101–125	18
126–150	28
151–200	8
201–300	2

(a) Draw a histogram to represent this data. (Note: unequal-width histogram.)

(b) How might this information be useful to the educational partnership?

Note: Answers to Self-Check Questions can be found on the instructor's website, www.pearsoned.co.uk/wall

1.5 Presenting data using frequency polygons and frequency curves

1.5.1 Frequency polygon

A *frequency polygon* is a straight line diagram that represents exactly the same area (i.e. frequency) as shown in the histogram. The frequency polygon is derived from the histogram by connecting the mid-points of the tops of each adjacent rectangle by straight lines, as in Figure 1.10, which represents the number and the age of international students on pre-university courses in the city in which the educational partnership is launching its first programme. If we then use straight lines to join the mid-points of the tops of the end two rectangles with the horizontal axis, as shown, then a key property of the frequency polygon

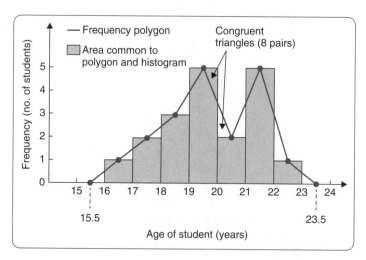

Figure 1.10 Frequency polygon: area enclosed identical to histogram

should quickly become apparent: namely that the area under the histogram is identical to the area under the frequency polygon.

The shaded area is common to both polygon and histogram and there are eight respective pairs of congruent triangles (side-angle-side), giving identical areas contained by polygon and histogram.

1.5.2 Frequency curve

From the previous discussion we can therefore state that the frequency distribution represented by the histogram can equivalently be represented by the straight line diagram known as the frequency polygon. Further, if the points to be connected by straight lines were close together then, as an approximation, we could represent the frequency polygon by the *frequency curve* shown in Figure 1.11. Indeed the frequency curve is the most usual way of representing a frequency table visually. However, it is simply an alternative means of displaying visually the properties of a frequency table already captured by the histogram and frequency polygon.

1.5.3 Cumulative frequency curve

Cumulative frequency is the 'running total' of the figures shown in the frequency column of a frequency table. As we shall see we can draw up cumulative 'more than' and cumulative 'less than' tables to represent data on income, wealth and many other variables. We can then draw cumulative frequency polygons or curves to give a visual picture of these tables.

Table 1.10 illustrates the frequency distribution of the overseas earnings of 153 UK universities. The educational partnership wants to work with universities experienced in their engagement with international students and is using the value of 'overseas fees and contracts' as an indicator of international experience and cultural awareness.

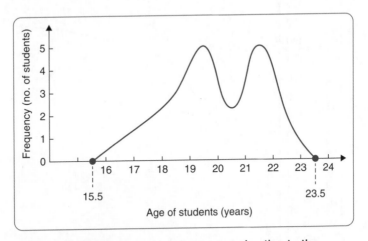

Figure 1.11 Frequency curve as an approximation to the frequency polygon

Table 1.10 Overseas fees and contracts (£m)

Overseas income (£m)	0–5	6–10	11–20	21–30	31–40	41–60	61–80	81–100
Frequency (f)	59	19	26	27	8	9	4	1

Table 1.11 Cumulative 'less than' frequency table for overseas fees and contracts (£m)

Overseas income (£m)	Frequency (*f*)	Fees less than (£m)	Cumulative frequency
0–5	59	5.5	59
6–10	19	10.5	78
11–20	26	20.5	104
21–30	27	30.5	131
31–40	8	40.5	139
41–60	9	60.5	148
61–80	4	80.5	152
81–100	1	100.5	153

We can, for example, produce a cumulative 'less than' frequency table (Table 1.11) from this data. This keeps a running total showing how universities have 'overseas fees and contracts' earnings less than a certain annual value. As we saw with unequal-width histograms, the width (size) of the class intervals varies from £5 million to £20 million. (Note also that the respective class boundaries meet at 5.5, 10.5, 20.5, etc.)

We now draw a cumulative frequency curve from this table by plotting the cumulative frequency (on the vertical axis) against the 'less than' value (on the horizontal axis). Here we join up the points we have plotted with a smooth curve. This frequency curve is also known as an 'ogive'. The curve plotted in Figure 1.12 is therefore the cumulative 'less than' curve (or ogive).

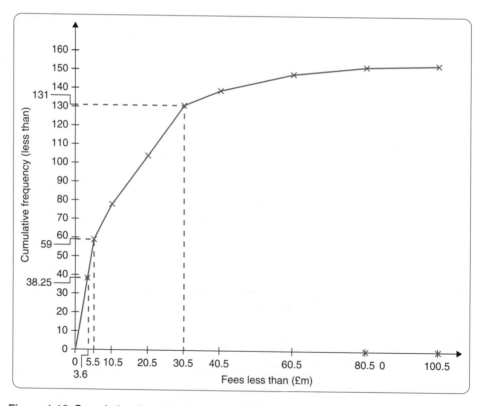

Figure 1.12 Cumulative 'less than' curve (or ogive)

You can take note of some useful information from such a curve. For example, all but 22 of the universities (i.e. 131 out of 153) have annual overseas earnings less than £30.5 million. On the other hand 59 universities out of 153 have overseas earnings of less than £5.5 million.

PAUSE FOR THOUGHT 1.4

Try to construct a cumulative 'more than' frequency table using the data in Table 1.10 but this time using the lower class boundaries (rather than the upper class boundaries) for each class interval. How might the information and data presented in the various histograms and frequency curves be useful to the partnership?

1.5.4   Cumulative frequency and percentiles

We can also use our cumulative 'less than' frequency curve to answer questions involving *percentiles*. A percentile is a particular value below (or above) which a given percentage of the distribution lies. We can easily convert the vertical axis from absolute numbers (0–153) to percentages (0–100%) when dealing with percentiles.

> ## Did you know?
>
> According to the OECD in 2012, China now provides 36.6% of the world's new higher education students, with its nearest rival being the United States, which has only 12.9% of the global total. This is a serious challenge to the stated ambition of the United States to lead the world in the proportion of graduates by 2020.

- *Lower quartile* (or first quartile) is that value for which a quarter (25%) of the distribution lies below it. We can therefore use our cumulative frequency curve to estimate the annual value of overseas income for which 25% of the distribution (38.25 students) will lie below that value. This value is shown as £3.6 million in Figure 1.12. We draw the horizontal line from 38.25 on the vertical (cumulative less than frequency) axis to the curve, and read down to £3.6 million on the horizontal axis.

- *Median* (or second quartile) is that value for which half (50%) of the distribution lies above it and half (50%) lies below it (76.5 students). We could draw the horizontal line from 76.5 on the vertical (cumulative less than frequency) axis to the curve and this would read down to £10.2 million on the horizontal axis.

- *Upper quartile* (or third quartile) is that value for which a quarter (25%) of the distribution lies above it and three quarters (75%) below it (114.75 students). We could draw the horizontal line from 114.75 on the vertical (cumulative less than frequency) axis to the curve and this would read down to £24.5 million on the horizontal axis.

Of course we can use the cumulative 'less than' distribution the other way round, this time starting on the horizontal axis and then moving to the vertical axis. For example, we can read off the number of universities having overseas earnings of less than a specific value. For example, 143 universities have overseas earnings of less than £50 million.

PAUSE FOR THOUGHT 1.5

At what value would you expect a cumulative 'more than' frequency curve to intersect a cumulative 'less than' frequency curve?

Self-check questions 1.5

Q1. The following table shows the distribution of the ages of 326 international students attending a pre-masters foundation course in the United Kingdom.

Age range (years)	21–23	24–26	27–29	30–32	33–35
No. of students	126	108	82	8	2

(a) Construct a cumulative frequency (less than) table.
(b) Draw the corresponding cumulative 'less than' curve on a graph.
(c) Use your curve to estimate:
   (i) the median age attending the pre-masters foundation course;
   (ii) the lower and upper quartile ages;
   (iii) the percentage of students aged 28 or over on the pre-masters foundation course.
(d) How might this information be useful to the educational partnership?

Q2. (a) Complete the cumulative 'more than' table below.

Overseas income (£m)	Frequency (f)	Fees 'more than' (£m)	Cumulative frequency
0–5	59	0	
6–10	19	5.5	
11–20	26	10.5	
21–30	27	20.5	
31–40	8	30.5	
41–60	9	40.5	
61–80	4	60.5	
81–100	1	80.5	

(b) Draw the cumulative 'more than' curve for Figure 1.12.
(c) What do you notice about the point at which the cumulative 'less than' and cumulative 'more than' curve intersect?

Note: Answers to Self-Check Questions can be found on the instructor's website, www.pearsoned.co.uk/wall

1.6 Presenting data using the Lorenz curve

The Lorenz curve is used to contrast the actual distribution of a variable with the distribution that would have occurred in a situation of 'perfect equality'. The distribution of variables such as income, wealth, profit, firm size and so on is often displayed visually using Lorenz curves. Since it is well known that higher income groups will spend a higher proportion of

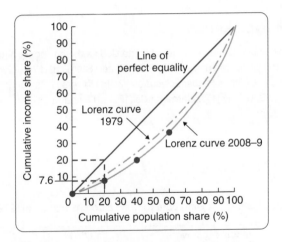

Figure 1.13 The Lorenz curve

Source: From *Applied Economics*, 12 ed., Pearson Education
(Griffiths, A. and Wall, S. 2012) Pearson.

their income on education, the distribution of income is certainly of interest to the educational partnership.

As we can see from Figure 1.13 the Lorenz curve uses cumulative percentages for each axis; one axis being the cumulative percentage figure for the variable (here income), the other being the cumulative percentage figure for the frequency (here people).

● The diagonal line represents perfect equality; for example, 20% of all people have 20% of all incomes, and so on.

● The Lorenz curve itself represents the *actual* distribution; for example, 20% of all people in the United Kingdom have only 7.6% of all income, and so on.

● The vertical distance between Lorenz curve and the diagonal represents inequality; for example, the bottom 20% of income earners should have had a further 12.4% of income had perfect equality existed.

The Gini coefficient is sometimes used together with the Lorenz curve as a measure of inequality. It is the ratio of the area between the Lorenz curve and diagonal to the total area beneath the diagonal.

● If there is perfect equality (i.e. the plotted Lorenz curve is the diagonal) then the Gini coefficient is zero.

● If there is perfect inequality (i.e. the plotted Lorenz curve is the horizontal axis until the last person who has all the income) then the Gini coefficient is one.

● The smaller the Gini coefficient, the greater the equality, and the larger the Gini coefficient the greater the inequality.

As we shall see from Self-Check Questions 1.6 the above conclusion may be invalidated should different Lorenz curves intersect one another. In this case we may have to trade off greater equality at one part of the distribution with greater inequality at another part, which may render the overall figure of the Gini coefficient less useful.

Did you know?

The United States is generally regarded as the strongest higher education nation in the world. In the global rankings of 2012 the United States had 75 universities in the world's top 200 universities (*Times Higher Education* World University Rankings), followed by the United Kingdom (32), Germany (12), Netherlands (12) and Canada (9).

Self-check questions 1.6

Q1. Use the following data to draw a Lorenz curve for 1979 on Figure 1.13.

Income receivers	1979	2009–10
Bottom 10%	4.7	2.6
Bottom 20%	11.0	7.1
Bottom 30%	17.5	12.6
Bottom 40%	24.2	19.1
Bottom 50%	32.2	26.6
Bottom 60%	41.2	35.3
Bottom 70%	51.8	45.3
Bottom 80%	64.3	57.0
Bottom 90%	79.6	73.4
Bottom 100%	100.0	100.0
Gini coefficient	0.248	0.340

Q2. Compare the 1979 and 2009–10 Lorenz curves and comment on any changes in inequality.

Note: Answers to Self-Check Questions can be found on the instructor's website, www.pearsoned.co.uk/wall

REVIEW QUESTIONS

*R1.1. We noted at the start of the chapter that the educational partnership was interested in developing 'flagship' programmes for pre-MBA study. It collects various data on MBA students and the outcomes of their studies from various sources of secondary data. This data is presented below. Use the data to respond to these questions.

(a) Select appropriate diagrams to display the data to show any patterns and trends to prospective MBA students.

(b) Suggest how the patterns and trends identified might be useful to the education partnership.

While various possible diagrams can be used in many cases, a 'hint' is given as to at least one possible diagram you might consider to represent each table.

Business school graduate salaries in eurozone

The data refers to salaries in 2011 of students who had graduated three years previously (in 2008) in three masters programmes:

- Master of Business Administration (MBA);
- Master of Science in Management (MSc);
- Executive MBA (EMBA).

The latter (EMBA) has more applied curriculum for more experienced executives entering an MBA programme.

The following data compares the median (50th percentile) salary of MBA graduates three years after graduation with that prior to their MBA studies, by location of study.

*Table R.1 Median salary increase (%) three years after graduation, compared with pre-MBA, by location of business school

Location	2007	2008	2009	2010	2011
Asia Pacific	67	66	48	59	46
North America	51	57	47	44	38
Europe (non-UK)	88	70	63	72	54
UK	51	61	68	64	55

Source: Adapted from Executive MBA Ranking 2011, *Financial Times* 24/11/2011, p. 24 (Jacobs, M.), Financial Times, © The Financial Times Limited. All Rights Reserved.

Hint: Line graph

The data in Table R.2 is a frequency distribution of MBA graduate salaries in 2011.

*Table R.2 Frequency table of MBA salaries in 2011 of 30 European business schools

Salary ($000)	Frequency (*f*)
71–90	4
91–110	11
111–130	8
131–150	7

Source: Adapted from Rankings, *Financial Times*, 05/12/2011, pp. 26–29 (Jacobs, M.), Financial Times, © The Financial Times Limited. All Rights Reserved.

Hint: Equal-width histogram

The data in Table R.3 is a frequency distribution of Masters in Management Science graduate salaries in 2011.

*Table R.3 Frequency table of MSc in Management salaries in 2011 of 62 European business schools

Salary ($000)	Frequency (*f*)
31–40	4
41–50	18
51–60	27
61–80	10
81–100	3

Source: Adapted from Rankings, *Financial Times*, 05/12/2011, pp. 26–29 (Jacobs, M.), Financial Times, © The Financial Times Limited. All Rights Reserved.

Hint: Unequal-width histogram

The data in Table R.4 gives absolute values for the respective salaries. It reminds us that a smaller percentage increase on a high absolute value can be worth more than a larger percentage on a small absolute value.

Table R.4 Average absolute salaries three years after graduation

MBA	€ 89,606
MSc	€ 46,700
EMBA	€ 103,600

Source: Adapted from Rankings, *Financial Times*, 05/12/2011, pp. 24–29 (Jacobs, M.), Financial Times, © The Financial Times Limited. All Rights Reserved.

Hint: Background information only

There is considerable official support for entrepreneurial and business start-up activity, seen as an engine of growth and job creation. The following data relates to MBA graduates in 2011, three years after graduating in 2008.

*Table R.5 Entrepreneurial start-ups: percentage of MBA graduates (three years after graduation)

Date	Female	Male	All
2005	6	12	10
2006	4	14	11
2007	3	12	8
2008	5	11	8
2009	5	12	9
2010	5	13	10
2011	5	15	11

Source: Adapted from Ranking: France loses stranglehold on the top, *Financial Times* 19/09/2011, p. 25 (Jacobs, M.), Financial Times, © The Financial Times Limited. All Rights Reserved.

Hint: Multiple bar chart

Internships are extremely popular: around two thirds of those graduating with a Masters in Management complete internships during their programme. Around half of these take place over-seas – that is, outside the country in which they are studying.

*Table R.6 Internships during studies for Masters in Management (2011), percentage by location

Country	All MSc Management	In country of study	Outside country of study
France	98	58	40
Germany	84	30	54
Belgium	98	21	77
Netherlands	28	12	16
United Kingdom	3	0	3
Other	30	14	16

Source: Adapted from Ranking: France loses stranglehold on the top, *Financial Times*, 19/09/2011 (Jacobs, M.), Financial Times, © The Financial Times Limited. All Rights Reserved.

Hint: Component bar chart or multiple bar chart

*R1.2. Our educational partnership is considering internationalising its operations and is comparing prospects for a start-up in two countries, A and B. It conducts some market research on the profitability of over one hundred educational companies in the same line of activity in each of these countries. The results are shown below.

Country A

LCB(£)	UCB(£)	f
−10,000	<0	2
0	<10,000	14
10,000	<20,000	18
20,000	<30,000	20
30,000	<40,000	28
40,000	<50,000	14
50,000	<70,000	16
	Total	112

Country B

LCB(£)	UCB(£)	f
−10,000	<0	5
0	<10,000	45
10,000	<20,000	30
20,000	<30,000	14
30,000	<40,000	12
40,000	<50,000	6
50,000	<70,000	4
	Total	116

(a) Draw a histogram for the profitability of educational companies in Country A and Country B.

(b) Compare the histogram for the profitability of the educational company in Country A with the histogram for country B. What do you conclude?

(c) What future policies might be suggested to the educational partnership by your histograms?

R1.3. The educational partnership wishes to review the performance of students on its Business Foundation Programme. A frequency distribution table was prepared from the data as follows:

% score	Number of students
40–45	4
45–50	13
50–55	17
55–60	44
60–70	59
70–80	7

From the given data construct

(a) a cumulative frequency curve (ogive).

(b) From your ogive estimate:

(i) the median score;

(ii) the interquartile range (the difference between the upper and lower quartiles);

(iii) the number of students with a score of less than 52%.

R1.4. The following total expenditure was incurred by the educational partnership in the last financial year.

Cost centre	£
Employees	1,139,410
Premises	69,004
Transport	52,524
Learning materials	83,205
Administration	23,205
Capital financing costs	71,282
Total	1,438,630

Construct a pie chart to illustrate the data.

What does the pie chart suggest?

R1.5. While investigating the number of students recruited from a particular country, the educational partnership collected the following data.

Year	Number of students
2004	120
2005	132
2006	170
2007	210
2008	230
2009	238
2010	220
2011	206
2012	194
2013	190

Use a vertical bar chart to illustrate the data. What does the bar chart indicate?

Note: Answers to Review Questions can be found on the instructor's website, www.pearsoned.co.uk/wall

Further practice

You can find more questions (with solutions) on techniques for collecting and presenting data on the instructor's website, www.pearsoned.co.uk/wall, including instructions on using spreadsheets to develop various types of graphs.

Spreadsheets: video guide

You can also find a step-by-step account that takes you through the actual use of a spreadsheet when solving the type of problems you have encountered in this chapter. Go to the instructor's website, www.pearsoned.co.uk/wall

Chapter 2

Making sense of data
Central location and dispersion

Introduction

We saw in Chapter 1 that the use of a wide range of tables, charts and graphs can help by giving a visual impression of patterns and trends in data, with the higher education sector the context for our discussion. Meaning can also be given to the original (raw) data by calculating various measures of central location (average) and dispersion (spread of data around the average).

In this chapter the context in which we will explore such measures involves the introduction of a new technique for mobile devices that allows them to access the internet using only one quarter of the current bandwidth. The introduction stage for this particular product and for information technology (IT) products more generally will help us see the importance of using measures of central location and dispersion to give meaning to raw (untreated) data.

Dr Sunil Singh is setting up a new business that involves producing a new type of technology for mobile phones. His idea is based on the research he has been undertaking in the laboratories of his university. He always wanted to establish his own business and now he believes he has made a technological breakthrough that will help him to do just that! The technology is a type of data compression that allows the internet to be accessed from the phone using only one quarter of the current bandwidth. In effect this means that internet access can now be four times faster for the end user or can take place at one quarter of the previous cost to the service provider. By appealing to both demand (users) and supply (providers) elements in the market place, Dr Singh is confident he will be able to establish a business based on this technology. He has applied for patent protection of his technology, and has been assured by specialists in the field that his breakthrough is sufficiently innovative for the patent to be granted. His technology is embedded in a device that can be inserted into existing mobile phones as well as new ones.

The following article provides useful insights for Dr Singh of both the opportunities and threats of entry into the fast-moving mobile and smartphone market sector.

Intel v ARM

Intel® launched its latest Intel® Core processors in 2013 in an attempt to revive desktop and laptop PC sales in which it has market dominance. However, these sales have been declining at around 12% per year in recent times as smartphones and tablets continue to capture market share, using chips mostly powered by designs licensed from ARM®, a smaller British firm whose energy-efficient designs are well suited for mobile devices. Intel® Atom™ processors targets the smartphone and tablet markets.

Intel is hoping that its power-efficient Intel Core processors will help revive PC and laptop sales by making possible thinner, quieter and faster machines that can run for 50% longer than before. Encouragingly for Intel, in 2013 Samsung chose the latest Intel Atom processor for its new range of Android-powered tablets.

Sunil will need to apply the statistical techniques reviewed in this chapter if he is to make sense of the emerging data and competing claims of the key 'players' in the mobile telephony market.

The focus in this chapter is on using measures of central location and dispersion to help Dr Singh analyse his business opportunities. We then extend the application of these measures to the IT sector as a whole. Of course he must be able to evaluate the demand (revenue) and supply (cost) elements of his new product line to justify investment by the venture capitalist company he has approached for finance, and he obviously also wants to be sure in his own mind that the investment of his own time and money in the new product will be worthwhile.

By the end of the chapter we should be able to identify how measures of central location and dispersion can help Dr Singh or any similar start-up company in the IT sector (or indeed any sector) evaluate a wide range of business opportunities. In 2013 some 60% of all internet users in Europe went to Google's search engines to locate information, so this is an important possible avenue for business development. Although our emphasis in this chapter is on the introduction stage of the product life cycle, Dr Singh's company will also need to use measures of central location and dispersion to evaluate data and opportunities in the subsequent growth stage.

Spreadsheets

The questions and activities in the Break-Out Boxes use spreadsheets which can be found on the student's website, www.pearsoned.co.uk/wall. Many of the Worked Examples, Self-Check Questions and Review Questions are set out for you as an Excel spreadsheet on the student's website and these questions are marked with an asterisk (*).

Learning objectives

When you have read this chapter you should be able to:

● identify and calculate the various measures of central location, such as arithmetic mean, median and mode, for both ungrouped and grouped data;

● understand when the various measures of central location will be similar and when they will differ, and calculate a measure for the extent of skew in the distribution;

- identify and calculate the various measures of dispersion such as interquartile range, mean deviation, variance and standard deviation, for both ungrouped and grouped data;
- understand and interpret measures that combine aspects of central location and dispersion, such as the coefficient of variation;
- apply these techniques to the issues faced by a start-up company in the IT sector and more generally.

2.1   Notation

Before we begin to apply these measures of central location and dispersion to Dr Singh's business we can usefully review some 'shorthand' ways of expressing information – that is, some important types of notation.

At least three types of average are in common use when seeking to describe raw data, namely arithmetic mean, median and mode. The formulae used to find these different types of average make use of a type of shorthand notation that will save you time and with which you should become familiar.

$$\sum = \text{Greek letter sigma} = \text{sum of}$$

The values of some variable X_i that are to be summed are indicated by the numbers written below and above the sigma sign. For example, suppose X_i refers to the number of days Dr Singh has spent with several different financial advisors and that he has spent three days with the first, five days with the second and one day with the third. Suppose we wish to sum (add together) the number of days he has spent with all three financial advisors, we would write:

$$\sum_{i=1}^{3} X_i = X_1 + X_2 + X_3$$
$$= 3 + 5 + 1$$
$$= 9 \text{ days}$$

Suppose Dr Singh now spends six days with a fourth advisor, but doesn't want to count the days spent with the first advisor. We would write:

$$\sum_{i=2}^{4} X_i = X_2 + X_3 + X_4$$
$$= 5 + 1 + 6$$
$$= 12 \text{ days}$$

More generally, when we wish to sum over n values of the variable we write:

$$\sum_{i=1}^{n} X_i = X_1 + X_2 + X_3 + \ldots X_n$$

where n can be any number.

Suppose Dr Singh is disappointed with the financial advice given and seeks out still more financial advisors, using eight altogether. Sometimes a particular number of days spent with an advisor might occur once or more than once with these eight different advisors. For example, he might spend four days with three of the eight financial advisors. In other words, four days occurs with a frequency 3.

For example, suppose we are given the following data on the number of days Dr Singh spends with eight different advisors:

$$4, 2, 5, 4, 2, 1, 4, 3$$

Let X_i = number of days

$\quad F_i$ = frequency with which X_i occurs

$\quad n$ = number of advisors

We can see that there are only five different number of days (X_i).

If we let X_1 = 1 day, occurs with frequency $F_1 = 1$

$\quad\quad\quad X_2$ = 2 days, occurs with frequency $F_2 = 2$

$\quad\quad\quad X_3$ = 3 days, occurs with frequency $F_3 = 1$

$\quad\quad\quad X_4$ = 4 days, occurs with frequency $F_4 = 3$

$\quad\quad\quad X_5$ = 5 days, occurs with frequency $F_5 = 1$

Note that if we sum the individual frequencies over the five different number of days spent with the eight advisors we get:

$$\sum_{i=1}^{5} F_i = F_1 + F_2 + F_3 + F_4 + F_5$$

$$\sum_{i=1}^{5} F_i = 1 + 2 + 1 + 3 + 1$$

$$\sum_{i=1}^{5} F_i = 8$$

So the sum of the individual frequencies for each of the five different number of days spent equals the total number of advisors, n, which in this case equals eight.

But the total number of days spent with all 8 advisors is 25. We can use our shorthand notation to express this as follows:

$$\sum_{i=1}^{5} F_i X_i = F_1 X_1 + F_2 X_2 + F_3 F_3 + F_4 X_4 + F_5 X_5$$

$$= (1 \times 1) + (2 \times 2) + (1 \times 3) + (3 \times 4) + (1 \times 5)$$

$$= 1 + 4 + 3 + 12 + 5$$

$$\sum_{i=1}^{5} F_i X_i = 25$$

You will come across the use of this shorthand notation involving the sigma sign throughout this chapter and in subsequent chapters. It will therefore be helpful to practise using the notation before going any further.

Self-check questions 2.1

Q1. Expand (write out in full) each of the following expressions:

(a) $\displaystyle\sum_{i=1}^{4} X_i$

(b) $\displaystyle\sum_{i=2}^{5} X_i$

(c) $\displaystyle\sum_{i=1}^{3} F_i X_i$

(d) $\displaystyle\sum_{i=3}^{6} F_i X_i$

Q2. Describe each of the following expressions using sigma notation:
   (a) $X_1 + X_2 + X_3 + X_4 + X_5$
   (b) $X_5 + X_6 + X_7$
   (c) $F_1 X_1 + F_2 X_2 + F_3 X_3 + F_4 X_4$
   (d) $F_2 X_2 + F_3 X_3 + F_4 X_4$

Q3. The following days are spent with 15 different financial advisors:

5, 6, 4, 3, 6, 5, 1, 1, 2, 4, 3, 1, 2, 4, 6

Find $\displaystyle\sum_{i=1}^{j} F_i X_i$

where j = the number of different days observed
   F_i = frequency of a particular number of days
   X_i = particular number of days

Note: From this point onwards, for simplicity, we will simply use the $\sum$ sign without the numbers below and above that sign.

Note: Answers to Self-Check Questions can be found on the instructor's website, www.pearsoned.co.uk/wall

2.2 Measures of central location

A number of measures of central location or 'average' are widely used in an attempt to give meaning to raw data. Here we consider the arithmetic mean, median and mode for both *ungrouped data* (all individual items known) and *grouped data* (items only identified within class intervals).

2.2.1 The arithmetic mean

This is the simple average of everyday use, and is often represented by the symbol $\overline{X}$.

Mean for ungrouped data

Where individual or ungrouped data is available, the following formula is commonly used:

$$\bar{X} = \frac{\sum X_i}{n}$$

where $\bar{X}$ = arithmetic mean

X_i = value of each item of data

n = number of items of data

<table>
<tr><td>**Worked example 2.1**</td><td>Suppose the revenue from the first five years of sales of Dr Singh's devices for mobile phones is projected to be as follows (in £m) in Table 2.1.</td></tr>
</table>

Table 2.1 Revenue projected in first five years of operation (£m)

	1	2	3	4	5
Yearly sales (£m)	0.4	0.9	1.5	2.5	2.7

Dr Singh wants to work out the average annual sales revenue over this five year period.

Solution

Using the formula:

$$\bar{X} = \frac{\sum X_i}{n} = \frac{X_1 + X_2 + X_3 + X_4 + X_5}{5} = \frac{0.4 + 0.9 + 1.5 + 2.5 + 2.7}{5}$$

$$\bar{X} = \frac{8}{5} = \text{£1.6 million per annum}$$

The average annual sales revenue is £1.6 million and this represents a typical annual figure around which the rest of the data will cluster over the five year period.

Did you know?

Here is some encouraging data for Dr Singh in terms of future possible sales of his mobile devices. The mean monthly *text messages per mobile connection* in the United Kingdom increased by over 900% over the past 10 years, from 36 text messages per month per mobile connection in 2003 to over 330 text messages per month per mobile connection in 2013. Similarly, the mean annual volume of *mobile-data traffic* has increased at the astonishing rate of over 1,000% per annum between 2008 and 2013. In 2013 over 8 billion mobile phones were in use, which is more than the global population at that date!

While still small in comparison, global sales of smartphones with internet linkage are the fastest growing, more than doubling each year to reach over 800 million in 2013.

Mean for grouped data

More usually (as we noted in Chapter 1), data is *grouped* into a frequency table with various class intervals. To deal with such data the simplifying assumption must be made that *within any given class interval* the items of data fall on the class mid-point. This is equivalent to assuming that the items of data are evenly spread within any given class interval.

We may now make use of the following formulae:

$$\bar{X} = \frac{\sum F_i X_i}{\sum F_i} = \frac{F_1 X_1 + F_2 X_2 + \ldots F_j X_j}{F_1 + F_2 \quad + \ldots F_j}$$

where F_i = frequency of ith class interval

$\qquad X_i$ = mid-point of ith class interval

$\qquad j$ = number of class intervals

*Worked example 2.2

Suppose that five different versions of devices for mobile phones will be sold in year 1, each having a different price range as indicated in Table 2.2 (five class intervals for prices).

Table 2.2 Price range for five different types of mobile device

Price of mobile device (£)	Number of devices sold (000)
1.5–2.5	10
2.5–3.5	20
3.5–4.5	40
4.5–5.5	20
5.5–6.5	10

Solution

We can use our formula for grouped data to calculate the average (arithmetic mean) price of the mobile phone devices sold (see Table 2.3).

Table 2.3 The average (arithmetic mean) price of mobile devices sold

Price range of device (£)	Class mid-point X_i	Number of devices sold (000) F_i	$F_i X_i$
1.5–2.5	2	10	20
2.5–3.5	3	20	60
3.5–4.5	4	40	160
4.5–5.5	5	20	100
5.5–6.5	6	10	60
		$\sum_{i=1}^{5} F_i = 100$	$\sum_{i=1}^{5} F_i X_i = 400$

$$\bar{X} = \frac{\sum F_i X_i}{\sum F_i} = \frac{400(000)}{100(000)} = 4$$

In other words, the average price of the mobile phone devices was £4.

2.2.2 The median

This is the value that divides the data set into two equal halves: 50% of values lying below the median, and 50% of values lying above the median.

The approach we consider below estimates the median value for both grouped and ungrouped data.

Median for ungrouped data

To find the median do the following.

Step 1. Construct an *array* (i.e. place the data in numerical order – whether rising or falling).

Step 2. Find the *median position* $\dfrac{n + 1}{2}$ where n = number of values.

Step 3. Find the *median value* (i.e. the value of the data corresponding to the median position).

Worked example 2.3

Find the median value of the output of Dr Singh's devices by a particular employee over a five day period (see Table 2.4).

Table 2.4 Daily output of devices by an employee of Dr Singh

Daily output				
310	340	360	320	330

Solution

Step 1. Place in an *array* 310 320 330 340 360.

Step 2. Find the *median position* using the equation $\dfrac{n + 1}{2}$ where n = the number of values. Median position = $\dfrac{5 + 1}{2}$ = third item arranged in order.

Step 3. Find the *value* of the third item in the array (i.e. 330 units).

Note: Where there is an *even* number of items there will be two middle items. If so, take the average of these two middle items. Suppose Dr Singh now produces his devices on a Saturday with 380 units of output recorded on that day.

The *median position* would now be $\dfrac{6 + 1}{2}$ = 3.5

The *median value* would now be $\dfrac{330 + 340}{2}$ = 335 daily output.

BREAK-OUT BOX 2.1

Central location – ungrouped data

Automatic example generator

In the Excel sheet Chapter2_Example_1 you will find an example generator for checking your ability to calculate the mean, median and mode for *ungrouped data*, using data from Dr Singh's business. You will find sales data that refers to the number of devices for mobile phones sold by one person each week over the past year in the sales department of Dr Singh's company. If you click on the 'Get another person's sales data' a new set of data will be automatically generated for you to work from. You can keep generating as much new data as you want. You can use your own calculations from our formulae to find the mean, median and mode and then check your answers with those provided by the spreadsheet.

You can check your answers by clicking on 'Formulas', then 'Insert function (*fx*)', then clicking on 'Average' (for mean), 'Median' and 'Mode' respectively.

Median for grouped data

The following steps can be used to calculate arithmetically the median value for grouped data presented in a frequency table.

Step 1. Find the median position.

Step 2. Find the class interval in which the median observation lies.

Step 3. Assume that all items in this class interval are equally spaced.

Step 4. Estimate the median.

Worked example 2.4

Find the median price for the five different versions of devices produced by Dr Singh, using the data given in Table 2.2 (p. 41).

Solution

$$\text{Median position} = \frac{n + 1}{2}$$
$$= \frac{100 + 1}{2}$$
$$= 50.5\text{th item in an array}$$

The 50.5th item will occur in the class interval £3.5–£4.5.

We assume that the 40 devices are evenly spread throughout the £3.5–£4.5 class interval.

Figure 2.1 gives a visual picture of how we find the median value for this grouped data.

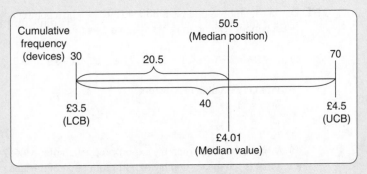

Figure 2.1 Median class interval for Table 2.2

The class interval in which the median position falls has a *lower class boundary* (LCB) of £3.5 and an *upper class boundary* (UCB) of £4.5, giving a *class width* of £1. Now the cumulative frequency up to the LCB of £3.5 is 30 devices, which is less than the median position which occurs with a cumulative frequency of 50.5 devices.

Clearly the median value is larger than £3.5 as we wish to go a further 20.5 (observations) to reach the median position. However, there are 40 devices assumed to be equally spaced along this class interval of £1. We therefore wish to go 20.5 ÷ 40 of the way along the £1 interval in order to find the median value of devices. This gives the formula:

$$£3.5 + \left(£1 \times \frac{20.5}{40} \right) = £3.50 + 0.51 = £4.01$$

Formula for finding median in grouped data

The median value can be found using the formula:

$$\text{LCB} + \text{class width} \times \frac{\text{number of observations to median position}}{\text{total number of observations in median class interval}}$$

where LCB = lower class boundary (of median class interval).

2.2.3 The mode

When data is ungrouped as in the example on p. 38 which gives the number of days Dr Singh spent with eight different financial advisors, the mode value can be identified; in this case it is four days, which occurs for three of the eight different advisors.

This is that value which occurs with the greatest frequency. When data is *grouped*, then the class interval with the highest frequency is referred to as the modal class interval. In Table 2.2 (p. 41) the class interval £3.5–£4.5 is the modal class interval, with 40(000) mobile devices in the interval.

Self-check questions 2.2

*Q1. Devices for mobile phones produced by Dr Singh's company for export (X_i) in thousands in each month during the past year were as follows:

69.3   75.7   76.3   94.4   88.7   77.2   86.4   75.5   79.0   83.3   82.2   78.1

(a) What is the value of X_i when:
   (i) $i = 4$
   (ii) $i = 7$
   (iii) $i = 10$
(b) What is the mean monthly export production of devices?
(c) What is the mean monthly export production of devices over the final six months?

(continued)

(d) What is the mean monthly export production of devices during months 4 to 9 inclusive?

(e) What is the median monthly export production of devices?

*Q2. The following figures show the annual salaries (£) of the 20 workers in Dr Singh's original business plan. Calculate the arithmetic mean, median and mode salary and comment on your results:

36,500	29,000	33,000	64,000	38,000
34,000	28,500	38,500	32,500	45,000
44,000	30,000	28,500	38,000	45,000
42,250	6,000	33,000	64,000	38,000

*Q3. Find the median value for the price of mobile devices using the data of Table 2.3 (p. 41). What do you notice?

*Q4. A major multinational is interested in purchasing Dr Singh's device to help increase its sales of mobile phones in the Chinese market. The multinational company has identified the younger Chinese consumers, whether male or female, as the most important buyers of its mobile phones. However, it is worried that the average age of male and female Chinese consumers is rising sharply.

(a) Use the data in Table 2.5 to comment on whether the average (*mean*) age of males and females has increased over the past 15 years.

(b) Would your answer to (a) be different if you used the *median* age of males and females?

We have already noted in Chapter 1 (p. 26) how the use of cumulative frequency curves (or ogives) can help find the median value by graphical methods.

Note: This will also be set out in an Excel spreadsheet on the instructor's website, www.pearsoned.co.uk/wall

Table 2.5 China's population (millions)

	1994		2009	
Age (years)	Male	Female	Male	Female
0–5	59	53	45	40
5–10	62	58	42	39
10–15	53	50	53	44
15–20	51	49	56	50
20–25	64	59	60	54
25–30	64	59	52	49
30–35	48	43	50	46
35–40	46	41	60	58
40–45	44	40	59	57
45–50	30	28	43	42
50–55	25	20	41	39
55–60	23	18	39	36
60–65	20	17	26	21
65–70	18	15	20	20
70–75	11	12	18	17
75–80	6	7	10	12
80–85	2	4	5	7
85–90	1	2	2	4
90 and above	1	2	2	3

(continued)

*Q5. A venture capitalist that Dr Singh has approached for further finance receives the following table of data (Table 2.6) showing the percentage changes in labour costs for the 100 employees now involved in producing his devices over a 12 month period. The highest change observed was +172% for a highly productive employee in one of Dr Singh's plants.

Table 2.6 Percentage change in employee annual labour costs

Percentage change	Frequency
−5 to under 0	2
0 to under 5	34
5 to under 10	25
10 to under 15	10
15 to under 20	8
20 to under 25	3
25 to under 30	2
30 to under 35	5
35 to under 40	4
40 to under 100	3
100 to 172	4

(a) What is the mean annual percentage change in labour costs for this company?
(b) What is the median annual percentage change?
(c) What is the modal class interval?

Note: Answers to Self-Check Questions can be found on the instructor's website, www.pearsoned.co.uk/wall

Did you know?

The biggest threat to IT businesses is not the eurozone crisis or credit restrictions, but the shortage of the so-called 'rare earth' metals such as tungsten, platinum and cobalt. In fact there are 17 'rare earth' metals and these are needed to make everything, from smartphones to plasma TVs, and China is responsible for around 95% of the global supply of such metals!

2.3 Normal and skewed distribution

When the set of data is distributed in a perfectly symmetrical way, as in Figure 2.2A, then all three types of average have the same value. Such a symmetrical distribution is often referred to as a *normal distribution*. However when, as is more usually the case, the set of data is *skewed* in one direction or another, as in Figure 2.2B and Figure 2.2C, then the three types of average will cease to be identical. In fact the arithmetic mean will always be most heavily influenced by the direction of the skew – that is, the direction being described by the tail of the distribution – which represents the side of the distribution with fewest

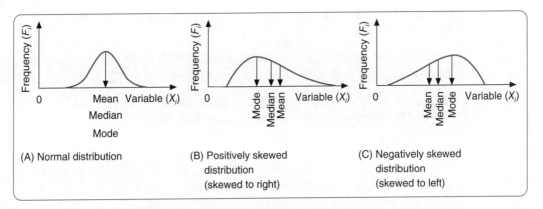

Figure 2.2 **Normal and skewed frequency distributions and measures of central location**

observations. In other words, the arithmetic mean will be most affected by a few extreme values, whether higher values (skewed to the right) or lower values (skewed to the left).

When data is skewed to the right or left, you must be careful about interpreting any loose talk on 'average' values. For example, if the distribution of wages in Dr Singh's business is skewed to the right, as in Figure 2.2B, Dr Singh might claim that he pays an 'average' wage of, say, £600 per week and the trade union might claim that he pays an 'average' of, say, £500 a week and both might be right! More generally the employers may be selecting the type of 'average' (arithmetic mean in this case) most likely to show them as a high paying company and the union may be selecting the type of average (median) most beneficial to their claim for higher wages.

PAUSE FOR THOUGHT 2.1

In what direction would you expect the UK income distribution to be skewed? How might this affect median and mean incomes? If you live outside the United Kingdom, what would your answer be for your country?

2.3.1 Measuring the skew

A useful measure of the direction and the extent of the skew is provided by *Pearson's coefficient of skewness* (SK).

$$SK = \frac{3(\text{mean} - \text{median})}{\text{Standard deviation}}$$

We consider the standard of deviation as a measure of spread or dispersion of the data in more detail in Section 2.4. Here we only concentrate on the numerator (top) of the expression for SK.

- In our earlier discussions involving a perfectly symmetrical (normal) distribution, we noted that the mean was exactly equal to the median, so that our formula will give SK = 0.

- If, however, there is a significant amount of skew, then the mean will be very different from the median, and the value of SK will be positive or negative and will rise or fall if there is any change in the extent of the skew.

Knowing the value (sign and size) of SK will therefore help us work out what the distribution looks like.

PAUSE FOR THOUGHT 2.2

When will the coefficient of skewness SK be positive and rising?
When will the coefficient of skewness SK be negative and falling?

*Worked example 2.5

Table 2.7 below shows the weekly output of the devices for mobile phones produced by the 200 production workers in Dr Singh's company.

Table 2.7 Weekly output of devices for mobile phones by production workers

Output (units)	Number of employees
100–160	1
160–180	5
180–200	10
200–220	35
220–240	55
240–260	74
260–300	20
	200

(a) Find the arithmetic mean of the weekly output.

(b) Find the median weekly output.

(c) Why do (a) and (b) differ?

PAUSE FOR THOUGHT 2.3

Before calculating the solution to Worked Example 2.5, look briefly at the table of data above and decide on the direction of skew and the likely impact this will have on the mean and median values.

Solution

(a) Since we are dealing with grouped data we must take class mid-points for the variable X_i. We then use the formula:

$$\bar{X} = \frac{\sum F_i X_i}{\sum F_i}$$

where F_i = class frequency

X_i = class mid-point

Worked example 2.5 (cont'd)

X_i (class mid-point)	F_i (class frequency)	F_iX_i
130	1	130
170	5	850
190	10	1,900
210	35	7,350
230	55	12,650
250	74	18,500
280	20	5,600
	$\sum F_i = 200$	$\sum F_iX_i = 46,980$

$$\overline{X} = \frac{\sum F_iX_i}{\sum F_i} = \frac{46,980}{200} = 234.9$$

The arithmetic mean of the weekly output is 234.9 units.

(b) The median position $= \dfrac{n+1}{2} = \dfrac{200+1}{2} = 100.5$ employees.

The median class interval for output is 220–240 units, as shown in Figure 2.3. Using our formula for the median, and assuming an equal spacing of the 55 employees along the median class interval with class width of 20 units of output, we have:

$$\text{Median} = \text{LCB} + \text{class width} \times \frac{\text{number of observations to median position}}{\text{total number of observations in median class interval}}$$

i.e.

$$\text{Median} = 220 + \left(20 \times \frac{49.5}{55}\right) = 238 \text{ units}$$

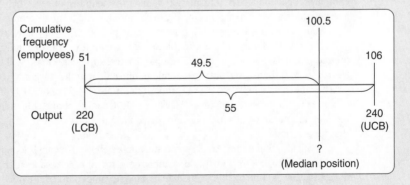

Figure 2.3 Finding the median value

49

Worked
example
2.5
(cont'd)

(c) The arithmetic mean output (234.9 units) is lower than the median output (238 units). We would expect this to be the case since the data is clearly skewed to the left. It is similar to Figure 2.2C and the arithmetic mean (simple average) will be pulled down by the few extremely low values.

The measure of skew (SK) will give us:

$$SK = \frac{3(234.9 - 238)}{\sigma} = \frac{-9.3}{\sigma}$$

The negative sign for SK tells us that the distribution is skewed to the left.

Did you know?

More good news for Dr Singh! There is a rapid growth in online shopping using mobile phones. In fact mobiles with internet access are at the forefront of what many see as a retail revolution! Smartphones accounted for over 50% of all new handsets sold in the United Kingdom in 2013, more than doubling their 26% market share of 2010. This rapid growth in smartphone demand is proving of major benefit to hard-pressed high street retailers. John Lewis, Tesco, M&S, Shop Direct, Mothercare and many others have adapted their websites to make them simpler and easier to navigate by smartphone. This is hardly surprising when retail analysts such as Verdict Research had accurately predicted that mobile internet sales would more than double between 2011 and 2013. In fact 79% of British consumers are predicted to use their mobile phones for retail sales by the end of 2014. Verdict Research's report suggests that by 2015 retail sales via smartphone mobile internet access will overtake those via PC access.

BREAK-OUT BOX 2.2

Using measures of central location for company comparisons

Dr Singh is often asked by potential investors how other companies in the IT sector are doing at that moment in time, to provide a benchmark against which they can assess the prospects for his company. A useful piece of information he likes to use in response to such questions involves the average share price of a major company in the mobile chip business, comparing its average share price today with the average in a previous time period. If he can show that the average share price is rising, Dr Singh will point to this as evidence for investors of a buoyant market for his and related products. Using Chapter2_Example_2 Excel spreadsheet you will be able to get the past 32 days of real share price data for mobile phone chip manufacturers.

The table below represents a snapshot *at that time* (i.e. 7 June 2013) of the previous 32 days of share price data on the US Stock Market of ARM, a large phone chip manufacturer. The mean, median and mode values for the share price have been calculated using the spreadsheet over that time period.

You will also find on the Excel spreadsheet noted above (Chapter2_Example_2) the *latest* share price data for you to work with for this company and for other companies in the IT sector. You can use the spreadsheet to find the mean, median and mode values of the share price for the past 32 days of ARM and then compare these current measures of average share price for ARM with those calculated for this earlier time period shown in the table below.

Date	Share price ($) close
07/06/2013	40.17
06/06/2013	41.22
05/06/2013	40.7
04/06/2013	42.07
03/06/2013	42.5
31/05/2013	43.88
30/05/2013	45.54
29/05/2013	44.61
28/05/2013	45.01
24/05/2013	45.1
23/05/2013	45.37
22/05/2013	45.82
21/05/2013	47.24
20/05/2013	49.89
17/05/2013	49.78
16/05/2013	49.89
15/05/2013	50.11
14/05/2013	49.41

Date	Share price ($) close
13/05/2013	49.11
10/05/2013	49.59
09/05/2013	49.5
08/05/2013	49.85
07/05/2013	48.91
06/05/2013	48.53
03/05/2013	48.5
02/05/2013	47.62
01/05/2013	47.54
30/04/2013	46.75
29/04/2013	45.74
26/04/2013	45.73
25/04/2013	45.9
24/04/2013	45.06

Mean:	46.46
Median:	46.33
Mode:	49.89

Now re-calculate the mean, median and mode using the most recent 32 day data on ARM's share price, using the Excel spreadsheet. What do you notice?

Self-check questions 2.3

Q1. Dr Singh reads an article in which researchers at Incomes Data Services reported in 2013 that pay rises for higher earning occupations in the United Kingdom have outstripped those for the rest of the workforce. As a result, the average (arithmetic mean) wage has been pulled upwards, leaving more and more occupations beneath it. In 2013 some 65% of the workforce earned less than the average weekly wage of £565 before tax, compared to only 60% in 1990. Dr Singh wants to check that the remuneration policy for his workforce is in line with national trends.

What does this study suggest to Dr Singh about the *direction* of skew for wages in the United Kingdom?

Q2. Dr Singh has calculated the mean and median values for the profits of two separate workshops that produce his mobile phone device. The results are shown in the following table. We also put in the values for the standard deviation for these workshops.

	Workshop A	Workshop B
Mean	£12,300	£18,776
Median	£7,679	£9,828
Standard deviation	17,476	19,688

(a) Use these results to calculate Pearson's coefficient of skewness (SK).

(b) What might Dr Singh conclude from these results?

Note: Answers to Self-Check Questions can be found on the instructor's website, www.pearsoned.co.uk/wall

2.4   Measures of dispersion

As well as measure of central tendency or average, it is helpful to have a measure of the extent of *dispersion* or spread around that average. The formulae and a brief outline for the most widely used measures of dispersion are presented here.

As we can see from Figure 2.4, two distributions showing the price of mobile devices of Dr Singh sold in two different outlets may have similar measures of central location, but may be very different in terms of dispersion around any 'average'. Clearly distribution B is more widely dispersed than distribution A around the same arithmetic mean $\bar{X}$.

- *Range:* Perhaps the simplest measure of dispersion is to take the absolute difference between the highest and lowest value of the raw data. In Figure 2.4 the range for distribution A is £30, but the range for distribution B is higher at £50.

- *Interquartile range:* This is the absolute difference between the upper and lower quartiles of the distribution. We saw how to calculate these quartiles in Chapter 1 (p. 27).

$$\text{Interquartile range} = \text{upper quartile} - \text{lower quartile}$$

- *Semi-interquartile range:* This is half the interquartile range. It is sometimes called the quartile deviation

$$\text{Semi-interquartile range} = \frac{\text{upper quartile} - \text{lower quartile}}{2}$$

All the measures of dispersion considered so far have involved comparing two different points on the respective frequency distributions, such as the maximum and minimum points (the range) or the upper and lower quartiles (the interquartile range). We now turn to more useful measures of dispersion which compare *all* the points on the respective frequency distributions.

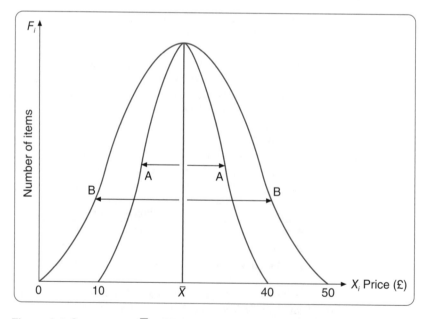

Figure 2.4 Same mean ($\bar{X}$), different dispersion for two distributions, A and B

Did you know?

The mean income for the top fifth of UK households is more than 20 times higher than that for the bottom fifth of UK households, before the impact of the tax and benefit system. After the impact of taxes and benefits, the respective mean incomes only differ by a factor of less than three.

2.4.1 Mean deviation

This is the average of the *absolute deviations* from the arithmetic mean, ignoring the sign. Of course if we did not ignore the sign, the average deviation from the arithmetic mean would always be zero! When two straight lines (rather than curved brackets) surround a number or variable it is referred to as the *modulus* and the straight lines tell us to ignore the sign.

The mean deviation is only rarely used as a measure of dispersion. However, it is worth some consideration as it is the basis for the more widely used measures of variance and standard deviation.

Mean deviation for ungrouped data

Suppose the hourly output (X_i) of devices for mobile phones by three employees of Dr Singh is as follows.

$$X_1 = 4, \ X_2 = 5, \ X_3 = 6$$

Clearly the arithmetic mean, $\bar{X}$, is 5. To find the mean deviation (MD) we need to find the average deviation from the mean, ignoring the sign:

$$\text{MD} = \frac{|X_1 - \bar{X}| + |X_2 - \bar{X}| + |X_3 - \bar{X}|}{n}$$

$$\text{MD} = \frac{|4 - 5| + |5 - 5| + |6 - 5|}{3} = \frac{|-1| + |0| + |+1|}{3} = \frac{2}{3}$$

On average, for each of the three employees, their hourly output of mobile devices is two thirds of a unit away from the average hourly output of 5.

Mean deviation for ungrouped data

$$\text{More generally MD} = \frac{\sum_{i=1}^{n} |X_i - \bar{X}|}{n}$$

where $||$ = modulus (i.e. ignore the sign)

n = number of observations

Mean deviation for grouped data

If we return to our example of the prices of 100 mobile devices of Dr Singh's company (Table 2.3) we can now use the mean deviation to give a measure of dispersion. We noted that the average price ($\bar{X}$) was £4 per device sold (p. 41). We now apply the formula for mean deviation with grouped data.

Mean deviation with grouped data

$$\text{More generally MD} = \frac{\sum_{i=1}^{j} F_i |X_i - \bar{X}|}{\sum_{i=1}^{j} F_i}$$

where F_i = class frequency

X_i = class mid-point

$\bar{X}$ = arithmetic mean

j = number of class intervals

$||$ = modulus (i.e. ignore the sign)

PAUSE FOR THOUGHT 2.4

How might you expect the mean deviation for the age of the UK population to change over time?

---

*Worked example 2.6

Find the mean deviation for the data shown in Table 2.3 (p. 41).

Solution

Price range of device (£)	Class mid-point X_i	Number of devices F_i	$|X_i - \bar{X}|$	$F_i |X_i - \bar{X}|$
1.5–2.5	2	10	$|-2|$	$|-20|$
2.5–3.5	3	20	$|-1|$	$|-20|$
3.5–4.5	4	40	$|0|$	$|0|$
4.5–5.5	5	20	$|+1|$	$|+20|$
5.5–6.5	6	10	$|+2|$	$|+20|$
	Total	100		80

Note: $\bar{X} = £4$

$$\text{MD} = \frac{\sum F_i |X_i - \bar{X}|}{\sum F_i} = \frac{80}{100} = £0.8$$

The average deviation from the arithmetic mean price is £0.8 per mobile device.

Did you know?

The mobile phone is becoming a key element in strategies to feed the world! A report by Oxfam in 2011 showed that even the most basic model at $5 can be used to give vital information on weather patterns, agricultural techniques and market prices to millions of small farmers in Asia and Sub-Saharan Africa. The report points to the vital role of the mobile phone in raising agricultural productivity for small rural farmers by as much as 11% within 10 years, so vital when one third of the world's food is produced by 500 million farms of less than 2 hectares. A 70% rise in food production will be needed by 2050 to feed the projected 9.2 billion people at that date.

2.4.2 Variance

If we *square* all the deviations from the arithmetic mean, then we no longer need to bother with the signs since all the values will be positive. We can then replace the straight line brackets (modulus) for the mean deviation with the more usual round brackets.

The resulting measure is now called the *variance*, which can then be regarded as the average of the squared deviations from the mean. Note that all the units are therefore squared: for example, square pounds, square metres, and so on.

Variance for ungrouped data

Variance for ungrouped data

$$\text{Variance } (s^2) = \frac{\sum \left(X_i - \bar{X} \right)^2}{n}$$

Worked example 2.7

Suppose we have to find the variance of the following eight items of raw data, representing the hourly earnings (£) of workers with very different productivity levels in Dr Singh's factories.

$$8, 10, 12, 14, 16, 18, 20, 22$$

Solution

$$\bar{X} = \frac{\sum X_i}{n} = \frac{120}{8} = £15$$

X_i	$(X_i - \bar{X})$	$(X_i - \bar{X})^2$
8	(−7)	49
10	(−5)	25
12	(−3)	9
14	(−1)	1
16	(1)	1
18	(3)	9

X_i	$(X_i - \bar{X})$	$(X_i - \bar{X})^2$
20	(5)	25
22	(7)	49
		168

$$s^2 = \frac{\sum (X_i - \bar{X})^2}{n} = \frac{168}{8} = 21 \text{ square pounds}$$

Variance $(s^2) = 21$ square pounds

Variance for grouped data

The formula for calculating the variance when data is grouped is as follows:

$$\text{Variance } (s^2) = \frac{\sum_{i=1}^{j} F_i \left(X_i - \bar{X} \right)^2}{\sum_{i=1}^{j} F_i}$$

where F_i = class frequency

X_i = class mid-point

$\bar{X}$ = arithmetic mean

j = number of class intervals

However, it can be shown that this formula simplifies to the following.

Variance for grouped data

Operational formula

$$\text{Variance } (s^2) = \frac{\sum F_i X_i^2}{\sum F_i} - \left(\frac{\sum F_i X_i}{\sum F_i} \right)^2$$

$$\text{Variance } (s^2) = \frac{\sum F_i X_i^2}{\sum F_i} - (\bar{X})^2$$

This is a useful formula for finding the variance since we will already have found the second term when calculating the arithmetic mean.

Worked example 2.8

Let us apply this formula to our earlier problem involving prices of mobile devices sold by Dr Singh in Table 2.3 (p. 41).

Price range of device (£)	Class mid-point X_i	Number of devices sold (000) F_i	F_iX_i	$F_iX_i^2$
1.5–2.5	2	10	20	40
2.5–3.5	3	20	60	180
3.5–4.5	4	40	160	640
4.5–5.5	5	20	100	500
5.5–6.5	6	10	60	360
	Total	100	400	1,720

$$s^2 = \frac{\sum F_iX_i^2}{\sum F_i} - \left(\frac{\sum F_iX_i}{\sum F_i}\right)^2$$

$$s^2 = \frac{1,720}{100} - \left(\frac{400}{100}\right)^2 = 17.2 - (4)^2$$

$$s^2 = 1.2 \text{ square pounds}$$

Note: $\sum_{i=1}^{j} F_iX_i^2 = F_1X_1^2 + F_2X_2^2 + \ldots F_iX_i^2$

In other words, the square is only on the X_i term and not on the F_iX_i term.

We can obtain the column $F_iX_i^2$ by either multiplying the F_iX_i column by the corresponding X_i or by multiplying the F_i column by the corresponding X_i^2. Check this yourself in the table above.

2.4.3 Standard deviation

Rather than use square units, it is more realistic to express solutions in terms of single units. The standard deviation does this by taking the square root of the variance.

The standard deviation (s) is then the square root of the average of the squared deviations from the mean.

The following formula applies to both ungrouped and grouped data:

$$\text{Standard deviation} = \sqrt{\text{variance}}$$

i.e. $$s = \sqrt{s^2}$$

BREAK-OUT BOX 2.3

Dispersion – ungrouped data

Automatic example generator

In the Excel spreadsheet Chapter2_Example_3 you will find an example generator for testing your ability to calculate the variance and standard deviation for ungrouped data, using data from Dr Singh's business.

The sales data refers to the number of devices for mobile phones sold each week in the past year by one person in the sales department of Dr Singh's company. Calculate the variance and standard deviation for weekly sales. You can check your answers by clicking on 'Formulas', then 'Insert function (fx)', then clicking on 'Varp' and 'Stdevp' respectively.

If you click on the 'Get another person's sales data' a new set of data will be automatically generated for you to work from. You can keep generating as much new data as you want.

*Worked example 2.9

Suppose Dr Singh now has 20 different production units for his mobile devices, spread across the United Kingdom and other countries. Table 2.8 presents the average hourly output of devices by employees in these different plants (production units).

Find the variance and standard deviation of average hourly production across the 20 different plants.

Solution

Table 2.8 Average hourly output of devices

Hourly output	Number F_i	Mid-point X_i	F_iX_i	$F_iX_i^2$
2.5–3.5	1	3	3	9
3.5–4.5	1	4	4	16
4.5–5.5	1	5	5	25
5.5–6.5	2	6	12	72
6.5–7.5	3	7	21	147
7.5–8.5	4	8	32	256
8.5–9.5	4	9	36	324
9.5–10.5	4	10	40	400
Total	20		153	1,249

$$\bar{X} = \frac{\sum F_iX_i}{\sum F_i} = \frac{153}{20} = 7.65 \text{ units}$$

$$s^2 = \frac{\sum F_iX_i^2}{\sum F_i} - \left(\frac{\sum F_iX_i}{\sum F_i} \right)^2$$

Worked
example
2.9
(*cont'd*)

$$s^2 = \frac{1,249}{20} - (7.65)^2$$

$$s^2 = 62.5 - 58.5 = 4$$

$$s^2 = \text{variance} = 4 \text{ square units}$$

$$s = \text{standard deviation} = \sqrt{4}$$

$$\text{i.e. } s = 2 \text{ units}$$

BREAK-OUT BOX 2.4

Using measures of dispersion for company comparisons

As we noted in Break-Out Box 2.2 (p. 50) Dr Singh is often asked by potential investors how other companies in the IT sector are performing. Another useful piece of information he likes to use in response to such questions involves measures of dispersion for the share price of a major company in the sector, comparing the measures of dispersion in its share price today with those in a previous time period. If he can show that these measures of dispersion are *falling* over time, he can argue that the sector is becoming less volatile (more certain) in terms of prospective returns for those investing in the sector. Using Chapter2_Example_4 Excel spreadsheet you will be able to obtain the past 32 days of real share price data for companies in the IT sector.

The table below represents a snapshot (*at that time*, i.e. 07.06.2013) of the previous 32 days of share price data on the US Stock Market of Microsoft. The variance, standard deviation and coefficient of variation values for the Microsoft share price have been calculated over that time period using the spreadsheet.

You can also find on the Excel spreadsheet noted above (Chapter2_Example_4) the *latest* share price data for you to work with for Microsoft and for other companies in the IT sector. You can use the spreadsheet to find the measures of dispersion in the share price for the most recent past 32 days of Microsoft and then compare these current measures of dispersion for Microsoft with those calculated for its share price in the earlier time period as shown in the table below.

Date	Share price ($) close	Date	Share price ($) close
07/06/2013	36.00	17/05/2013	35.00
06/06/2013	35.00	16/05/2013	34.00
05/06/2013	35.00	15/05/2013	34.00
04/06/2013	35.00	14/05/2013	34.00
03/06/2013	36.00	13/05/2013	33.00
31/05/2013	35.00	10/05/2013	33.00
30/05/2013	35.00	09/05/2013	33.00
29/05/2013	35.00	08/05/2013	33.00
28/05/2013	35.00	07/05/2013	33.00
24/05/2013	34.00	06/05/2013	34.00
23/05/2013	34.00	03/05/2013	33.00
22/05/2013	35.00	02/05/2013	33.00
21/05/2013	35.00	01/05/2013	33.00
20/05/2013	35.00	30/04/2013	33.00

Date	Share price ($) close
29/04/2013	33.00
26/04/2013	32.00
25/04/2013	32.00
24/04/2013	32.00

Mean	33.96875
Median	34
Mode	35
Coefficient of variation	0.033842773

Now re-calculate these measures of dispersion using the most recent 32 day data on Microsoft's share price, using the Excel spreadsheet. What do you notice?

Self-check questions 2.4

Q1. Look back at the data in question 1 of Self-Check Questions 2.2 (p. 44). Find the variance and standard deviation for monthly exports of Dr Singh's mobile devices.

Q2. Look back at the data in question 5 of Self-Check Questions 2.2 (p. 46). Find the variance and standard deviation for the percentage change in annual labour costs for 100 employees of Dr Singh.

Note: Answers to Self-Check Questions can be found on the instructor's website, www.pearsoned.co.uk/wall

2.5   Coefficient of variation (C of V)

This is a widely used measure of relative dispersion. It relates an absolute measure of dispersion (the standard deviation) to the absolute value of the arithmetic mean around which the dispersion takes place. Clearly, a data set A with a standard deviation (s) of 10 units and mean ($\overline{X}$) of 10 units has a greater *relative dispersion* than a data set B with a higher absolute standard deviation (s) of 20 units but a still higher absolute mean ($\overline{X}$) of 50 units.

$$\text{C of V}_A = \frac{s}{\overline{X}} = \frac{10}{10} = 1.0$$

$$\text{C of V}_B = \frac{s}{\overline{X}} = \frac{20}{50} = 0.4$$

The coefficient of variation can be expressed as a decimal (as here) or as a percentage. To obtain a percentage we simply multiply by 100, giving 100% and 40% for this example. The data set with the highest coefficient of variation has the greatest relative dispersion.

2.5.1   Risk assessment and the coefficient of variation

Dr Singh is trying to assess the 'risk' should he decide to give exclusive rights to his mobile phone technology to one of five possible technology hardware companies listed by the *Financial Times Share Service*. He decides to use the coefficient of variation of the share price of the five companies over the past 12 months as a measure of the 'risk' the market associates with each company. Table 2.9 gives the mean share price and standard deviation of the share

Table 2.9 Assessing risk in five different technology hardware companies

Technology hardware company	Mean share price* (pence)	Standard deviation of share price*	High/low share price in past 52 weeks (pence)
Pace	174.7	2.08	243.8/56.5
Psion	91.8	1.66	124/30.5
Sepura	52.9	0.64	61/30
Vislink	23.8	0.15	32/18
Xaar	83.8	0.06	107.8/52

Table 2.10 Ranking of risk for hardware companies

Technology hardware company	Coefficient of variation	Ranking (C of V)	High:low ratio	Ranking high:low
Pace	0.012	3=	4.32	5
Psion	0.018	5	4.07	4
Sepura	0.012	3=	2.03	2
Vislink	0.006	2	1.78	1
Xaar	0.001	1	2.07	3

price for the five hardware companies over a five day period using the *Financial Times Share Service*. As he has to make a rapid decision Dr Singh will use the data in Table 2.9 to rank the five companies in terms of market risk.

Can you suggest what conclusions Dr Singh might make from the data in Table 2.9?

We can work out the coefficient of variation ($S/\overline{X}$) for each company, as in Table 2.10.

Using the coefficient of variation for the share price data in that week, the least risky company in terms of the relative dispersion in its share price would seem to be Xaar, followed by Vislink, with Pace and Sepura joint third and Psion last.

However, if we use the *whole year* data, and observe the highest and lowest share price for each company over 52 weeks, then we can use the *ratio* of highest to lowest share price for each company over the past year as a 'risk' indicator. This gives the least risky company as Vislink (1.78), followed by Sepura (2.03), Xaar (2.07), Psion (4.07) and Pace (4.32). The respective rankings in Table 2.10 have some similarities: for example, Vislink is second and first on the respective coefficient of variation and high:low ratio rankings in terms of least risk.

Of course a more sophisticated assessment of risk would involve a longer period of observation, with perhaps the mean value of each share price identified over several years and the daily deviations recorded over those years before working out the coefficient of variation ($S/\overline{X}$) for each company.

BREAK-OUT BOX 2.5

Sunil Singh's own risk index

In fact Dr Singh has decided to use his own risk index, using the following equation.

Dr Singh's risk index:

$$\frac{\text{Average of past 32 days share price } - \text{ 52 week low share price}}{\text{52 week high share price } - \text{ 52 week low share price}}$$

The *top part* (numerator) of the equation is the difference between the mean share price of the most recent 32 days trading minus the lowest share price experienced in the past 52 weeks (year). This top part can be positive or negative: the bigger the positive value, the greater the confidence that the trend of the share price is upward (less risky).

The *bottom part* (denominator) of the equation is the *range* between the highest weekly share price and the lowest weekly share price experienced over the past 52 weeks (year). This bottom part will be positive, and the bigger the positive value the greater the annual dispersion (more risky).

Overall a high and positive numerator and low denominator will suggest smaller risk to Dr Singh. Dr Singh has therefore worked out his own risk index.

Dr Singh's risk index
0 or minus – high risk
0.5 or thereabouts – medium risk
1 or above – low risk

To test his risk index, Dr Singh applies it to data on Microsoft.

Using the Chapter2_Example_5 Excel spreadsheet you will be able to obtain the past 32 days of real share price data for Microsoft and for other companies in the IT sector.

Self-check question 2.5

Dr Singh decides to sell his device through two different outlets, Store A and Store B.

£	Store A	Store B
0.0–2.5	27	1
2.5–5.0	114	3
5.0–7.5	333	31
7.5–10.0	530	142
10.0–12.5	504	328
12.5–15.0	334	498
15.0–17.5	121	504
17.5–20.0	29	351
20.0–22.5	5	110
22.5–25.0	2	29
25.0–27.5	1	3
	2000	2000

Find:
(a) The mean expenditure in each store.
(b) The standard deviation in each store.
(c) The coefficient of variation for sales revenue in each store.
(d) What do your results suggest for Dr Singh?

Note: Answers to Self-Check Questions can be found on the instructor's website, www.pearsoned.co.uk/wall

REVIEW QUESTIONS

R2.1. All parts of this review question refer to the involvement of Dr Singh's company with a major manufacturer of his devices and with which he has established a joint venture.

(a) His joint venture partner is a major mobile phone manufacturer which, at the moment, purchases similar devices from both Dr Singh's company and from a rival company. The daily supply of devices (in 000 units) over the past two weeks from the two companies is shown below.

Dr Singh's company (output, 000)						
357	262	319	412	398	330	341
329	332	309	229	259	337	383

Rival company (output, 000)						
364	295	352	380	314	343	290
291	306	348	333	291	324	315

Calculate the following for each company:
(i) the mean and median values;
(ii) the range, the interquartile range and the semi-interquartile range;
(iii) the variance, standard deviation and coefficient of variation.
Use your calculations to compare and contrast the relative contributions of each company to the major mobile phone manufacturer. What do your results show?

(b) His mobile phone manufacturing partner suggests, after market research into global sales, that Dr Singh's devices be designed to operate effectively even when average temperatures in which the mobile phones are used fall to $-10°C$ over a 30 day period. Dr Singh suspects that the device he has designed is not meeting this standard so he decides to test over a 30 day period by seeing how many of his devices stop working effectively between $0°C$ and $-10°C$, using 10,000 tests.

Temperature °C	Devices failed (%)
0 to (−1)	1
−1 to (−2)	11
−2 to (−3)	25
−3 to (−4)	30
−4 to (−5)	20
−5 to (−6)	6
−6 to (−7)	4
−7 to (−8)	1
−8 to (−9)	1
−9 to (−10)	1

(i) Calculate the mean and median values for the data.
(ii) Calculate the variance, standard deviation and coefficient of variation for the data. What do you notice?

(c) The number of visitors (in hundreds) recorded in each of 150 days to Dr Singh's stand at a major mobile phone trade show were as shown in the frequency table below:

Daily visitors (00)	Frequency
6–8	4
8–10	17
10–12	61
12–14	47
14–16	18
16–18	3

Calculate

(i) Mean and median values for the numbers of visitors.

(ii) Variance, standard deviation and coefficient of variation for the numbers of visitors. What do you notice?

(d) A new production line developed by his joint venture partner for manufacturing the mobile phone devices has a mean daily rejection rate of 4 units with a standard deviation of 2 units in the first three months of operation. In the next three months of operation the mean daily rejection rate was 3 units with a standard deviation of 1 unit. Find the coefficient of variation in each case and use it to comment on the relative dispersion of the production line over the two time periods.

(e) Dr Singh's joint venture partnership is also evaluating a separate market in which its devices can be used in television set-top boxes. His partner has close links with a major flat screen TV set manufacturer. The TV set manufacturer approaches some of its own existing customers to determine if there is a market for the devices to be used in its set-top boxes. It produces two different types of set-top box and asks 50 customers purchasing each type of set-top box to estimate how many set-top boxes incorporating Dr Singh's devices they would purchase each year to enhance the quality of their product.

Number of set-top boxes	Frequency	
with Dr Singh's devices (000)	Customer group A	Customer group B
0–20	5	2
20–40	10	7
40–60	22	12
60–80	7	28
80–100	6	1

Calculate

(i) the mean and median purchases of set-top boxes incorporating Dr Singh's devices by each customer type;

(ii) the variance, standard deviation and coefficient of variation for each customer type. What do you notice?

R2.2. The table below uses grouped data to show the prices of the five different types of mobile device and the number sold per year by Dr Singh's company. Use the spreadsheet Chapter2_Example_6 to find the mean and median values for the overall price of the mobile device.

Price of mobile devices (£)	Number of items sold (F_i)
0.15–0.25	8,308
0.25–0.35	19,566
0.35–0.45	44,369
0.45–0.55	21,616
0.55–0.65	9,677

R2.3. The table below uses grouped data to show the prices of the five different types of mobile device and the number sold per year by Dr Singh's company. Use the spreadsheet Chapter2_Example_7 to find the variance and standard deviation for the overall price of the mobile device.

Price of item (£)	Number of items sold
0.15–0.25	9,226
0.25–0.35	24,993
0.35–0.45	35,502
0.45–0.55	16,205
0.55–0.65	9,602

Note: Answers to Review Questions can be found on the instructor's website, www.pearsoned.co.uk/wall

Further practice

You can find more questions (with solutions) on techniques for collecting and presenting data on the instructor's website, www.pearsoned.co.uk/wall, including instructions on using spreadsheets to develop various types of graph.

Spreadsheets: video guide

You can also find a step-by-step account that takes you through the actual use of a spreadsheet when solving the types of problems you have encountered in this chapter. Go to the instructor's website, www.pearsoned.co.uk/wall

Chapter 3

Financial decision making
Project appraisal

Introduction

The 'clean technology' sector in general, and solar power in particular, are the contexts for our study of how to allocate scarce finance among alternative investment projects. The clean technology sector has benefited from a global recognition of the importance of 'carbon-lite' technologies, given the widely accepted association of greenhouse gas emissions with adverse climate changes.

We pay particular attention to a company called Solar Spot Ltd, which seeks to provide an online information service to households and businesses that are considering whether or not to install solar panel heating. Solar Spot wishes to use various investment appraisal techniques to evaluate which of its possible projects should be given priority.

The growth potential of solar power-related businesses derives not only from government concerns to reduce carbon emissions, but also from a sharp reduction in the cost of photovoltaic cells, the main component of solar panels. The cheaper photovoltaic cells are very much down to China, which is acutely aware of the need for pollution avoidance given predictions that it will produce as much CO_2 between 2010 and 2035 as the United States, the European Union and Japan combined! In seeking to avoid the environmental damage from such an outcome, China has funded a major increase in the supply of the photovoltaic cells used in solar panels. This increase in supply has resulted in a significant fall in the price of solar panels, cost reductions for firms installing them worldwide and extra potential business for those involved in the delivery of services supporting solar power, such as Solar Spot.

The boxed material below provides a useful summary of the business plan submitted by Solar Spot when it secured its initial start-up funding from an Angel investor.

Solar Spot Ltd

Solar Spot is in the clean technology sector and delivers a software service to end-users to help them make the most of their solar technology investment. Solar Spot has developed a patented algorithm that applies satellite imagery to a house or business premises in which solar panels might be installed, and its 'cloud-based' web service automatically calculates the best type of solar panel technology to be installed on a property and the best roof location.

(continued)

A study has shown that 70% of people installing solar panels on their houses make the wrong trade-off between minimising the initial installation investment on the type of solar technology and maximising the longer-term returns from energy savings. In other words, they make poor investment choices due to a lack of easily accessible information. This has led to a rapid expansion in the need for third-party information about home solar panel technology, such as that provided by Solar Spot.

The online advertising of Solar Spot will attract users to its website. Solar Spot has formed partnerships with major national solar panel installers in key geographies around the world who want to see their customers making the most appropriate solar panel investment choices through better access to information. While the basic service will be offered free to users, referral revenue to Solar Spot will result from click-through sales orders to major solar panel installers.

While there are other online solar technology information sources, Solar Spot's unique and patented image technology allows it to identify the shape, orientation and gradient of the roof of a house or building, which are the essential measurements required for optimum panel placement to maximise the amount of sunlight received.

After reviewing the various techniques of investment appraisal in this chapter in the context of the clean technology sector, we will apply them to the collaborative project outlined in the 'Business Applications' box below and for which Solar Spot is seeking funding.

Business applications

Collaborative venture in China

Solar Spot has demonstrated its technology at an international trade fair and has attracted interest from a major Chinese manufacturer and installer of solar panels. After extensive discussions it has developed the following scenarios for this major collaborative project.

Solar Spot Ltd	Financials	Year 1	Year 2	Year 3	Year 4	Year 5
	Revenues	£30k	£110k	£800k	£1,400k	£2,800k
	Expenditures	£50k	£250k	£530k	£900k	£1,200k
	Profit (net revenue)	−£20k	−£140k	£270k	£500k	£1,600k

Review Question R3.1 at the end of the chapter will return to this business application.

Spreadsheets

The questions and activities in the Break-Out Boxes use spreadsheets which can be found on the student's website, www.pearsoned.co.uk/wall. Many of the Worked Examples, Self-Check Questions and Review Questions are set out for you as an Excel spreadsheet on the student's website and these questions are marked with an asterisk (*).

Learning objectives

When you have read this chapter you should be able to:

● examine the nature and importance of financial decision making in the context of project appraisal;

● use the discounting process to find the present value (PV) of future streams of income and expenditure;

● evaluate the advantages and disadvantages of various techniques such as payback, accounting rate of return (ARR), net present value (NPV) and internal rate of return (IRR) when comparing alternative investment projects;

● apply these techniques to specific projects in the clean technology sector, especially solar power, and to projects in other sectors.

3.1 Investment and financial decision making

Making investment decisions follows the logical process outlined in Figure 3.1.

The part of the process that we focus on in this chapter involves Solar Spot in selecting between alternative projects. This will involve gathering data about the investment projects the company is considering, including the following:

● the revenues and their time profile over the 'life time' of the project;

● the initial capital cost and the time profile of any further expenditures over the 'life time' of the project;

● the type and level of interest rate we will use for our calculation.

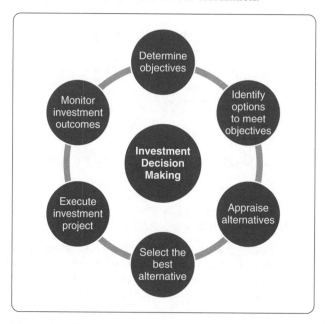

Figure 3.1 The investment process

After a brief discussion of the role of time in project appraisal, we review the contribution of each of these factors in helping Solar Spot select between alternative uses of its financial and other resources.

3.1.1 Time value of money

When we compare different potential projects, we must be careful to consider the *time profile* of any revenues from, or expenditures on, these projects. Otherwise we could easily make an unwise decision as to which, if any, project to pursue.

This idea of the time value of money can easily be illustrated in terms of the fact that, say, £100 today is certainly *not* the same as £100 in one year's time. Suppose the interest I could receive on £100 placed in my bank account was 10% per annum. Then in one year's time my £100 would be worth £100 + £100 (0.10) = £110, since I can get my £100 back and earn 10% interest (0.10 as a decimal) on the £100 held by the bank for that year. I might therefore regard £100 now as equivalent to £110 in 12 months' time rather than £100 in 12 months' time.

When different projects yield different monetary returns over successive time periods (i.e. have different time profiles) it is even more important that we have a clear framework by which the time factor can be taken into account. Only then can we be sure that we are comparing 'like with like' in terms of the different monetary returns that flow from the various projects.

Just as the monetary *returns* on a project can vary over time, so too can the monetary *costs* of investing in the project. If, say, the total costs for two alternative projects are identical, but one requires a higher proportion of these costs to be incurred *later* than the other, then for the reasons already mentioned we could regard this as the less costly project. For example, £110 of costs incurred next year could be paid for by putting aside £100 now at 10% interest, but £110 of costs incurred in two years' time could be paid for by putting aside *less than* £100 now at 10% interest.

Clearly, the time profile of both monetary returns and monetary costs must explicitly be taken into account if we are to take appropriate business decisions, as must the rate of interest we will apply in our calculations. It is to the interest rate issue that we now turn.

Did you know?

There is considerable pressure on governments to support the use of clean technologies such as solar energy. For example, the International Energy Agency (IEA) reported in 2012 that 80% of the CO_2 deemed 'safe' to be emitted between 2009 and 2035 had already been emitted! Without further governmental action to support 'clean energy', the IEA estimates that as early as 2017 the 'safe' levels of CO_2 emissions will have been exceeded and a forecast temperature increase as high as +2°C can then be expected by 2035, causing catastrophic climate change.

Self-check questions 3.1

Q1. Explain why, at an interest rate of 10%, I would prefer £1,000 now to £1,000 in one year's time.

Q2. Explain why, at an interest rate of 5%, I would prefer £1,100 in one year's time to £1,000 now.

Note: Answers to Self-Check Questions can be found on the instructor's website, www.pearsoned.co.uk/wall

3.2   Interest rates and project appraisal

It will be useful to remind ourselves of the different types of interest rates that might be involved in Solar Spot's project appraisal. The ideas of simple and compound interest will be introduced, and we will see how compound interest underpins calculations to find the present value of different time profiles of revenues and costs.

An *interest rate* is usually quoted as a *percentage*, and indicates the amount received (or paid) for each £1 saved (or borrowed). For example, an interest rate (i) of 10% per annum indicates the receipt of 10 pence on each £1 saved over the year.

If we know the amount received (or paid) over some time period and the initial amount saved (or borrowed) at the start of that period, then we can calculate the rate of interest (i).

$$i = \frac{\text{interest received (or paid) for the period}}{\text{initial amount saved (or borrowed) at start of period}}$$

So if £20 is received on £200 saved in a bank account over one year, then:

$$i = \frac{20}{200} = \frac{10}{100} = 0.10 \text{ per annum}$$

To convert this decimal to a *percentage*, multiply by 100, to get

$$i = 0.10 \times 100 = 10\% \text{ per annum}$$

The amount of interest received (or paid) each year will depend not only on the value of i, but also on whether the calculation involves *simple interest* or *compound interest*.

3.2.1   Simple interest (SI)

If an interest payment is received on money saved and that interest is not reinvested at the end of each period, then the savings scheme offers *simple interest* (SI).

The simple interest (SI) earned over a number of time periods is calculated as follows.

Formula for simple interest

$$SI = P \times \frac{i}{100} \times T$$

where SI = simple interest earned

P = principal (i.e. initial amount at start of period)

i = rate of interest as a *percentage*

T = number of time periods.

Worked example 3.1

Calculate the simple interest earned by Solar Spot over five years if £1,640 is invested at a rate of interest of 9% per annum.

Solution

$$SI = P \times \frac{i}{100} \times T$$

$$SI = 1,640 \times \frac{9}{100} \times 5$$

$$SI = \textbf{£738}$$

BREAK-OUT BOX 3.1

Simple interest

Chapter3_Example_1 Excel spreadsheet will show you the different simple interest rates that various governments must pay when they borrow monies by issuing government bonds for different periods of time. You can use these interest rates to calculate the amount of money the investor in government bonds in that country would receive after investing £500m for bonds of 1, 5 and 10 years to maturity. You can then find the total amount of simple interest received on such investment.

3.2.2 Compound interest (CI)

Most types of account receive (or pay) compound interest (CI). For example, if an interest payment is received on money saved and that interest *is then reinvested*, the savings scheme offers *compound interest*.

In this chapter you may assume that any interest received or paid is compound interest, unless stated otherwise.

Table 3.1 shows the payment of compound interest on an initial amount of £100 (principal) invested at a 10% per annum compound interest rate.

Note: For all compound interest rate problems we express i, the rate of interest, as a *decimal*.

PAUSE FOR THOUGHT 3.1

Can you extend Table 3.1 so that it covers the situation after four years? Can you see a pattern emerging?

Finding end value (A_t) after period t

We can easily derive a formula from Table 3.1 for finding A_t, the value of the initial amount of £100 at the end of any time period (t) when it grows at a compound rate of i (as a decimal).

Formula for compound interest

$$A_t = P (1 + i)^t$$

where A_t = value at end of time period t

P = principal (i.e. initial amount at start of period)

i = compound interest rate, as a *decimal*

t = end of time period in question

Thus, from Table 3.1:

at end of $t = 1$

$$A_1 = 100 (1 + 0.10)^1 = £110$$

at end of $t = 2$

$$A_2 = 100 (1 + 0.10)^2 = £121$$

at end of $t = 3$

$$A_3 = 100 (1 + 0.10)^3 = £133.10$$

Table 3.1 Compound interest

Principal	After 1 year	After 2 years	After 3 years
£100	100 + 100 (0.10)	110 + 110 (0.10)	121 + 121 (0.10)
	= 100 (1 + 0.10)^1	= 110 (1 + 0.10)	= 121 (1 + 0.10)
	= £110	= 100 (1 + 0.10)^2	= 100 (1 + 0.10)^3
		= £121	= £133.10

Worked example 3.2

Solar Spot has placed £30,000 in an account to provide 'back-up' to its operations. It earns 5% compound interest rate. How much would the account be worth to Solar Spot after 10 years?

Solution

$$A_t = P (1 + i)^t$$

i.e. $A_{10} = 30,000 (1 + 0.05)^{10}$

$$A_{10} = 30,000 (1.6289)$$

$$A_{10} = £48,867.$$

Of course this same formula could be used by Solar Spot to find out how much it would need to set aside *now* if it wishes to purchase, say, some new equipment in the future.

Worked example 3.3

Solar Spot wants to know how much it needs to invest now in order to be able to purchase some equipment it needs in five years' time. To calculate this, the same formula can be used when calculating how much Solar Spot would receive if it invested its money in the bank; the formula was:

$$A_t = P(1 + i)^t$$

This formula can be rearranged to apply to Solar Spot's specific situation. The company wants to know how much money it needs to place in the bank now in order to have £30,000 available to spend on a machine in five years' time if the interest rate is, say, 6%. The rearranged formula would be:

$$P = \frac{A_t}{(1 + i)^t}$$

$$P = \frac{30,000}{(1 + 0.06)^5}$$

$$P = \frac{30,000}{1.3382} = £22,418$$

So Solar Spot would need to invest £22,418 now at an interest rate of 6% in order to have £30,000 available in five years' time to spend on the new machine.

Did you know?

The carbon (CO_2) emissions from some countries are increasing at an even faster rate than their GDP. The United Kingdom is a case in point, with 2012 data showing that for the first time in over 15 years the United Kingdom's annual CO_2 emissions had increased by 3.5% but its GDP had only grown by 1.3% – that is, an increase in 'carbon intensity' of 2.2%. Increases in carbon intensity were also recorded for Brazil (3.5%), Russia (2%), United States (1.2%) and China (0.1%), but reductions in carbon intensity were recorded in Australia (−10.9%), Mexico (−5.1%), Turkey (−2.6%) and India (−0.5%). Overall carbon intensity increased by an average of 0.1% for EU countries in 2012, and 1.2% globally. Solar Spot can only benefit from such studies that place severe pressure on governments to continue to support carbon-lite alternatives, such as solar power.

If fact China is likely to be a source of considerable potential business for Solar Spot and similar clean technology companies. A report in 2013 by collaborative universities (MIT, Tsinghua, Peking and others) used decades of pollution data to show that China's air pollution has cut life expectancy by an average of 5.5 years in the north of the country which has a policy for distributing free coal for heating in winter.

Self-check questions 3.2

Q1. Calculate the simple interest earned over five years if Solar Spot invests £20,000 now at a rate of interest of 6% per annum.

Q2. Calculate the value to Solar Spot at the end of four years of an initial investment of £10,000 at a compound interest rate of 5% per annum.

Note: Answers to Self-Check Questions can be found on the instructor's website, www.pearsoned.co.uk/wall

3.3 Compound factors, discounting and present value

We can apply this 'compound' idea to help us understand how to discount future income streams to a present value equivalent.

3.3.1 Compound factors

Tables of compound factors can simplify many of the calculations considered so far. These compound factors tell us the number of times (multiple) by which an initial amount will have grown, for any compound interest rate (i) and any time period (t). In Worked Example 3.2, we noted that £30,000 invested by Solar Spot at 5% (0.05) per annum will have grown by the *compound factor* 1.6289 by the end of period (year) 10.

We can use Table 3.2 (or similar tables) to solve many relevant calculations:

- £1,000 invested by Solar Spot at a compound interest rate of 15% (0.15) will, by the end of period (year) 20, have grown by a *compound factor* of 16.3665, being worth £16,366.5.

- £1,000 invested by Solar Spot at a compound interest rate of 20% (0.20) will, by the end of period (year) 20, have grown by a *compound factor* of 38.3376, being worth £38,337.6, and so on.

If we go *down any of the columns* in Table 3.2, we can see the significance of growth taking place at a given compound interest rate. For example, at a given compound interest rate of, say, 0.10 (10%) the compound factors get progressively larger for each five year increase in time. Between 5 and 10 years the compound factor grows from 1.61 to 2.59, but between 10 and 15 years the compound factor grows much more rapidly from 2.59 to 4.17 and so on.

Similarly, if we go *across any of the rows* in Table 3.2, we can see that for any given time period, the compound factors get progressively larger for each 0.05 (5%) increase in interest rate. For example, at the 10 year time period, between 0.15 (15%) and 0.20 (20%) interest rates the compound factor grows from 4.04 to 6.19, but grows much more rapidly from 6.19 to 9.31 for the next 0.05% (5%) increase in interest rates from 0.20 (20%) to 0.25 (25%).

Table 3.2 Compound factors at various interest rates (i) as decimals and at the end of various time periods (t)

Time (t) years	Interest rate (i) as decimal					
	0.05	0.10	0.15	0.20	0.25	0.30
1	1.05	1.1	1.15	1.2	1.25	1.3
5	1.2763	1.6105	2.0114	2.4883	3.0518	3.7129
10	1.6289	2.5937	4.0456	6.1917	9.3132	13.7859
15	2.0789	4.1772	8.1371	15.4070	28.4217	51.1859
20	2.65353	6.7275	16.3665	38.3376	86.7362	190.0497
25	3.3864	10.8347	32.9190	95.3692	264.6978	705.6412
30	4.3219	17.4494	66.2118	237.3763	807.7936	2619.9963

3.3.2 Discounting and present value (PV)

We have already noted that £100 invested at an interest rate of 10% per annum will give a return of £110 in one year's time. Put another way, at an interest rate of 10% per annum we can expect an investor to regard £110 in one year's time as being equivalent to £100 now (since they can readily convert the one into the other). This process of converting a future money value into a PV equivalent is referred to as discounting.

The discounting process essentially involves *reversing* the growth process involving compound interest rates already discussed. Looking back at Table 3.1 (p. 72) we can see that £100 invested at an interest rate of 10% per annum would be worth £133.10 after 3 years; reversing the process we can say that £133.10 after 3 years would only be worth £100 now if we discount at an interest rate of 10%.

We have already derived an equation (p. 72)

$$A_t = P\,(1 + i)^t$$

where A_t is the value of some initial amount, the principal (P), at the end of period t when it grows at a compound interest rate i (as a decimal).

So, from Table 3.1, for $P = £100$, $t = 3$ years, and $i = 0.10$

$$A_3 = £100\,(1 + 0.10)^3 = £133.10$$

Re-arranging gives us:

$$£100 = £133.10 \times \frac{1}{(1 + 0.10)^3}$$

More generally:

> Present value = future amount × discount factor

In other words, £133 received after three years at a 10% (0.10) interest rate, is *equivalent* to £100 received now.

- We call the £100 the *PV* equivalent of the £133.10 in three years' time.
- We call the £133.10 the future amount to be *discounted*.
- We call the factor $\dfrac{1}{(1 + 0.10)^3}$ by which we multiply the future amount (£133.10) to get the PV equivalent, the *discount factor*.
- We call the process of reducing any future amount to its PV equivalent, *discounting*.
- We call the rate of interest (i) we apply in the discounting process, the *discount rate*.

In general, we can express the discount factor as follows.

> ### Formula for the discount factor
>
> $$\text{Discount factor} = \frac{1}{(1 + i)^t}$$
>
> where i = discount rate (interest rate) as a decimal
>
> t = time period in question.

Table 3.3 Discount factors at various interest (discount) rates as decimals and at the end of various time periods

Time (t) years	Interest rate (discount rate)					
	0.05	0.10	0.15	0.20	0.25	0.30
1	0.9524	0.9091	0.8696	0.8333	0.8000	0.7692
5	0.7835	0.6209	0.4972	0.4019	0.3277	0.2693
10	0.6139	0.3855	0.2472	0.1615	0.1074	0.0725
15	0.4810	0.2394	0.1299	0.0649	0.0352	0.0195
20	0.3769	0.1486	0.0611	0.0261	0.0115	0.0053
25	0.2953	0.0923	0.0304	0.0105	0.0038	0.0014
30	0.2314	0.0573	0.0151	0.0042	0.0012	0.0004

Notice that:

- the higher the rate (i) at which we discount, the bigger the denominator and the *smaller the discount factor*.

- the higher the number of time periods (t) over which the discounting takes place, the bigger the denominator and the *smaller the discount factor*.

Remember, the discount factor is the number (or factor) by which we multiply the future amount to find its PV equivalent. The *smaller the discount factor*, the smaller will be the PV equivalent for any future amount.

It is often helpful to refer to a *table of discount factors*, as in Table 3.3.

The *compound* nature of the discounting process can be seen from Table 3.3.

- For any given interest rate (discount rate), the discount factor falls progressively more rapidly as time increases. Here we are *moving down the columns*. Thus at a 0.10 (10%) interest (discount) rate, an estimated amount in 5 years' time will be worth (today) 0.6209 or 62.09% of its nominal value; but an estimated amount in 20 years' time will be worth (today) only 0.1486 or 14.86% of its nominal value at that time.

- For any given time period, the discount factor falls progressively more rapidly as the interest (discount) rate increases. Here we are *moving across the rows*. Thus if we discount an estimated amount in 10 years' time at a discount rate of 0.05 (5%), it will be worth (today) 0.6139 or 61.39% of its nominal value; but if we discount that same amount in 10 years' time at a discount rate of 0.20 (20%), it will be worth (today) only 0.1615 or 16.15% of its value at that time.

Did you know?

Discounting can be used as an 'excuse' for shifting environmental costs onto future generations. For example, if the impact of nuclear waste is valued at £1,000 million damage in 100 years' time, then the PV of that damage at, say, a discount rate of 8% (0.08) would only be £450,000. Such a small PV figure might lead decision makers to ignore this future cost and, by doing nothing now, pass these environmental costs onto future generations.

Present value

From this analysis we can derive a simple formula for the *PV* of an amount, £A, received at end of time period t.

Formula for present value

Present value (*PV*) of £A received at end of time period *t*:

$$PV = £A_t \times \frac{1}{(1 + i)^t}$$

where A_t = expected amount received at end of time period t

i = rate of discount (as a decimal)

t = end of time period in question

$\dfrac{1}{(1 + i)^t}$ = discount factor

Worked example 3.4

Use Table 3.3 to find the PV of £1,000 received by Solar Spot at the end of five years' time when discounted at an annual rate of 10%.

Solution

$$PV = £1,000 \times \frac{1}{(1 + 0.10)^5}$$

$$PV = £1,000 \times 0.6209$$

$$PV = £620.9$$

In other words, under these conditions Solar Spot would be indifferent between a sum of £1,000 at the end of five years' time and a sum of £620.9 today.

Did you know?

Global 'clean technology' investment in energy has increased dramatically in the past few years, from only $50 billion in 2004 to over $400 billion in 2013.

Self-check questions 3.3

Q1. Use Table 3.2 (p. 74) to calculate the value to Solar Spot of an initial amount of £1,000 growing at a compound rate in each of the following circumstances.

   (a) compound interest rate 0.05 (5%) after 15 years

   (b) compound interest rate 0.10 (10%) after 25 years

   (c) compound interest rate 0.15 (15%) after 20 years

   (d) compound interest rate 0.20 (20%) after 30 years

   (e) compound interest rate 0.25 (25%) after 10 years

   (f) compound interest rate 0.30 (30%) after 25 years

(continued)

Q2. Use Table 3.3 (p. 76) to estimate the PV of £100,000 received in the future with the characteristics outlined below.
(a) in 1 year's time at a discount rate of 0.25 (25%)
(b) in 5 years' time at a discount rate of 0.10 (10%)
(c) in 10 years' time at a discount rate of 0.30 (30%)
(d) in 15 years' time at a discount rate of 0.05 (5%)
(e) in 20 years' time at a discount rate of 0.15 (15%)
(f) in 25 years' time at a discount rate of 0.20 (20%)
(g) in 30 years' time at a discount rate of 0.10 (10%)

Note: Answers to Self-Check Questions can be found on the instructor's website, www.pearsoned.co.uk/wall

3.4 Cash flow and financial decision making

Before Solar Spot can apply project appraisal techniques it needs to identify the projected cash outflows and inflows for the alternative projects being appraised. A typical project would have a cash outflow at the start as it makes an initial capital investment with the benefits of that investment coming through for several years afterwards. Let us imagine that Solar Spot purchases a piece of equipment for £800,000; Solar Spot expects it to generate positive cash flow for five years and then expects to be able to sell it for 25% of its initial value. The equipment will need maintenance throughout its life at a cost of £25,000 a year, falling to £10,000 in its final year.

The *cash flow* position relating to this investment would be as shown in Table 3.4.

Being familiar with the construction and use of cash flow tables is important for project appraisal and the self-check question below gives you further practice in this.

Table 3.4 Cash flow position

Year	Cash outflow (£000)	Cash inflow (£000)	Net cash flow (£000)
0	800		−800
1	25	200	175
2	25	250	225
3	25	350	325
4	25	350	325
5	10	350	340
Sale		200	200
Total	910	1700	790

Did you know?

A major report by the International Energy Agency in January 2012 has forecast that renewable energy sources (solar, wind, hydro-electric) will grow at around 8.2% per year, much faster than the growth of non-renewable energy sources (e.g. oil, gas, coal) in the period to 2030. Gas would only grow at 2.1% per year and oil is actually forecast to decline over this period. Renewable energy sources are expected to provide 11% of all the world's electricity by 2030, with total world demand for energy expected to rise by 1.6% a year to 2030.

Self-check question 3.4

Solar Spot is considering purchasing a new piece of equipment for an activity it expects will be withdrawn from the market in five years' time but will generate £175,000 of income per year for each year it is undertaken. The equipment will cost £500,000 and have a scrap value of £25,000. Included in this price is a one year service guarantee from the supplier of the equipment. Each additional year the equipment is in use Solar Spot will take out another service contract with the supplier at a cost of £7,500.

Complete the cash flow table (Table 3.5) for this project and find the total net cash flow that will be generated.

Table 3.5 Cash flow for the purchase of a new piece of equipment

Year	Cash outflow (£000)	Cash inflow (£000)	Net cash flow (£000)
0			
1			
2			
3			
4			
5			
Sale			
Total			

Note: Answers to Self-Check Questions can be found on the instructor's website, www.pearsoned.co.uk/wall

3.5 Investment appraisal: non-discounting techniques

Our analysis of discounting and PV is highly relevant to attempts by Solar Spot to appraise or rank different investment projects. As we shall see, discounting and PV underpin the techniques of net present value (NPV) and internal rate of return (IRR) which Solar Spot can use for investment appraisal. However, here we briefly consider some *non-discounting* techniques that Solar Spot can apply to its alternative investment projects.

3.5.1 Payback period

This is a crude but widely used method of investment appraisal that does *not* rely on the discounting process. In its simplest form, the firm will select that project with the shortest payback period – that is, the project that requires the shortest time to pay back (in nominal terms) any initial capital outlay.

Suppose Solar Spot has the following information on the expected cash flows (£m) for two projects, A and B, over the eight time periods ($t = 0$ being today) it regards as the 'life' of each project (see Table 3.6).

Table 3.6 Expected cash flows (£m) of two investment projects over eight time periods.

Time period t	$t = 0$	$t = 1$	$t = 2$	$t = 3$	$t = 4$	$t = 5$	$t = 6$	$t = 7$	$t = 8$
Project A	−18	0	0	5	6	7	8	9	10
Project B	−6	2	2	2	2	2	0	0	0

The cash flows are expressed in *nominal terms* – that is, in the money values expected to be received in future. These values correspond to *net revenues* (i.e. revenue – cost) or *profits* expected in future time periods.

Project A is a capital intensive project with £18 million expected to be spent on capital outlay this year ($t = 0$), but no net revenues are received until $t = 3$, though net revenues rise steadily thereafter.

Project B, in contrast, is a less capital intensive project, but also a less 'productive' project. Only £6 million is expected to be spent on capital outlay this year ($t = 0$) and net revenues are expected from next year onwards. However, the net revenues remain static in value from $t = 1$ to $t = 5$ and are expected to cease altogether by $t = 6$.

- Project A is expected to pay back the initial capital outlay of £18 million by time period $t = 5$.
- Project B is expected to pay back the initial capital outlay of £6 million by time period $t = 3$.

On the strict application of the payback criterion, Project B would be preferred by Solar Spot to Project A as it is expected to repay the initial capital outlay quicker.

Of course this investment decision can be criticised. While Project B may be 'less risky' in terms of a more rapid payback, it would also seem 'less productive' in that little subsequent net revenue is generated for Solar Spot after payback by Project B compared to Project A. Further, all future values are expressed in nominal terms whereas the PV equivalent of those future values would be a more realistic basis for comparing the two projects.

Worked example 3.5

Let us use our cash flow tables to consider the *payback period* for the previous example (p. 79) of Solar Spot considering the purchase of a new piece of equipment.

The payback period is the time taken for the cash inflows resulting from an investment to equal the cash outflows.

We can add a *cumulative cash flow column* to the cash flow table so that we can easily see when the cash flow turns from negative to positive (see Table 3.7).

Table 3.7 Cumulative cash flow table

Year	Cash outflow (£000)	Cash inflow (£000)	Net cash flow (£000)	Cumulative cash flow (£000)
0	500		−500	−500
1		175	175	−325
2	7.5	175	167.5	−157.5
3	7.5	175	167.5	10
4	7.5	175	167.5	177.5
5	7.5	175	167.5	345
Sale		25	25	370
Total	530	900	370	

Worked
example
3.5
(cont'd)

The payback period comes just before the end of year 3. As we can see from the cumulative cash flow a positive cash flow of £10,000 has been generated at the end of year 3 so the payback period actually comes about three weeks before the end of this year, assuming that the cash flows are evenly distributed throughout the year.

3.5.2 Average rate of return (ARR)

The *rate of return* method, also known as *average rate of return* (ARR), can also be used by Solar Spot to choose the best investment option between two or more projects.

The ARR expresses the average annual profits arising from a project as a percentage of the original capital investment.

So the formula would be:

$$ARR = \frac{\text{average annual net income} \times 100\%}{\text{initial capital cost}}$$

Worked
example
3.6

Work out the ARR for Solar Spot on Projects A and B as shown in Table 3.8 below.

Table 3.8 Expected cash flows (£m) of two investment projects over eight time periods

Time period t	$t = 0$	$t = 1$	$t = 2$	$t = 3$	$t = 4$	$t = 5$	$t = 6$	$t = 7$	$t = 8$
Project A	−18	0	0	5	6	7	8	9	10
Project B	−6	2	2	2	2	2	0	0	0

Solution

- Project A: Total net income $= 45 - 18 = 27$

$$ARR = \frac{(27 \div 8)}{18} \times 100$$

$$ARR = 18.75\% \text{ per annum}$$

- Project B: Total net income $= 10 - 6 = 4$

$$ARR = \frac{(4 \div 8)}{6} \times 100$$

$$ARR = 8.33\% \text{ per annum}$$

Notice that whereas the payback criterion results in Project B being preferred by Solar Spot to Project A, the ARR criterion results in Project A being preferred to Project B. Again, however, we could criticise the ARR approach for expressing future values only in nominal terms.

Worked example 3.7

In the earlier Solar Spot example in Table 3.7 (Worked Example 3.5, p. 80), where the initial capital cost was £500,000 and the total net income over the whole project of five years was £370,000, what would be the ARR for this project?

Solution

£370,000 is the net total income generated by this project which is divided over the life of the project, five years.

$$\text{ARR} = \frac{(370 \div 5)}{500} \times 100 = \frac{74}{500} \times 100 = 14.8\%$$

We now consider rather more sophisticated methods of investment appraisal which look beyond the payback period and which consider 'real' rather than nominal values for expected future returns.

Self-check question 3.5

*Solar Spot is considering two major investment projects which each have the same initial capital outlay of £100,000. The expected net revenues (profit) on the respective projects over the next four years are shown in the table below.

	Project A (£)	Project B (£)
Year 0	−100,000	−100,000
Year 1	40,000	20,000
Year 2	60,000	30,000
Year 3	80,000	50,000
Year 4	100,000	120,000

1. Compare Projects A and B using the payback method.
2. Compare Projects A and B using the ARR method.

Note: Answers to Self-Check Questions can be found on the instructor's website, www.pearsoned.co.uk/wall

---

3.6 Investment appraisal: discounting techniques

3.6.1 Net present value (NPV)

The idea here is for Solar Spot to first find the *PV* of all the expected future net revenues from its project(s) expressed in nominal terms. In other words, we use the *discounting process* to find the PV (p. 75) of the future cash flows.

From this PV we then subtract any initial capital outlay in the current time period ($t = 0$). (Of course if the capital outlay extends beyond the current time period, then we will have to discount this also.)

$$NPV = PV - K$$

where NPV = net present value

PV = present value of future net revenues

K = initial capital outlay

Let us consider in more detail how Solar Spot finds the PV of a stream of expected net revenues (i.e. profits). We use our formula for PV (on p. 77), but apply this to *each* time period:

$$PV = £A_t \times \frac{1}{(1 + i)^t}$$

where $£A_t$ = expected return in time t

i = rate of discount (as a decimal)

t = time period in question

$\frac{1}{(1 + i)^t}$ = discount factor

Worked example 3.8

Suppose Solar Spot uses a discount rate of 0.10 (10%) and applies this formula to the net revenues it expects for Project B in Table 3.6 (p. 80). We have:

- $t = 1$ $PV = £2(m) \times \dfrac{1}{(1 + 0.10)^1} = £2(m) \times 0.909 = 1.818$

- $t = 2$ $PV = £2(m) \times \dfrac{1}{(1 + 0.10)^2} = £2(m) \times 0.826 = 1.652$

- $t = 3$ $PV = £2(m) \times \dfrac{1}{(1 + 0.10)^3} = £2(m) \times 0.751 = 1.502$

- $t = 4$ $PV = £2(m) \times \dfrac{1}{(1 + 0.10)^4} = £2(m) \times 0.683 = 1.366$

- $t = 5$ $PV = £2(m) \times \dfrac{1}{(1 + 0.10)^5} = £2(m) \times 0.621 = 1.242$

There are no net revenues after $t = 5$. We must then *sum* these PVs calculated for each future time period to get the total PV of expected net revenues for Project B. In this case the sum of these PVs over the five time periods for Solar Spot is £7.58 million.

$$NPV = PV - K$$

$$NPV = £7.58 \text{ million} - £6 \text{ million}$$

$$\textbf{NPV} = \textbf{£1.58 million for Project B}$$

Using our sigma notation from Chapter 2 (p. 37), we can write a general formula for NPV.

Formula for net present value

$$\text{NPV} = \sum_{t=0}^{n}\left[A_t \times \frac{1}{(1 + i)^t}\right] - K$$

where n = number of time periods

A_t = net revenue in time period t

i = rate of discount (as a decimal)

t = end of time period in question

K = initial capital outlay

Note: When $t = 0$, the discount factor for net revenue is:

$$\frac{1}{(1 + i)^0} = \frac{1}{1} = 1$$

This is because anything raised to the power 0 is 1 (see Appendix 1, p. 323).

Did you know?

The IEA has forecast the future price of oil to rise from $90 per barrel in 2011 to as much as $150 per barrel by 2015. The $150 per barrel scenario will follow if the governments of North Africa and the Middle East feel they must cut investment in new oil production facilities to boost social spending, which the IEA regards as quite likely given global economic uncertainties and the political impacts of the 'Arab Spring'. Even if investment in oil is maintained, the oil price is still forecast to rise to $120 per barrel by 2015.

Such forecasts do, of course, favour Solar Spot and other renewable energy providers, raising still higher expected future net revenues for their various investment projects, and thereby making these projects more likely to be undertaken, whatever the investment appraisal technique adopted.

3.6.2 Discounted cash flow tables

In fact we can set down these calculations for NPV using cash flow tables. These are often called discounted cash flow tables. Instead of subtracting the initial capital outlay at the end, a *negative* figure is recorded for time period 0 – that is, the start of the project.

We illustrate this using our data for investment Projects A and B from Table 3.9 (p. 85). Note that nominal cash flow (NCF) is the original data, whereas discounted cash flow (DCF) is the original data discounted, here using a discount rate of 0.10 (10%).

As we can see, the NPV for Project A (sum of the DCFs) is £7.989 million. This is higher than the NPV for Project B of only £1.580 million. The usual 'decision rule' would be that if a scarcity of financial resources means choosing between these projects, then choose the project with the higher NPV, namely Project A.

Table 3.9 Discounted cash flows for Projects A and B (£m) with a 0.10 (10%) discount rate

| Time (year) | Nominal cash flow (NCF) | | | Discounted cash flow (DCF) | |
	NCF (Project A)	NCF (Project B)	Discount factor	DCF (Project A)	DCF (Project B)
0	−18	−6	1.000	−18.000	−6.000
1	0	2	0.909	0.000	1.818
2	0	2	0.826	0.000	1.652
3	5	2	0.751	3.755	1.502
4	6	2	0.683	4.098	1.366
5	7	2	0.621	4.347	1.242
6	8	0	0.564	4.512	0.000
7	9	0	0.513	4.617	0.000
8	10	0	0.466	4.660	0.000
Sum	27	4		7.989	1.580
			NPV	7.989	1.580

Worked example 3.9

We return to the example in Table 3.7 (p. 80) of Solar Spot purchasing a new piece of equipment for an activity that is due to be withdrawn from the market in five years' time although it will generate £175,000 of income per year for each year it is undertaken. The equipment will cost £500,000 and have a scrap value of £25,000. Included in this price is a one year service guarantee from the supplier of the equipment. Each additional year the equipment is in use the company will take out another service contract with the supplier at a cost of £7,500. The interest rate to be applied is 7% (0.07) (see Table 3.10).

Table 3.10 Present value table with 0.07 (7%) discount rate

Year	Cash outflow (£000)	Cash inflow (£000)	Net cash flow (£000)	Discount factor	Present value (£)
0	500		−500	1	−500,000
1		175	175	0.935	163,625
2	7.5	175	167.5	0.873	146,228
3	7.5	175	167.5	0.816	136,680
4	7.5	175	167.5	0.763	127,803
5	7.5	175	167.5	0.713	119,428
Sale		25	25	0.713	17,825
Total	530	900	370		211,589

For each year we can calculate the *PV* of the net cash flow by applying a *discount factor*. Remember that the discount factor is calculated using the formula:

$$\frac{1}{(1 + i)^t}$$

Worked example 3.9 (cont'd)

where i = discount rate

t = time period.

The *discount rate* applied in this example is 7%. The easiest way to find discount factors is to use the PV tables. Use the PV table on p. 85 to check that you understand where the *discount factors* in this example have come from.

The PV is the net cash flow multiplied by the discount factor.

$$PV = A_t \times \text{discount factor}$$

Table 3.10 shows the sum of all the individual PVs for each year of the project, which is £211,588.

Note that the NPV is NOT the total net cash flow from the project multiplied by a discount factor.

Let's look at an example where Solar Spot seeks to use NPV to determine which of two project options is better.

Worked example 3.10

Solar Spot has an option of being paid £150,000 now for a project that will spread over this year and four more years (Option 1) or to receive a payment of £40,000 now and in each of the next four years (Option 2).

If the current interest rate is 8%, which option would you advise Solar Spot to take?

This table is available for you to complete in an Excel spreadsheet on the companion website.

Solution

Option 1

Taking £150,000 for the project now means that it is not necessary to calculate NPV as the *PV* is clearly £150,000.

Option 2

Year	Cash flow (£)	Discount factor	Present value (£)
0	40,000	1	40,000
1	40,000	0.926	37,040
2	40,000	0.857	34,280
3	40,000	0.794	31,760
4	40,000	0.735	29,400
Total	200,000		172,480

Therefore Option 2 is the one that Solar Spot should choose as it gives the higher NPV at £172,480.

BREAK-OUT BOX 3.2

Discount rate and NPV

The discount rate we use in calculating NPV for a project can make all the difference as to whether that project will prove viable and be undertaken. Using Chapter3_Example_2 Excel spreadsheet you will be able to see how the NPV of the following project changes with different discount rates.

Year	Net cash flow
0	−£30,000.00
1	−£8,000.00
2	−£20,000.00
3	£40,000.00
4	£80,000.00
5	£140,000.00

Did you know?

When managers are comparing projects that have different degrees of 'risk', a higher rate of discount is often applied to the more risky project(s). This means a *lower* discount factor, and therefore a smaller PV for any future returns expected from that more risky project(s).

3.6.3 Internal rate of return (IRR)

In finding the net present value (NPV) for Projects A and B in Table 3.9 we used a *discount rate* of 0.10 (10%). Of course we could have used lower or higher rates of discount to find the NPV of each project.

Figure 3.2 shows an inverse relationship between the NPV for a project and the rate of discount; in other words, the higher the rate of discount we use in calculating NPV, the lower the value of NPV.

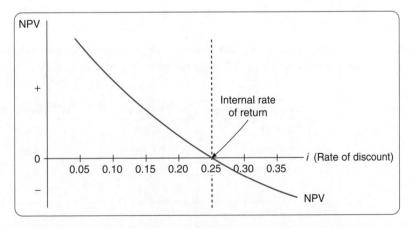

Figure 3.2 NPV varies inversely with the rate of discount (i). IRR occurs where NPV = 0

In Figure 3.2 we can see that the NPV falls as the rate of discount, i, rises. At some rate of discount, here $i = 0.25$ (25%), the value of NPV is zero. We call this rate of discount that makes NPV = 0, the *internal rate of return* (IRR).

> **IRR** is that rate of discount that makes NPV = 0 for any project.

Worked example 3.11

Find the IRR for Project A and for Project B in Table 3.8 (p. 81).

Solution

We apply the procedure for calculating the NPV of each project at a 0.10 (10%) rate of discount. However, we repeat this procedure for a *range* of possible discount rates.

In Table 3.11 we work out the *discount factors* for each of the eight time periods (years) using discount rates of 0.05 (5%), 0.10 (10%), 0.15 (15%) and 0.20 (20%) respectively.

Table 3.11 Discount factors for each time period at various discount rates

Time	0.05 (5%)	0.10 (10%)	0.15 (15%)	0.20 (20%)
0	1.000	1.000	1.000	1.000
1	0.952	0.909	0.870	0.833
2	0.907	0.826	0.757	0.694
3	0.863	0.751	0.658	0.578
4	0.822	0.683	0.573	0.482
5	0.782	0.621	0.497	0.402
6	0.745	0.564	0.433	0.334
7	0.709	0.513	0.377	0.278
8	0.675	0.466	0.328	0.232

Applying these discount factors to the respective nominal cash flows for each project shown in Table 3.9 (p. 85) gives the following results for NPV (£m).

Rate of discount	NPV Project A	NPV Project B
0.05 (5%)	15.812	2.652
0.10 (10%)	7.989	1.580
0.15 (15%)	2.344	0.710
0.20 (20%)	−1.910	−0.022

We can usefully plot the NPV curve for Project A on a diagram, as in Figure 3.3.

Worked example 3.11 *(cont'd)*

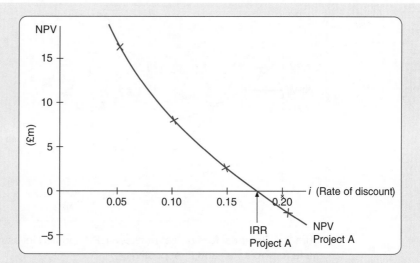

Figure 3.3 Finding IRR for Project A

As we can see, the NPV curve for Project A intersects the horizontal axis in between the 0.15 (15%) and 0.20 (20%) discount rates. This intersection point of the NPV curve with the horizontal axis is the IRR for Project A.

PAUSE FOR THOUGHT 3.2

Plot the NPV curve for Project B on this same diagram. What do you notice?

To find the *exact* rate of discount at which the intersection takes place we would need to use discount rates that vary by, say, 0.01 (1%) instead of 0.05 (5%) as here. This is an iterative (step-by-step) process which is easily solved by statistical packages on a computer.

For appraising financial investment options it is preferable to look at *both* of these measures together.

Using NPV and IRR criteria

To *use* the investment criteria we have discussed, the *decision rules* are as follows.

If selecting between alternative projects

● choose that project which has the *highest NPV* at the rate of discount applied;
● choose that project which has the *highest IRR*.

Often these decision rules will give the same result, but not always.

In the case of our two projects, A and B, using the NPV criterion at a discount rate of 0.10 (10%) clearly favours Project A: NPV of £7.989 million for Project A compared to only £1.580 million for Project B.

However, the decision is much closer in terms of the IRR criterion with both projects having NPV = 0 at rather similar rates of discount. It is when the respective NPV curves intersect

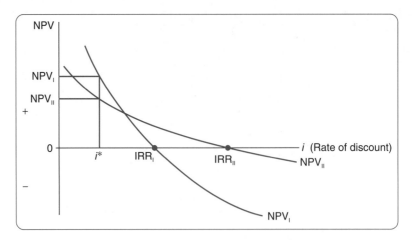

Figure 3.4 Potential for conflict between NPV and IRR investment criteria for Projects I and II respectively

above the horizontal axis that the two types of decision rule may give conflicting advice (see Figure 3.4).

In Figure 3.4, at a rate of discount i^*, Project I has the highest NPV. However, because the respective NPV curves intersect above the horizontal axis, Project II has the highest IRR.

PAUSE FOR THOUGHT 3.3

Can you suggest how a manager might *measure* risk? In other words, can you think of any statistical measures that might give a manager some idea of the different levels of risk between two investment projects with similar NPVs?

Self-check questions 3.6

*Q1. Two major investment projects being considered by Solar Spot each have the same initial capital outlay of £50,000. The expected net revenues on the respective projects over the next four years are outlined below (£000).

	Project A (£000)	Project B (£000)
Year 0	−50	−50
Year 1	10	40
Year 2	70	40
Year 3	80	40
Year 4	70	40

Calculate the NPV for the respective projects using a 0.10 (10%) rate of discount. Set out your answer in the form of a discounted cash flow table.
Comment on your results.

(*continued*)

*Q2. The table below presents the calculation of the PVs by Solar Spot for each year of cash flow, with the total being the NPV for the project. Use this table to calculate the IRR for this project.

Year	Cash outflow (£000)	Cash inflow (£000)	Net cashflow (£000)	Discount factor	Present value (£)
0	500		−500	1	−500,000
1		175	175	0.935	163,625
2	7.5	175	167.5	0.873	146,228
3	7.5	175	167.5	0.816	136,680
4	7.5	175	167.5	0.763	127,803
5	7.5	175	167.5	0.713	119,428
Sale		25	25	0.713	17,825
Total	530	900	370		211,589

*Q3. Use *all* the methods of investment appraisal to consider the relative merits of the two investment projects outlined below. Each investment project has the same initial capital outlay (£100,000) but different flows of net revenue thereafter.

Nominal cash flow Year	Project I	Project II
0	−£100,000	−£100,000
1	£38,000	£5,000
2	£30,000	£57,000
3	£23,000	£60,000
4	£22,500	£12,000
5	£21,500	£1,000

Comment on your results.

Note: Answers to Self-Check Questions can be found on the instructor's website, www.pearsoned.co.uk/wall

REVIEW QUESTIONS

R3.1. Here we return to the business application we raised at the start of the chapter.

Business applications

Collaborative venture in China

Solar Spot has demonstrated its technology at an international trade fair and has attracted interest from a major Chinese manufacturer and installer of solar panels. After extensive discussions it has developed the following scenarios for this major collaborative project.

Solar Spot Ltd	Financials	Year 1	Year 2	Year 3	Year 4	Year 5
	Revenues	£30k	£110k	£800k	£1,400k	£2,800k
	Expenditures	£50k	£250k	£530k	£900k	£1,200k
	Profit (net revenue)	−£20k	−£140k	£270k	£500k	£1,600k

(a) Find each of the following
(i)   payback;
(ii) ARR;
(iii) NPV (assume $i = 6\%$);
(iv) IRR.
(b) What decisions might Solar Spot make in view of these results?
(c) How might Solar Spot introduce risk factors into the analysis?

R3.2. The discount rate applied in a NPV calculation can have a significant effect on the valuation of the company. You can use the spreadsheet provided (Chapter3_Example_3) to change the discount rate to see how it affects the NPV and therefore the percentage of the company owned by an investor (Solar Spot) who makes a £300,000 investment.

*R3.2. After conducting a preliminary analysis Solar Spot has identified three investment opportunities. The initial capital outlay and net revenue flows from each project (in £m) were:

Year	Project A	Project B	Project C
0	−22.00	−20.00	−15.00
1	1.00	2.00	3.00
2	3.38	3.86	4.76
3	5.98	6.81	7.21
4	7.82	8.94	8.64
5	8.90	10.25	9.05
6	9.22	12.74	8.44
7	8.78	13.41	6.81
8	7.58	9.26	4.16
9	5.62	7.29	0.49

The financial director's team considered that an interest rate of 8% would be a prudent figure on which to appraise the three investment opportunities.
(a) Which project would be chosen using the payback method?
(b) What is the average rate of return on each of the projects?
(c) Which project would be chosen using NPV (discounted cash flows)?
(d) Plot the respective NPV curves on a diagram. Is there any conflict between the NPV and IRR criteria? Explain your answer.

*R3.3. Solar Spot is considering investing in a new production line for solar panels at a cost of £450,000. The projected end of year profits from installing the new production line are as follows:

Year	Profit (£000)
1	−20
2	105
3	110
4	115
5	120
6	125
7	130
8	125
9	120
10	115

Calculate the NPV of the project if the discount rate is 6%. If the discount rate increased to 10% what effect would it have on the project?

Note: Answers to Review Questions can be found on the instructor's website, www.pearsoned.co.uk/wall

Further practice

You can find more questions (with solutions) on techniques for making financial decisions on the instructor's website, www.pearsoned.co.uk/wall, including instructions on using spreadsheets to solve these questions.

Spreadsheets: video guide

You can also find a step-by-step account that takes you through the actual use of a spreadsheet when solving the type of problems you have encountered in this chapter. Go to the instructor's website, www.pearsoned.co.uk/wall

PART TWO

Growth stage of product life cycle

The emphasis in this part of the book is on the quantitative techniques most widely used when evaluating strategies for growing the revenue, profit or market share of a product that has already been introduced to the market. Even the global credit crunch since 2007 has not prevented the United Kingdom from nurturing some 4,000 fast-growing medium-sized firms, or 'gazelles', often identified as those growing revenues at more than 20% per annum.

The benefits of analysing data to better understand the current and future growth potential for a product or business has been usefully indicated by a recent film, *Moneyball*. If you ever thought business decision making had little to do with calculations and data analysis, then this film will have been something of an eye-opener! It tells the true story of how data analysis in baseball helps a previously little known team, Oakland A, to compete effectively and win against all the richer and better established US baseball teams. Billy Beane, the general manager of Oakland A, adopts the language and practices of Wall Street and uses computer simulations to transform the fortunes of the team. Beane's idea is to use extensive data on the performance of baseball players to find 'undervalued assets in an inefficient market' – that is, players who are far better in terms of the data on their actual achievements in key aspects of baseball than is reflected in their market valuation. Such 'undervalued assets' are then acquired at bargain prices by Oakland A on the transfer market, with immediate benefits to team performance.

Chapter 4 reviews a financial services company, Lendright, which is seeking to grow its business by specialising in lending to, and investing in, companies currently considering merger and acquisition (M&A) activities. We review various techniques the financial services company can use to forecast the likely outcome of the proposed merger or acquisition, forecasts that are so important if it is to 'pick winners' and lend and invest wisely. Techniques of regression and correlation will help our financial services company identify and understand the linkages between the key variables that will determine future success or failure for the merged businesses it is considering funding or investing in. Forecasting future outcomes will also be helped by reviewing past annual, quarterly or monthly data to determine both annual trends and seasonal (quarterly or monthly) variations around those trends, which can also improve the accuracy of its forecasts.

Chapter 5 examines a company in events management, Stage-it, in order to identify and assess the contribution of probability and probability distributions to management decision making. There has been a rapid growth in revenues from live music performances and festivals in recent years, contrasting sharply with declining revenues from conventional CD and record sales, in an era of legal and illegal downloading. However, Stage-it is well aware that the careful analysis of data, especially the trade-off between risk and return, will be a key element in its effective management and co-sponsorship of events. The probability characteristics embedded in expected values, decision trees, game theory and various probability distributions (normal, binomial and Poisson) will play a key role in decision making and growth for Stage-it.

Chapter 6 investigates a company that produces electronic components in the motor vehicle sector, Electrofit, which seeks to grow by progressively aligning its expertise in component design and production with developments in electronic and hybrid vehicles. Electrofit is well aware that it must continually challenge conventional assumptions (hypotheses) in the motor vehicle sector if it is to grow its business via both cost reduction and revenue generation. As it cannot inspect *all* the items involved in its inputs and outputs, sampling is of particular significance for all aspects of its quality control. Drawing the 'correct' conclusions (inferences) from sample results will be a key factor in making appropriate managerial decisions.

Chapter 4

Regression, correlation and time series

Introduction

The financial services sector in general, and the finance of mergers and acquisitions (M&A) in particular, provide the context for our study in this chapter of some key forecasting techniques involving regression, correlation and time series analysis. We review how Lendright, a financial services business with over 30 years' experience of funding business start-ups, can use these forecasting techniques to extend its funding and investing operations from supporting business start-ups to supporting larger, more established businesses seeking to grow still further via M&A activities. The article below indicates some of the reasons why Lendright is seeing carefully targeted support of M&A activity as a key growth strategy.

M&A

Latest studies show that half of all merger and acquisition (M&A) deals actually destroy (rather than create) value, but this is still an improvement on the 1980s and 1990s where 60–70 per cent of all deals were found to destroy value! It means that in the last few years, with the annual value of M&A deals running at $2,000bn to $2,700bn, about a trillion dollars ($1,000bn) a year has evaporated into thin air! Scott Moeller, director of the M&A research centre at Cass Business School, says executive boards are blithely waving through deals that are 'at best a 50/50 flip of the coin'. However, Cass research for the UK government still shows that successful deals generated better returns than failed ones destroyed.

 Source: Lucas, L. (2012) *Spending on M&A Often Wasteful*. Financial Times. 13 April.
© The Financial Times Limited. All Rights Reserved.

Lendright believes that its long experience of funding business start-ups has given it key insights into the attributes that businesses require for sustained growth. The poor outcomes for shareholders from previous M&A, as reported in the article, have convinced Lendright that it can do far better itself in identifying successful potential mergers than the financial intermediaries currently involved. It sees the prospect of growth for both its revenue and profit in providing consultancy services to the parties involved in potential mergers and also in providing funding for, and investing in, those mergers it believes to be particularly attractive. The withdrawal of some major financial intermediaries from higher-risk investment banking to concentrate on less risky 'retail' banking, and the problems many businesses are currently finding in securing funding for investment, are providing still further opportunities for new market entrants such as Lendright.

Lendright has long advocated 'data mining' and sees its experience in data analysis as giving it a key competitive advantage in allocating its available financial resources to funding and investing in those companies and proposed mergers that are most likely to succeed. Of course it is also aware that the track record for those forecasting the benefits of M&A activity is hardly encouraging! Nevertheless Lendright strongly believes that its previous success in data analysis for business start-ups can be replicated for more established firms seeking to grow via M&A.

In this chapter we will be reviewing how regression, correlation and time series techniques can help Lendright and other businesses improve their forecasts of outcomes for a wide range of business decision making, including proposed M&A.

Spreadsheets

The questions and activities in the Break-Out Boxes use spreadsheets which can be found on the student's website, www.pearsoned.co.uk/wall. Many of the Worked Examples, Self-Check Questions and Review Questions are set out for you as an Excel spreadsheet on the student's website and these questions are marked with an asterisk (*).

Learning objectives

When you have read this chapter you should be able to:

- find the least squares (regression) line to establish relationships between variables and forecast into the future;
- calculate various measures to establish the confidence you can have in forecasting from your regression line;
- use time series analysis to identify both the trend line and the seasonal variation around the line, and use these to forecast into the future;
- evaluate the factors influencing the reliability of such forecasts;
- apply all these techniques to forecast future outcomes for proposed M&A activities, and more generally.

4.1   Regression analysis

Lendright prides itself on having developed considerable expertise in analysing data to establish the nature of any relationship between two or more variables considered relevant to forecasting the future prospects of a business. The term regression analysis is often applied to the techniques it uses to establish such relationships. For example, in evaluating the prospects for a proposed merger, it will be useful to know:

- *whether there is a linkage between size and costs*: will the extra size of the combined firms help reduce costs of production and increase competitiveness?
- *whether there is a linkage between price and sales revenue*: will the lower price (now possible via lower costs for the combined firms) increase turnover and market share?
- *whether there is a linkage between a more global presence and profitability*: will the now higher proportion of international (non-UK) activity for the combined firms increase profitability?

These, and many other possible relationships between variables, will crucially determine whether the proposed merger or acquisition is likely to be a 'success'. It is important, therefore, that Lendright establishes whether there is a relationship between these and other key variables. If a relationship does exist between the variables then what is the precise nature of that relationship and can it be measured? When only two variables (e.g. X and Y) are involved we call this *linear regression* because we try to fit a straight line to our data. When more than two variables are involved we call this *multiple regression* because we then try to fit a (non-linear) curve or surface to our data.

When, in linear regression, we talk about the 'line of best fit' it is useful to remember that this is also called the 'least squares line'. This is because it is the line through the data on a scatter diagram that minimises the sum of squared deviations from the line. Finding this line is sometimes called 'regression analysis'.

4.1.1 Simple linear regression

Here we initially illustrate how we find a straight line (linear) relationship between two variables, although more sophisticated approaches can establish non-linear relationships and involve more than two variables. In 'simple' regression analysis we assume two variables only: Y, the dependent variable, and X, the independent variable.

Look at the scatter diagram in Figure 4.1, which shows the straight line $Y = mX + c$, which best fits the data. As for any straight line, m is the slope of the line and c is the intercept (i.e. the value of Y when $X = 0$).

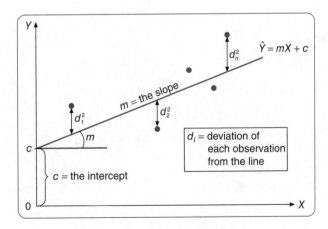

Figure 4.1 Finding the least squares line

We consider the equation of a straight line (linear equation) in more detail in Appendix 1 (p. 314). Here we note that the general equation of a straight line is

$$Y = mX + c$$

where Y = dependent variable

X = independent variable

m = gradient of the line

c = point where the line intersects the Y axis

Figure 4.1 shows a scatter diagram with dots representing the different co-ordinates (X, Y) plotted on the diagram. Our aim is to find an estimated line ($\hat{Y} = mX + c$) that best fits the data. We use the symbol $\hat{Y}$ to refer to the estimated value of Y from the least squares line.

One possibility would be to find that line which minimises the sum of deviations (d) of each observation from the line. However, some observations would have positive deviations (above the line) and some would have negative deviations (below the line). We would then be faced with the same problem noted in Chapter 2 for the mean deviation (p. 53) of identifying these signs $\pm$ and then ignoring them. It is much easier to square all these deviations so that all the signs will be positive.

Least squares line

That (unique) line for which:

$d_1^2 + d_2^2 + \ldots d_n^2$ is a minimum

$\sum_{i=1}^{n} d_i^2$ is a minimum.

If we look at the scatter diagram in Figure 4.2A, we can see four observations. In Figure 4.2B, we can see the least squares line that best fits this data.

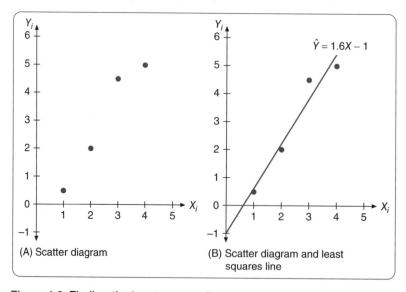

(A) Scatter diagram

(B) Scatter diagram and least squares line

Figure 4.2 Finding the least squares line

- The least squares line has a gradient (m) of $+1.6$. In other words, the estimated value of Y is rising by 1.6 units for every 1 unit rise in X.
- The intercept (c) on the vertical axis is -1. In other words, when X is 0 the estimated value of Y is -1.

Did you know?

If Lendright can use its data analysis techniques effectively to lend and invest wisely, it knows that there will be considerable demand for its financial services. The need for more funding for growing businesses was clearly demonstrated in May 2012 with the announcement that Wonga, the online 'payday' lender that has been criticised for charging annual interest rates of 4,000% on short-term personal loans, had launched a similar service for cash-strapped small- and medium-sized enterprises (SMEs). Wonga is charging between 0.3% and 2% a week for business loans of up to £10,000, which can be available in as little as 15 minutes, but which are usually repaid on a weekly basis with upfront fees and potential penalty payments meaning that a £10,000 loan for one year might cost as much as £21,000 altogether! Wonga said it hoped to provide an alternative source of funding for the 'broken' small business market.

Comparative data between countries further emphasises the need for well-targeted business lending, especially in countries such as the United Kingdom. Between 2009 and 2012, business lending *rose* by 62% in China, 53% in Russia, 49% in India, 39% in Brazil, 27% in Mexico and by over 15% in the Netherlands, Romania and Slovakia. However, business lending in the United Kingdom *fell* by 13% over the same period, with falls also being recorded in the United States (-16%), Denmark (-29%) and Ireland (-42%). It is in the countries in which business lending is falling that the greatest potential for additional sources of funding can be found.

4.1.2 Finding the least squares line: coding formula

How then can we find this least squares line?

The slope (m) and intercept (c) of this unique line can be found using the following approach, which is sometimes referred to as using the 'coding formula'.

It makes use of the fact that the regression (least squares) line must go through the point of means ($\overline{X}, \overline{Y}$), as shown in Figure 4.3. This allows us to change the origin from zero to the point of means ($\overline{X}, \overline{Y}$) and to redefine the data to establish two new axes, x and y. We do this by subtracting $\overline{X}$ from each original value of X, and $\overline{Y}$ from each original value of Y. As we can see from Figure 4.3, a single observation (9,8) is re-expressed as (4,2) using the new axes (x, y) when $\overline{X} = 5$ and $\overline{Y} = 6$.

So the two new axes, x and y, are:

$$x = X - \overline{X}$$
$$y = Y - \overline{Y}$$

If we use the redefined data for x and y then the following formula will help us calculate m and c for the least squares line.

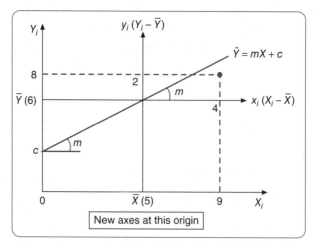

Figure 4.3 Changing the origin from zero to the point of means $(\bar{X}, \bar{Y})$ to establish the coding formula. Here a single observation (9,8) is re-expressed as (4,2) using the new axes (x,y) when $X = 5$ and $Y = 6$

Coding formula

Here we change the origin from zero to the point of means $(\bar{X}, \bar{Y})$

$$m = \frac{\sum xy}{\sum x^2}$$

where $x = X - \bar{X}$

$y = Y - \bar{Y}$

Having calculated m (the slope of the least squares line) at the new origin $(\bar{X}, \bar{Y})$ we revert to the zero origin to calculate c (the intercept). The slope, m, is of course identical at each of these origins for the linear least squares line.

Since $\bar{Y} = m\bar{X} + c$ (least squares line $\hat{Y}$ goes through point of means)

$$c = \bar{Y} - m\bar{X}$$

Worked example 4.1

Suppose Lendright has the sales revenue data (£bn) of a target acquisition. Lendright decides to use regression analysis to find the trend line to forecast the future revenue potential of this takeover target.

The revenue data for the years 2008 to 2011 is shown in the table, where $X = 1$ represents 2008, $X = 2$ represents 2009 and so on.

X (years)	Y (£bn)
1 (2008)	0.5
2 (2009)	2
3 (2010)	4.5
4 (2011)	5

Worked example 4.1 (cont'd)

Question

Calculate the least squares line using the coding formula.

Solution

Here we use the new origin $(\bar{X}, \bar{Y})$, namely $(2.5, 3)$, and redefine the data using the axes $x(X - 2.5)$ and $y(Y-3)$ (see Figure 4.4).

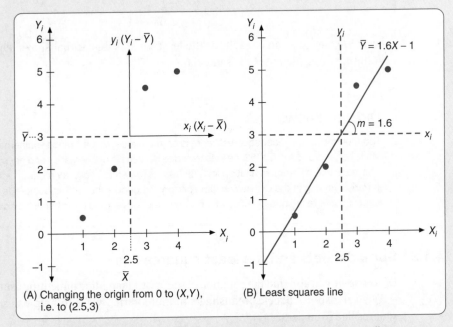

(A) Changing the origin from 0 to (X,Y), i.e. to (2.5,3)

(B) Least squares line

Figure 4.4 Using redefined data (x_iy_i) to calculate the least squares line

We can set the data out in the columns needed to calculate m and c using the coding formula for redefined data, as follows.

X	Y	x(X) – (X̄)	y(Y) – (Ȳ)	x y	x²
1	0.5	−1.5	−2.5	3.75	2.25
2	2	−0.5	−1	0.50	0.25
3	4.5	0.5	1.5	0.75	0.25
4	5	1.5	2	3.00	2.25
$\sum X = 10$	$\sum Y = 12$			$\sum xy = 8.00$	$\sum x^2 = 5.00$

$$\bar{X} = \frac{\sum X}{4} = \frac{10}{4} = 2.5$$

$$\bar{Y} = \frac{\sum Y}{4} = \frac{12}{4} = 3$$

$$m = \frac{\sum xy}{\sum x^2}$$

$$m = \frac{8.00}{5.00} = 1.6$$

$$m = \mathbf{1.6}$$

<table>
<tr><td>

Worked
example
4.1
(cont'd)

</td><td>

We have now calculated m for the least squares line at the new origin, which is of course the same as m at the 'true' zero origin. We now revert to the zero origin to find c, the vertical intercept.

$$c = \bar{Y} - m\bar{X}$$
$$c = 3 - 1.6(2.5)$$
$$c = 3 - 4$$
$$c = -1$$
$$\hat{Y} = 1.6X - 1$$

Note: We have the same result for the least squares line as that shown earlier in Figure 4.2B (p. 100) which uses the same data.

</td></tr>
</table>

Did you know?

The founder of the 'least squares' regression technique was a French mathematician, Adrien-Marie Legendre. Born in 1752, he was awarded degrees in mathematics and physics. Having lost his wealth in the French revolution in 1789 he was forced to 'work' for a living, lecturing in maths in Paris, working at the Greenwich Observatory in London and writing books. He developed the least squares technique in 1805, which was further developed by UK statistician Robert Gauss.

4.1.3 Spreadsheets and the least squares line

Of course we can also find the equation of the least squares line directly by using a spreadsheet.

We can also use Excel spreadsheets in more varied ways to help us estimate the least squares line from data.

BREAK-OUT BOX 4.1

Regression analysis by Lendright

Automatic example generator

In the Excel sheet Chapter4_Example_1 you will find data on revenue and on gross profit over the past 208 weeks (4 years) for a potential acquisition.

When evaluating the attractiveness of such a potential acquisition, Lendright carefully analyses past data of the target company.

Question

You have been asked to use the spreadsheet to find the following:

- the equation of the least squares line (regression line) for revenue over the past four years;
- the equation of the least squares line (regression line) for gross profit over the past four years.

Use your regression lines to forecast revenue and gross profit in year 7.

You will see instructions on the spreadsheet on how to find the regression lines from which you can forecast.

When you have done this for the company shown on the spreadsheet, you can press the button identified and find data on another target acquisition.

4.1.4 Forecasting

Once we have obtained our estimated least squares line we can use it for prediction (forecasting). We can insert values of the independent variable (X) not yet experienced and predict future values for the dependent variable (Y). Of course, the confidence we can have in any such prediction will depend upon:

- the past relationship between Y and X continuing into the future;
- the estimated least squares line ($\hat{Y}$) fitting the past data rather well.

We return to the 'goodness of fit' of the least squares line in the next section. In our previous example we could substitute the value X = 10 into our equation:

$$\hat{Y} = 1.6X - 1$$
$$\hat{Y} = 1.6(10) - 1$$
$$\hat{Y} = 16 - 1 = 15$$

Our predicted value for Y is 15, should X be given the value of 10.

PAUSE FOR THOUGHT 4.1

Under what circumstances would you be reasonably confident in using your least squares line for prediction? Can you think of any problems that might arise to make these predictions unreliable?

4.1.5 Multiple regression

Our analysis has, until this point, concentrated on relationships involving only two variables: a dependent variable (Y) and an independent variable (X). In many relationships, however, more than two variables are involved and attempts to fit lines (or surfaces) of 'best fit' to such variables are termed multiple regression. Here we merely touch upon a few of the issues involved.

As we can see in Figure 4.5, the variable (Y) depends on more than one independent variable, namely both X and Z. As the independent variable (X) rises, Y falls, but as the independent variable (Z) rises, Y rises, and the best fitting relationship between the variables is shown by the surface BCDE.

For example, Lendright might find from its data analysis that the profitability (Y) of a company it is considering funding falls as the number of administrative staff (X) increases, but rises as the number of operational staff (Z) increases.

Did you know?

A further variable Lendright might introduce into a forecasting model for the profitability of an overseas company or one that trades heavily from the United Kingdom with particular overseas countries is 'risk'. This risk variable (Z) can be represented by the current market price of credit default swaps (CDS) for various countries overseas.

(continued)

A credit default swap is a financial instrument that provides insurance against a country defaulting on its five year government bonds and is therefore a useful measure of how the market views the risk of lending to that country. A CDS of 100 basis points (1%) means it costs €100,000 per year to insure €10 million of a country's debt. In 2013, whereas the CDS for Germany was only 1%, that for Greece was as high as 60%, so that as much as €6 million is needed to insure against a €10 million loan to Greece. The market value of the CDS for each country therefore provides a useful guide to the degree of risk for companies in dealings with those countries.

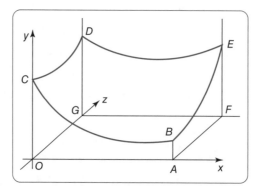

Figure 4.5 Multiple regression

Self-check questions 4.1

Q1. The data below shows how total exports Y (£000) for a firm that Lendright is considering funding have varied over the years (X) from 2006 to 2013, where $X = 1$ is 2006, $X = 2$ is 2007 and so on.

X	1	2	3	4	5	6	7	8
Y (£000)	2	5	6	7	9	12	15	16

(a) Use the data to create a scatter diagram.
(b) Find the regression line relating Y (exports) to X (time).
(c) Comment on your results.

Q2. The data below shows that employment (Y) for a firm Lendright is considering funding for proposed merger activity has varied over the years (X) from 2004 to 2013, where $X = 1$ is 2004, $X = 2$ is 2005 and so on.

X	1	2	3	4	5	6	7	8	9	10
Y (000)	19	18	16	16	20	13	6	6	11	9

(continued)

(a) Use the data to create a scatter diagram.

(b) Find the regression line relating Y (employment) to X (time).

(c) Comment on your results.

Q3. The data below shows the number of countries (X) in which a firm that Lendright is considering funding has been active over the past 15 years and the average profitability (Y in £m) per country.

X	4	5	6	12	13	13	16	16	17	17	18	19	20	22	24
Y (£m)	47	111	124	240	211	205	276	305	309	302	259	334	302	371	241

(a) Find the 'line of best fit' (least squares line) relating average profitability (Y) to the number of countries in which the firm operates (X).

(b) What do your results suggest?

Q4. The data shows the budget deficit (public expenditure minus tax revenue) as a percentage of national income for nine countries and the market value of their CDS in 2012, expressed as a percentage. We noted above that the higher the percentage CDS for a country, the greater the market perception of risk from lending to that country.

Country	CDS as a percentage	Budget deficit as a percentage of national income
France	1.9	5.9
Germany	1.0	2.1
Greece	60.0	9.8
Ireland	8.6	10.2
Italy	5.1	3.9
Portugal	12.1	5.8
Spain	3.9	6.3
UK	0.9	8.1
US	0.5	10.1

(a) Find the 'line of best fit' relating a country's CDS value (Y) to its budget deficit (X).

(b) What do your results suggest?

Note: Answers to Self-Check Questions can be found on the instructor's website, www.pearsoned.co.uk/wall

Analysts at Lendright have been made aware of a recently published study by David Blanchflower and Andrew Oswald (2013). The main findings of the study are reviewed in the box below. Suggest how this study might be relevant to the advice Lendright is about to give to a client on its proposed acquisition of a large multinational house-building company in the European Union.

Home ownership and unemployment

Blanchflower and Oswald found that rises in the home ownership rate in a US state were followed by sharp rises in the unemployment rate. This positive relationship between the two variables was linked to higher home ownership resulting in less labour mobility, greater time spent in commuting to work and fewer new business start-ups.

The authors then reviewed unemployment rates and home ownership across 28 EU and OECD countries, and obtained the result shown in Figure 4.6.

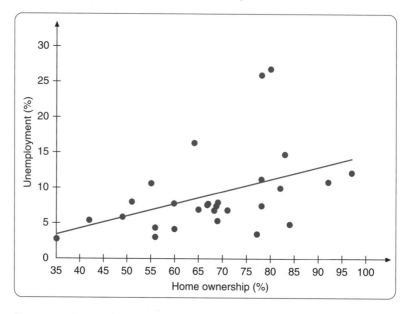

Figure 4.6 Unemployment rates and home ownership

What implications might this study have for Lendright's advice on the proposed merger of its client with a major EU house-building company?

4.2   Correlation

The key idea here is to measure how well the regression line fits the actual data. Two key measures are frequently used in this respect:

- the coefficient of determination (R^2);
- Pearson's coefficient of correlation (R).

Did you know?

The use of data to find relationships between variables and measures of correlation can be really helpful in identifying possible M&A targets for the growth of a business. For example, Eric Siegel, in his book *The Power to Predict Who Will Click, Buy, Lie or Die* (2013), shows how

(continued)

the extensive analysis of data from a wide range of sources has provided important insights into consumer behaviour. Siegel shows that if consumers buy nappies, they are more likely to buy beer, which might encourage a pharmacy chain to consider a conglomerate merger with a drinks company. However, Professor Siegel also strikes a cautionary note on assuming that correlation always reflects causation! For example, he shows that the annual closing price of the S&P 500 Stock Market index could have been predicted from 1983 to 1993 by the rate of butter production in Bangladesh!

Before considering formulae for calculating these measures, it will be helpful to define the concepts of deviation and variation that underpin them. Figure 4.7 is used for illustration.

Deviation (d) is the difference between the actual value of an observation (Y) and its arithmetic mean ($\overline{Y}$). This deviation can be split into two separate parts:

- an explained part (d_e), which is predicted or accounted for by the regression line;
- an unexplained part (d_u), which is not predicted or accounted for by the regression line.

$$\text{Deviation} = d = Y - \overline{Y}$$
$$\text{Deviation} = \text{explained deviation} + \text{unexplained deviation}$$
$$\text{Deviation} = d = d_e + d_u$$

Summing such deviations across all n observations gives total deviation:

$$\sum d = \sum d_e + \sum d_u$$

i.e. total = explained + unexplained
deviation   deviation   deviation

Variation (d^2) is the square of the difference between the actual value of an observation (Y) and its arithmetic mean ($\overline{Y}$). As before, squaring the deviations avoids the problem of first identifying then dropping the sign $\pm$ of each deviation.

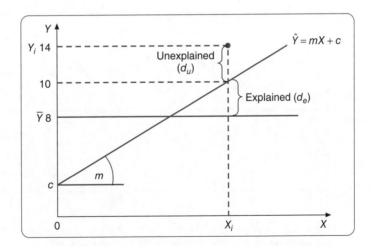

Figure 4.7 Deviation for each observation (d) is the actual value (Y) minus the arithmetic mean ($\overline{Y}$). This can be split into two parts: explained deviation (d_e) and unexplained deviation (d_u)

Summing the squared deviations across all n observations gives total variation. It can be shown that:

$$\sum d^2 = \sum d_e^2 + \sum d_u^2$$

i.e. total = explained + unexplained
variation   variation   variation

PAUSE FOR THOUGHT 4.2

How does total variation differ from the variance we discussed in Chapter 2?

4.2.1 Coefficient of determination R^2

The coefficient of determination (R^2) is the ratio of 'explained variation' to 'total variation'.

$$R^2 = \frac{\text{explained variation}}{\text{total variation}}$$

- When $R^2 = 1$, as in Figure 4.8A, then all the deviation and therefore all the variation can be explained or accounted for by the regression line. We have a perfect fit.
- When $R^2 = 0$ (or close to 0), as in Figure 4.8B, none of the deviation and therefore variation can be explained or accounted for by the regression line. We effectively have a random scatter of points to which any regression line fits as well as any other.
- The closer R^2 is to 1, the better the fit of the least squares line to the actual data.

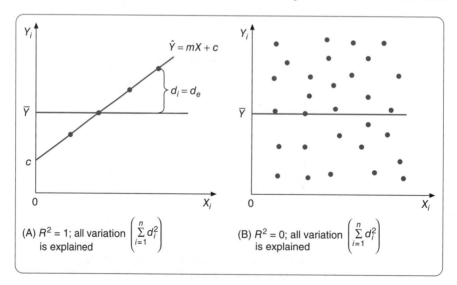

(A) $R^2 = 1$; all variation $\left(\sum_{i=1}^{n} d_i^2 \right)$ is explained

(B) $R^2 = 0$; all variation $\left(\sum_{i=1}^{n} d_i^2 \right)$ is explained

Figure 4.8 Coefficient of determination (R^2)

4.2.2 Pearson's coefficient of correlation (R)

Pearson's coefficient of correlation (R) is the square root of the coefficient of determination (R^2)

$$R = \sqrt{R^2}$$

$$R = \sqrt{\frac{explained\ variation}{total\ variation}}$$

Just as R^2 varies between 1 and 0, so R varies between ± 1 and 0.

Figure 4.9 outlines the various possible values for R, the coefficient of correlation. This is often called Pearson's coefficient of correlation and can have values between $+1$ and -1.

$$(A)\ R = +1$$

This is perfect positive correlation. Here the relationship between Y and X is direct (positive), as both variables rise and fall together. The sign for R is therefore positive, and the value is $+1$ since the fit of the least squares line is perfect (all the variation is explained).

$$(B)\ R > 0 \text{ but} < 1$$

Lendright has found in the past that the survival rate of new business start-ups (Y) is closely and positively correlated with the time and effort put into developing the initial business plan (X). This would suggest a direct (positive) relationship between Y and X with each variable moving in the same direction, so the sign is positive for R. The value for R is <1, since not all of the variation is explained.

$$(C)\ R = 0 \text{ (random scatter)}$$

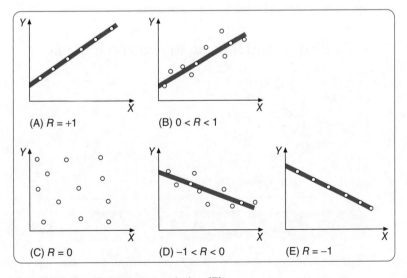

Figure 4.9 Coefficient of correlation (R)

Essentially there is no relationship between Y and X. All the variation is unexplained.

$$\text{(D) } R < 0 \text{ but } > -1$$

Lendright has found in the past that a key measure of profitability (Y) has tended to fall as the number of layers of management (X) has increased. Here the relationship between Y and X is indirect (negative or inverse) as each variable moves in the opposite direction; when one variable rises the other falls, and vice versa. The sign for R is therefore negative but the value is > -1 since not all of the variation is explained.

$$\text{(E) } R = -1$$

This is perfect negative correlation. The relationship between Y and X is indirect (negative or inverse) and the value is -1 since the fit of the least squares line is perfect (all the variation is explained).

Did you know?

The easiest way to interpret the meaning of a particular value of R, the Pearson coefficient of correlation, is to square it. For example, a value $R = +0.8$ means that $R^2 = (+0.8)^2 = 0.64$ that is, 64% of total variation can be 'explained' or accounted for by your regression line.

Finding R^2 and R: coding formula

As when we found the regression line, we can find R^2 and R by changing the origin from zero to the point of means $(\overline{X}, \overline{Y})$ since the regression line goes through this point, and then using the 'coding formula'.

So the two new axes, x and y, are:

$$x = X - \overline{X}$$
$$y = Y - \overline{Y}$$

If we use the redefined data for x and y then the following coding formula will help us calculate R^2 and R for the least squares line.

Finding R^2 and R using the coding formula

$$R^2 = \frac{\left[\sum xy \right]^2}{\left[\sum x^2 \sum y^2 \right]}$$

where $x = X - \overline{X}$

$$y = Y - \overline{Y}$$
$$R = \sqrt{R^2}$$

PAUSE FOR THOUGHT 4.3

What part of the formula for R^2 have you already found when calculating the equation of the least squares line?

Worked example 4.2

Here we apply our coding formula to the data on sales revenue (£bn) for a target acquisition already presented on p. 102. We used the data to find the least squares line, $\hat{Y} = 1.6X - 1$, but here we use the data to find R^2 and R. We reproduce our earlier workings below, noting that this time we need an extra column for y^2.

Solution

X	Y	x(X−X̄)	y(Y−Ȳ)	x y	x²	y²
1	0.5	−1.5	−2.5	3.75	2.25	6.25
2	2	−0.5	−1	0.50	0.25	1
3	4.5	0.5	1.5	0.75	0.25	2.25
4	5	1.5	2	3.00	2.25	4
$\sum X = 10$	$\sum Y = 12$			$\sum xy = 8.00$	$\sum x^2 = 5.00$	$\sum y^2 = 13.50$

$$\bar{X} = \frac{\sum X}{4} = \frac{10}{4} = 2.5$$

$$\bar{Y} = \frac{\sum Y}{4} = \frac{12}{4} = 3$$

Using our coding formula

$$R_2 = \frac{\left[\sum xy\right]^2}{\left[\sum x^2 \sum y^2\right]} = \frac{(8.00)^2}{(5.00)(13.50)} = \frac{64.00}{67.50} = 0.948$$

$$R^2 = 0.948$$

In other words, 94.8% of the total variation of sales revenue is accounted for by our regression line.

Worked example 4.3

In this example we see how the profits of a company (Y) in £million have varied since it was established six years ago ($X = 1$).

(a) Calculate the regression line relating profits to time.

(b) How confident can you be in using this regression line for forecasting?

X	Y	x(X−X̄)	y(Y−Ȳ)	xy	x²	y²
1	−4	−2.5	−4.5	11.25	6.25	20.25
2	−3	−1.5	−3.5	5.25	2.25	12.25
3	−1	−0.5	−1.5	0.75	0.25	2.25
4	2	0.5	1.5	0.75	0.25	2.25
5	3	1.5	2.5	3.75	2.25	6.25
6	6	2.5	5.5	13.75	6.25	30.25
$\sum X = 21$	$\sum Y = 3$			$\sum xy = 35.5$	$\sum x^2 = 17.5$	$\sum y^2 = 73.50$

Worked example 4.3 (cont'd)

$$\bar{X} = \frac{\sum X}{6} = \frac{21}{6} = 3.5$$

$$\bar{Y} = \frac{\sum Y}{6} = \frac{3}{6} = 0.5$$

Using the coding formula

$$m = \frac{\sum xy}{\sum x^2} \qquad c = \bar{Y} - m\bar{X} \qquad\qquad R^2 = \frac{\left(\sum xy\right)^2}{\left(\sum x^2\right)\left(\sum y^2\right)}$$

$$m = \frac{35.5}{17.5} \qquad c = 0.5 - (2.03)3.5 \qquad\qquad R^2 = \frac{1{,}260.25}{1{,}286.25}$$

$$\qquad\qquad\qquad\qquad\qquad\qquad\qquad\qquad R^2 = 0.98$$

$$m = 2.03 \qquad c = -6.6 \qquad\qquad\qquad R = \sqrt{0.98}$$

$$\hat{Y} = 2.03X - 6.6 \qquad\qquad\qquad\qquad R = 0.99$$

(a) Y rises by 2.03 units for every 1 unit rise in X; in other words, profits (Y) are rising by £2.03 million in each year (X).

(b) We can be confident in forecasting in that $R^2 = 0.98$ so that 98% of the total variation is explained or accounted for by the regression line.

Spreadsheets and correlation

The Excel spreadsheet Chapter4_Example_2 applies these ideas to finding both the regression line and the 'goodness of fit' of that line to original data.

BREAK-OUT BOX 4.2

Co-efficient of determination (R^2)

Automatic example generator

In the Excel spreadsheet Chapter4_Example_2 you will find data on 50 past acquisitions from the London Stock Exchange.

Lendright is interested in identifying the relationship between the total market value of the acquired company at the point of purchase and its value three years after the point of purchase.

As well as using the approach in Break-Out Box 4.1 (p. 104) to find the regression line, it also wishes to find the coefficient of determination (R^2) to assess how well the regression line actually fits the data.

Question

You have been asked to use the spreadsheet to find the following:

- the equation of the least squares line (regression line) for value three years after purchase (Y) and value at the point of purchase (X);
- the coefficient of determination (R^2) for this least squares (regression) line.

You will see instructions on the spreadsheet on how to find the regression line and R^2.

When you have done this for the 50 company acquisitions shown on the spreadsheet, you can press the button identified and find data on another 50 company acquisitions.

PAUSE FOR THOUGHT 4.4

Can you suggest how Lendright might use the analysis from the spreadsheet to inform its decision making?

Self-check questions 4.2

Q1. This is the earlier data from Q1 of Self-Check Questions 4.1 (p. 106) which shows how total exports Y (£000) for a firm that Lendright is considering funding varied over the years (X) from 2006 to 2013 where $X = 1$ is 2006, $X = 2$ is 2007 and so on.

X	1	2	3	4	5	6	7	8
Y (£000)	2	5	6	7	9	12	15	16

(a) Find the coefficient of determination.
(b) Find Pearson's coefficient of correlation.
(c) Comment on your results.

Q2. This is the earlier data from Q2 of Self-Check Questions 4.1 (p. 107) which shows how employment Y (000) for a firm that Lendright is considering funding varied over the years (X) from 2004 to 2013 where $X = 1$ is 2004, $X = 2$ is 2005 and so on.

X	1	2	3	4	5	6	7	8	9	10
Y (000)	19	18	16	16	20	13	6	6	11	9

(a) Find the coefficient of determination.
(b) Find Pearson's coefficient of correlation.
(c) Comment on your results.

Q3. This is the earlier data from Q4 of Self-Check Questions 4.1 (p. 107) which shows the budget deficit (public expenditure minus tax revenue) as a percentage of national income for nine countries and the market value of their CDS in 2012, expressed as a percentage. We noted above that the higher the percentage CDS for a country, the greater the market perception of risk from lending to that country.

(continued)

Country	CDS as a percentage	Budget deficit as a percentage of national income
France	1.9	5.9
Germany	1.0	2.1
Greece	60.0	9.8
Ireland	8.6	10.2
Italy	5.1	3.9
Portugal	12.1	5.8
Spain	3.9	6.3
UK	0.9	8.1
US	0.5	10.1

(a) Find the coefficient of determination.

(b) Find Pearson's coefficient of correlation.

(c) Comment on your results.

Note: Answers to Self-Check Questions can be found on the instructor's website, www.pearsoned.co.uk/wall

4.3   Spearman's coefficient of rank correlation

Sometimes data is presented in rank order, whether descending (first to last) or ascending (last to first). It may be that the ranking comes from two separate sources, as when applicants for a post are ranked both by interview and by psychological tests. We might then wish to check to what extent the different rankings agree! In such situations Spearman's coefficient of rank correlation (R_s) might be calculated. The formula for R_s is as follows:

$$R_s = 1 - \frac{6 \sum d^2}{n^3 - n}$$

where R_s = Spearman's rank correlation coefficient

d = difference in ranking of a given observation

n = number of observations

If $R_s = 1$, then clearly we have perfect agreement between the respective rankings. This follows from the fact that each d would be zero when the respective rankings are identical, giving $R_s = 1 - 0$ in the above expression. The closer to 1 the value of R_s, the better the agreement between the respective rankings.

Worked example 4.4

Ten candidates for a managerial post at Lendright were ranked by interview and psychological test in the following manner:

	A	B	C	D	E	F	G	H	I	J
I Interview	4	2	7	1	5	6	9	3	10	8
II Psychological test	3	2	5	1	4	9	6	7	8	10

Worked example 4.4 (cont'd)

Question

Calculate Spearman's rank correlation coefficient and discuss whether it represents a measure of agreement between the two types of test.

Solution

Step 1. Take the difference in the ranks (d).

Step 2. Square each of these differences.

Step 3. Sum the squares of the differences.

Step 4. We then substitute the result into the formula.

d	1	0	2	0	1	3	3	4	2	2
d^2	1	0	4	0	1	9	9	16	4	4

$$\sum d^2 = 48$$

$$R_s = 1 - \frac{6 \sum d^2}{n^3 - n} = 1 - \frac{6 \times 48}{10^3 - 10} = 1 - \frac{288}{990} = 0.709$$

The Spearman's rank correlation coefficient shows some agreement in ranking between the two types of procedure.

We can use Spearman's coefficient of rank correlation (R_s) whenever the data for two variables is given in rank order (i.e. the data is ordinal). Whenever data is given in terms of absolute values (i.e. the data is cardinal) we would usually use the earlier coefficient of correlation (R). However, we can convert two sets of data that are given in absolute values into rank order should we wish to calculate R_s. Further, should one set of data be given in terms of absolute values (cardinal) and the other in terms of rank order (ordinal) then only by converting the cardinal data to ordinal and calculating R_s might we be able to establish a measure of 'goodness of fit' between the two types of data.

Self-check questions 4.3

Q1. The data below shows the number of countries (X) in which the firm that Lendright is considering acquiring has been active over the past 15 years and the average profitability (Y in £m) per country.

X	4	5	6	12	13	13	16	16	17	17	18	19	20	22	24
Y (£m)	47	111	124	240	211	205	276	305	309	302	259	334	302	371	241

(a) Find the coefficient of determination.

(b) Find Pearson's coefficient of correlation.

(c) Comment on your results.

Q2. Lendright has used two different methods of forecasting in the past, and wishes to identify one method to use in the future. For a recently acquired company it seeks to check how well each forecasting method would have performed in predicting actual sales over the past year in eight different regions.

(continued)

The data below gives the actual sales of the company (£000) in each of the eight regions, together with the forecast of sales by two different methods. Lendright wishes to compare the actual sales recorded with what the two forecasting methods used by Lendright would have predicted.

Region	Actual sales (£000)	Forecast sales (£000): method 1	Forecast sales (£000): method 2
A	15	13	16
B	19	25	19
C	30	23	26
D	12	26	14
E	58	48	65
F	10	15	19
G	23	28	27
H	17	10	22

(a) Calculate the rank correlation coefficient between
  (i) actual sales and forecast method 1;
  (ii) actual sales and forecast method 2.
(b) Which forecasting method would you recommend that Lendright use in the future?

Note: Answers to Self-Check Questions can be found on the instructor's website, www.pearsoned.co.uk/wall

4.4   Time series and forecasting

Data can be collected for purposes of analysis in a number of ways. For example, data for household saving can be collected in different locations (nation, region, city, etc.) at a single point of time. These are called *cross-sectional* data. Alternatively data for household saving can be collected for a given location (nation, region, city, etc.) at different points in time. This is called *time series* data.

In this section we consider the use by Lendright of such time series data as a basis for estimating both trend and seasonal variation. As we shall see, such estimates can then be used as a basis for forecasting and can be combined with our earlier work on finding the least squares line to give even more accurate forecasts.

4.4.1   Time series components

Many types of data have been recorded through time, such as monthly, quarterly or annual data for output, sales revenue, profit, employment, unemployment, prices and so on. Typically such time series data exhibits one or more of the following components:

● *Trend component* (*T*), whereby the variable appears to broadly rise or fall (or remain unchanged) through time.

● *Seasonal component* (*S*) whereby the variable moves in regular cycles within a year around that trend line. For example, within a broadly rising value of sales through time (trend), an ice cream manufacturer may regularly experience peaks for sales in summer months and troughs for sales in winter months (seasonal). Note that although the term 'seasonal' has been applied to such short-term cycles, these may involve any units of time within a year: for example, days within a week (e.g. high sales on Fridays and low sales on Mondays), weeks within a month, months or quarters or other 'seasons' within a year.

- *Cyclical component* (*C*), whereby the variable moves in a rather less regular cycle over the medium to longer term around the trend line. For example, some have claimed to observe a business cycle of some 8 to 10 years between periods of 'boom' and 'bust' in modern industrialised economies. Others have claimed to observe still longer cycles over 50 years, with the peaks of such cycles related to new technological breakthroughs, such as water power, steam, electricity, microelectronics and so on. These have sometimes been referred to as Kondratief cycles, after a Russian economist of that name.

Note that the period of a cycle is often referred to as the time between successive peaks or successive troughs.

- *Irregular component* (*I*), which is entirely unpredictable. The 'credit crunch' of 2007–8 was, for example, a dramatic and unexpected departure from trend in terms of global economic activity.

PAUSE FOR THOUGHT 4.5

Can you list six products (goods or services) for which you might expect the demand to experience seasonal variation within a year?

Can you name three irregular components other than the so-called 'credit crunch' that have influenced global economic activity in the past 10 years?

Figure 4.10 presents two possible time series profiles for the value of a dependent variable (*Y*).

In Figure 4.10A a clear upward trend is evident, around which there is seasonal variation, with quarter 1 representing successive peaks and quarter 3 successive troughs within each year. In Figure 4.10B a clear downward trend is evident, around which there is a cyclical component with a period of around 10 years between successive peaks or successive troughs.

Of course many variants are possible for such profiles. We may, for example, have a shorter-term seasonal variation (e.g. quarterly or monthly) superimposed on a time series showing both a cycle and trend using longer-term (e.g. annual) data.

Did you know?

The construction industry is widely regarded as a barometer for economic prospects throughout the economy. Traditionally it is one of the earliest sectors to be affected by economic recession and one of the earliest sectors to experience higher demand when economic recovery occurs.

Additive or multiplicative model

We can represent or 'model' our time series using the four components already identified. We can do this in one of two ways: either adding or multiplying the respective components.

- $Y = T + S + C + I$ (additive model)
- $Y = T \times S \times C \times I$ (multiplicative model)

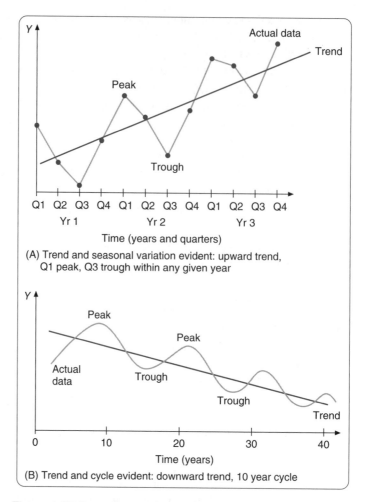

(A) Trend and seasonal variation evident: upward trend,
Q1 peak, Q3 trough within any given year

(B) Trend and cycle evident: downward trend, 10 year cycle

Figure 4.10 Some time series profiles

As we shall see, we can use either of these models to calculate any trend line or seasonal variation. However, there may be circumstances in which one approach is more appropriate than another!

In Figure 4.11A the additive model is the most appropriate as deviations from the trend line are of a similar *absolute magnitude* from one peak (or trough) to another, with Q2 providing peaks and Q4 troughs. The same principle would equally apply if we were using annual data and comparing successive peaks or troughs in a business cycle over, say, an 8 to 10 year period.

However, in Figure 4.11B the multiplicative model is the most appropriate as deviations from the trend line are of a similar *percentage* from one peak (or trough) to another. We can see that the absolute magnitude of the deviations from the trend line grows over time as the dependent variable (Y) rises, but that the percentage deviations remain roughly constant.

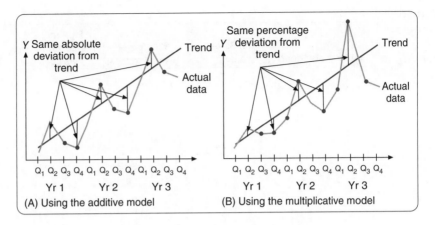

Figure 4.11 Choosing an appropriate time series model

Moving average

As we shall see in this section, we can use the idea of a moving average to find the trend of the data. To find the moving average we initially find the simple average (arithmetic mean) for a specified number of items of data. We then recalculate that average having dropped the initial item of data and added a subsequent item of data.

In the worked example below, involving quarterly data for sales value, we initially find the simply average for four items of data, and then move the average along. Because the four quarter moving average falls in between the second and third quarters, we include an extra column to centre the data to align with a particular time period.

Worked example 4.5

Find a four quarter centred moving average for the data in Table 4.1 on sales value (£000).

Table 4.1 Time series of quarterly sales value (£000)

(1) Year and quarter		(2) Sales value (Y)	(3) Four quarter moving total	(4) Four quarter moving average	(5) Centred four quarter moving average (T)
2010	1	87.5			
	2	73.2			
			314.0	78.5	
	3	64.8			78.9
			316.8	79.2	
	4	88.5			79.6
			319.6	79.9	
2011	1	90.3			80.5
			324.0	81.0	

Worked example 4.5 (cont'd)

(1) Year and quarter		(2) Sales value (Y)	(3) Four quarter moving total	(4) Four quarter moving average	(5) Centred four quarter moving average (T)
	2	76.0			81.8
			330.2	82.6	
	3	69.2			83.1
			333.8	83.5	
	4	94.7			83.8
			336.2	84.1	
2012	1	93.9			84.5
			339.0	84.8	
	2	78.4			85.5
			344.6	86.2	
	3	72.0			
	4	100.3			

It is often helpful to find the four quarter centred moving average in stages.

- *Four quarter moving total (column 3)*. Here we simply sum the data for the initial four quarters in column 2 to find the four quarter moving total. Notice that the moving totals fall in between the actual quarterly data in column 2. For example, the first moving total falls in between quarter 2 and quarter 3 for 2010.

- *Four quarter moving average (column 4)*. We then divide the respective four quarter moving totals in column 3 by 4 to find the four quarter moving average.

- *Four quarter centred moving average (column 5)*. It will help to align the moving averages with the specific quarterly data in column 2. For this reason we centre the data in column 4 by summing respective pairs of data and dividing by 2.

Did you know?

Survey evidence suggests that the technique of moving averages is used by around 25% of UK businesses in an attempt to forecast future demand.

Finding the trend

In practice we are often presented with monthly or quarterly data over a number of years for which no obvious business cycle (C) of 8 to 10 years is present. We can therefore regard the actual data, Y, as having only three of the four components previously mentioned:

$$\text{i.e. } Y = T + S + I \text{ (additive)}$$

$$\text{or } Y = T \times S \times I \text{ (multiplicative)}$$

If we calculate an appropriate moving average for the monthly or quarterly data, then we can eliminate both the seasonal variation component (S) and the irregular component (I) from the actual data. This will leave us with T, the required trend value.

- Using a four quarter moving average in column 4 of the worked example above means that we can eliminate any seasonal variation (S) as regards high or low quarters. For example, in column 3 after our initial calculation of 314 we drop the first quarter of 2010 but add the first quarter of 2011 to get 316.8. Our four quarter moving total therefore continually takes in all quarters, both high (as for quarter 1) and low (as for quarter 3) quarters. In this way column 4 helps eliminate S, the seasonal component.

- In calculating column 4 we are averaging, and in finding the centred moving average in column 5 we are also averaging. Any averaging process helps eliminate any irregular component, so the data in column 5 can be regarded as having eliminated I, the irregular component.

$$\text{If } Y = T + S + I$$
$$\text{or } Y = T \times S \times I$$

Then by calculating column 5 we have eliminated S and I, leaving us with T, the trend component.

Figure 4.12 plots the original quarterly data (Y) of column 2 and the trend component (T) of column 5. Straight lines are often used to connect successive points on the scatter diagram. An alternative approach would, of course, be to draw a single least squares line that 'best fits' the points on the scatter diagram that correspond to the trend. We consider this alternative approach below.

PAUSE FOR THOUGHT 4.6

Can you name three products (goods or services) for which an upward sales trend is well established, and three products for which a downward sales trend is well established?

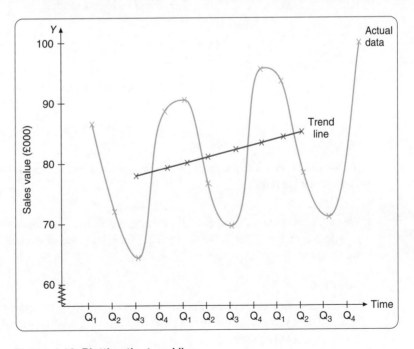

Figure 4.12 Plotting the trend line

The nature of the data will define the type of moving average required to eliminate S and I and therefore leave only the trend, T.

Using moving averages to find the trend (T)

Quarterly data: use four quarter centred moving average to eliminate S and I, and leave T.

Monthly data: use 12 month centred moving average to eliminate S and I, and leave T.

Finding and eliminating the seasonal variation

When the original data (Y) has no obvious longer-term business cycle, we have already noted that it can be represented as either:

$$Y = T + S + I \text{ (additive model)}$$

$$\text{or } Y = T \times S \times I \text{ (multiplicative model)}$$

Finding the seasonal variation (S)

We can easily extend our work in using moving averages to find T, the trend component, so that we can find S, the seasonal variation component. Essentially we need only add an extra column to the calculations we have already undertaken to find T. This extra column which gives us S (and I) will be ($Y-T$) in the case of the additive model or $\left(\dfrac{Y}{T}\right)$ in the case of the multiplicative model, for the following reasons:

$$Y = T + S + I \text{ (additive model)}$$
$$MA = T$$
$$Y - MA = S + I$$
$$\text{Or}$$
$$Y = T \times S \times I \text{ (multiplicative model)}$$
$$MA = T$$
$$\frac{Y}{MA} = S \times I$$

As we shall see, a further simple averaging process will remove I, leaving S, the seasonal variation that we require.

Worked example 4.6

We can demonstrate this approach by using the earlier data for sales value (Y) and calculations for trend (T) in Table 4.1 (p. 121) for sales value in Worked Example 4.5. Here we shall use the additive model (Table 4.2).

Solution

Subtracting our trend values (T) from the corresponding quarterly sales values (Y) gives us $S + I$ over successive quarters. The averaging process will then help to remove I, leaving us with S as required.

Worked
example
4.6
(cont'd)

A simple table can usefully illustrate this process (Table 4.3).

The averaging process for each quarter leaves us with S, the seasonal variation for that quarter. Clearly quarters 1 and 4 are high sales quarters for this product, whereas quarter 2 and especially quarter 3 are low sales quarters.

Table 4.2 Time series of quarterly sales value (£000)

		Y (original data)	T (four quarter centred moving average)	S + I (Y – T)
2010	Q1	87.5		
	Q2	73.2		
	Q3	64.8	78.9	−14.1
	Q4	88.5	79.6	8.9
2011	Q1	90.3	80.5	9.8
	Q2	76.0	81.8	−5.8
	Q3	69.2	83.1	−13.9
	Q4	94.7	83.8	10.9
2012	Q1	93.9	84.5	9.4
	Q2	78.4	85.5	−7.1
	Q3	72.0		
	Q4	100.3		

Table 4.3 Finding the seasonal variation factors (£000)

	Q1	Q2	Q3	Q4
2010			−14.1	8.9
2011	9.8	−5.8	−13.9	10.9
2012	9.4	−7.1		
Total	19.2	−12.9	−28.0	19.8
Average (S)	9.6	−6.45	−14.0	9.9

Did you know?

Business confidence is a key factor in stimulating M&A and the demand for financial services. The official national income (GDP) data plays a key role here, involving both trend and irregular factors. Two successive falls in quarterly GDP is the official definition of 'recession' and trends in such quarterly data are carefully scrutinised. However, irregular factors (I) can influence such quarterly data. For example, the Diamond Jubilee (60 years of reign by the monarch) in the United Kingdom in June 2012 resulted in an extra day of national holiday. The extra day of holiday is estimated to have reduced the second quarter GDP figures for the United Kingdom by as much as 0.3% of GDP.

Finding the adjusted seasonal variation factor (S)

The data shown in the 'Average' row of Table 4.3 for S is actually *unadjusted*. If we sum the plus values we have $+19.5$ $(9.6 + 9.9)$ but if we sum the negative values we have -20.45 $(-6.45 + -14.0)$. In other words, there is a net value for S of -0.95.

Strictly speaking the plus and minus values should cancel out. We can compensate for the -0.95 by adding $+0.95/4$ (i.e. $+0.24$) to each of the four quarterly values for S. These values would then be the adjusted values for S (see Table 4.4).

It is these *adjusted values* for S that we usually refer to as the seasonal variation components. Here we can see that sales are normally 9.84 above trend for Q1, but 6.21 below trend for Q2 and so on (all values in £000).

Eliminating the seasonal variations (S)

Having found S, the seasonal variation component, our next step is to eliminate S from the original data, Y (see Table 4.5). We will then have an estimate of Y without any 'distortion' resulting from seasonal influences on Y. Such data, with the seasonal variation removed, is sometimes called *deseasonalised* data.

Notice that in eliminating S by subtracting S from Y, we sometimes have $-- = +$, as in Q2 of 2010.

Using the adjusted seasonal variation component, S, calculated above we can easily eliminate S from the original data, Y. Here we use the additive model for illustration purposes and therefore subtract S from Y for each quarter (in the multiplicative model we would divide S into Y for each quarter).

Table 4.4 **Finding the adjusted seasonal variation factors (£000)**

	Q1	Q2	Q3	Q4
Unadjusted S (0.95 net)	+9.6	−6.45	−14.0	+9.9
Adjusted* S (zero net)	+9.84	−6.21	−13.76	+10.14

$* +\left(\dfrac{0.95}{4}\right)$ i.e. +0.24 added to each quarter

Table 4.5 **Eliminating the seasonal variation from the original data (i.e. deseasonalising the data)**

Year and quarter		Original data (Y)	S Adjusted seasonal variation	Y − S (deseasonalised data)
2010	Q1	87.5	+9.84	77.66
	Q2	73.2	−6.21	79.41
	Q3	64.8	−13.76	78.56
	Q4	88.5	+10.14	78.36
2011	Q1	90.3	+9.84	80.46
	Q2	76.0	−6.21	82.21
	Q3	69.2	−13.76	82.96
	Q4	94.7	+10.14	84.56
2012	Q1	93.9	+9.84	84.06
	Q2	78.4	−6.21	84.61
	Q3	72.0	−13.76	85.76
	Q4	100.3	+10.14	90.16

4.4.2 Forecasting: trend and seasonal variation

We have already looked at prediction (forecasting) using the simple regression analysis. Here we combine the ideas of finding a least squares line (line of 'best fit') with our analysis of time series components. We can then extrapolate (take forward) the regression line that best fits the trend estimates to derive a forecast of future sales into a particular year and into a specific month (or quarter).

Figure 4.13 shows the equation of the least squares line that best fits the data presented earlier in Table 4.2 (p. 125).

$$\hat{Y} = 0.975X + 77.8$$

where X represents successive quarters, Q3 (2010) $= 1$

Of course any forecast for the sales (Y) in a particular quarter (X) will be more accurate if it takes into account the seasonal variation (S) components already identified as well as the trend (T). The adjusted values for S were as follows (£000):

Q1 (+9.84)   Q2 (−6.21)   Q3 (−13.76)   Q4 (+10.14)

We must add or subtract these seasonal variation values to our trend forecast if we are to be more realistic about the likely future sales in a particular quarter (see Table 4.6). For example, we can forecast the trend using the equation

$$\hat{Y}_T = 0.975X + 77.8$$

where $X = 1$ for Q3, 2010

This gives the trend forecast for Q2, 2013 as follows:

When $X = 12$ (i.e. Q2, 2013)

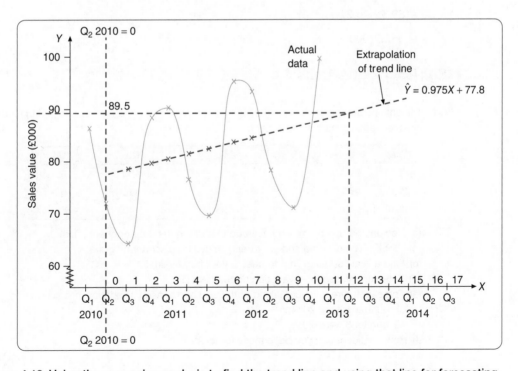

Figure 4.13 Using the regression analysis to find the trend line and using that line for forecasting

Table 4.6 Forecast ($\hat{Y}_{T+S}$) for sales value (£000) over the period 2013–15 inclusive

Year and quarter		X^*	$\hat{Y}_T$ Trend forecast	S Adjusted seasonal variation	$\hat{Y}_{T+S}$ Overall forecast
2013	Q1	11	88.5	+9.84	98.34
	Q2	12	89.5	−6.21	83.29
	Q3	13	90.5	−13.76	76.74
	Q4	14	91.5	+10.14	101.64
2014	Q1	15	92.4	+9.84	102.24
	Q2	16	93.4	−6.21	87.19
	Q3	17	94.4	−13.76	80.64
	Q4	18	95.4	+10.14	105.54
2015	Q1	19	96.4	+9.84	106.24
	Q2	20	97.3	−6.21	91.09
	Q3	21	98.3	−13.76	84.54
	Q4	22	99.3	+10.14	109.44

*Quarter 3 2010 = 1

$$\hat{Y}_T = 0.975(12) + 77.8$$
$$\hat{Y}_T = 89.5$$

However, Q2 also has a seasonal component.

$$S = -6.21$$

So our forecast for $\hat{Y}_{T+S}$ with both T and S included is:

$$\hat{Y}_{T+S} = 89.5 - 6.21$$
$$\hat{Y}_{T+S} = 83.29(000)$$

Self-check questions 4.4

Q1. The data below shows revenue (£000) for a company that Lendright is considering funding over various years and quarters.

Year	Q1	Q2	Q3	Q4
2010	44	80	120	60
2011	52	88	126	62
2012	60	98	140	68

(a) Use an appropriate moving average to find the trend component (T).
(b) Plot the original data and your trend values on a scatter diagram.
(c) Find a 'least squares line' to best fit your trend values.
(d) Estimate the seasonal variation component (S).
(e) Forecast future revenue, taking both trend and seasonal variation into account in:
   (i) quarter 1, year 2014;
   (ii) quarter 3, year 2015.
(f) How confident can you be in these forecasts?

(continued)

Q2. The spreadsheet with instructions can be found on the instructor's website, www.pearsoned.co.uk/wall, and provides a template for calculating the components of time series data. Although the layout here is for quarterly data, the concept can be adapted for any time series data.

As you will see, you are using the technique of a four quarter centred moving average to estimate the trend of the data (had the data been monthly, you would have used a 12 month centred moving average to estimate the trend). You are also finding the (adjusted) seasonal factors. If you are using your trend values for forecasting you will need to add or subtract the seasonal factors from each quarterly trend estimate to get a more accurate forecast.

The quarterly data values shown below are entered on the spreadsheet.

Year	Q1	Q2	Q3	Q4
Year 1	196.9	295.5	349.4	389.3
Year 2	324.1	418.0	447.5	456.4
Year 3	415.2	528.6	550.6	615.3
Year 4	513.6	650.8	670.6	754.4

(a) Calculate the trend values.
(b) Calculate the seasonal variation factors.

Note: Answers to Self-Check Questions can be found on the instructor's website, www.pearsoned.co.uk/wall

REVIEW QUESTIONS

The Review Questions below all relate to the operations of Lendright itself or to the operations of the companies to which Lendright is considering providing funding or in which it is considering becoming an active investor.

All the questions identified with an asterisk (*) are already set out for you as a spreadsheet on the instructor's website, www.pearsoned.co.uk/wall. You can use the spreadsheet directly for your calculations or you can use it to check that you obtain the same answer as you did when you used a calculator.

*R4.1. Sales of products (£000) for the past 12 years in a company of interest to Lendright are shown below. Use linear regression to forecast sales for the next three years.

Year	2001	2002	2003	2004	2005	2006	2007	2008	2009	2010	2011	2012
Sales	890	740	920	1,230	1,020	1,390	1,520	1,280	1,830	1,480	1,660	1,790

Comment on the reliability of your results.

*R4.2. The weather was considered an important element in the sales pattern of a certain product for a company in which Lendright holds shares. Over a four month period the average daily air temperature was recorded and the average daily sales of the product were calculated for each temperature. The results were as follows.

Temp (°C)	10	11	12	13	14	15	16	17	18	19	20	21	22	23	24
Average daily sales (000)	103	104	95	83	81	75	68	47	53	40	43	40	38	39	35

(a) Plot a scatter diagram of the data. What does this suggest?

(b) Calculate the linear regression equation that best fits the data.

(c) Plot the least squares regression line on your scatter diagram.

(d) Use the regression equation to estimate the number of products that will be sold if the temperature reaches 30°C.

*R4.3. Lendright has invested in a privately operated train franchise. The data below shows the lateness of trains (in minutes) arriving at a station and the number of passengers on those trains. The train operator believes that the number of passengers (Y) will be greater if the train arrives a little later (X minutes) than scheduled.

Minutes late	No. of passengers
1	1,459
3	395
0	534
2	641
7	927
3	650
4	447
5	392
0	569
11	713
1	401
12	2,691
1	443
7	883
12	1,577
11	147
7	568
2	455
3	632
4	531

(a) Plot a scatter diagram of the data.

(b) Calculate the linear regression equation that best fits the data.

(c) Plot the least squares regression line on your scatter diagram.

(d) Is there any evidence to suggest that there is a relationship between the number of passengers and the punctuality of the train?

*R4.4. A manager in a company of which Lendright has a majority shareholding needs to determine the relationship between the company's advertising expenditure and its sales revenue. If the relationship is a strong one, then the company will be able to forecast the sales revenue for a given advertising expenditure. The following data have been collected over the past eight years.

Advertising (£000)	Sales (£000)
8.73	400.285
8.78	390.423
9.25	470.389

Advertising (£000)	Sales (£000)
9.54	450.707
10.29	470.711
11.22	520.500
12.92	530.727
13.99	640.389

(a) Plot a scatter diagram of the data.
(b) Calculate the linear regression equation that best fits the data.
(c) Estimate the sales revenue when advertising is:
    (i) £15,000
    (ii) £20,000
    (iii) £25,000
(d) Is the relationship sufficiently strong to use as a forecasting method?

*R4.5. The data below shows an index of economic activity and the sales revenue for a firm that has been funded by Lendright over a 14 year period.

Index of economic activity	Sales revenue (£000)
103	1,188
104	1,224
104	1,243
105	1,239
105	1,242
107	1,138
108	1,481
108	1,562
109	1,554
109	1,566
110	1,598
111	1,562
112	1,609
112	1,499

(a) Calculate the regression line relating the two sets of data. Let sales revenue be the dependent variable. Comment on your result.
(b) How well does your regression line fit the data?

*R4.6. A quality control manager in a firm funded by Lendright believes that the number of rejected items on an assembly line is related to the length of time between breaks (the work period) for the assembly staff. The period between breaks is measured as well as the percentage of rejects produced by the operatives with the following results.

Work period (minutes)	Rejects %
60	2.3
65	2.5
70	2.7
75	2.9

Work period (minutes)	Rejects %
80	3.2
85	3.6
90	3.5
95	3.7
100	4.0
105	4.4
110	4.3
115	4.6
120	4.7
125	3.3
130	5.1
135	5.2

    (a) Calculate the regression line and use it to consider if there is any evidence to support the quality control manager's theory.

    (b) Given the above data, is there a case to suggest that work periods not exceeding two hours would reduce the number of rejects to below 5%?

    (c) How well does your regression line fit the data?

*R4.7. The marketing department of a company funded by Lendright believes that consumer tastes for beer are related to geographical area. They have therefore commissioned research to investigate the popularity of six leading brands of beer. Two different panels, one from the north, the other from the south, tasted the products and ranked them in their order of preference. To avoid bias, the name of the products was withheld and substituted with the labels A–F. The results of the blind testing were as follows:

Product	Northern panel	Southern panel
A	3	2
B	4	4
C	5	3
D	2	6
E	6	5
F	1	1

Is there any statistical evidence to suggest that the tastes of consumers are related to geographical region?

*R4.8. Lendright has been alerted to the fact that a motoring organisation has commissioned two independent testing laboratories to assess the safety of eight of the best-selling models of car in the mid-range family saloon market. This is of interest to Lendright as it has invested heavily in this segment of the car market. The laboratories used different testing procedures and methods before ranking the models in order of safety (where 1 = safest, 8 = least safe) as follows:

Product	Lab 1	Lab 2
Chimera 205	1	2
Apollo T7	6	5

Product	Lab 1	Lab 2
Pastiche	7	8
Ganymede	4	6
Callisto LX	3	4
QM4	5	3
Alfredo GT	8	7
Arctura	2	1

Is there any correlation between the two sets of results?

*R4.9. Lendright is considering investing in a company that manufactures snow chains and helping it fund a new production plant to cope with growing demand as average temperatures continue to fall across Europe.

Unit sales 2009–12

Year	Q1	Q2	Q3	Q4
1	444.1	397.7	396.1	472.8
2	476.4	454.4	450.8	553.5
3	580.7	573.2	571.6	703.6
4	692.0	676.5	659.9	752.7

(a) Calculate the trend line using the moving average method.
(b) Plot the original data and the trend values on a scatter diagram.
(c) Estimate and then eliminate the season variation component. In other words, find the de-seasonalised data.
(d) Find the least squares (regression) line to fit the trend values and forecast sales in 2015, Q4.

*R4.10. Lendright is considering investing in a proposed merger in which a company producing torches is negotiating with a company for the supply of torch bulbs. Lendright has been asked to help assess how the bulb company needs to plan its production to meet the needs of the torch company by using that company's quarterly sales figures over the past three years to forecast future demand. The sales figures are as follows:

Quarterly sales figures 2010–12 (000)

Year	Q1	Q2	Q3	Q4
1	349.4	295.5	196.9	389.3
2	447.5	418	324.1	456.4
3	550.6	528.6	415.2	615.3

(a) Using the moving average technique find the trend observations and the seasonal variation.
(b) Fit a least squares regression line to the trend observations.
(c) Use this trend regression line and your estimates of the seasonal variation factors to forecast future demand for the four quarters of year 4 for torches.

Note: Answers to Review Questions can be found on the instructor's website, www.pearsoned.co.uk/wall

Further practice

You can find more questions (with solutions) on regression, correlation and time series analysis on the instructor's website, www.pearsoned.co.uk/wall.

Spreadsheets: video guide

You can also find a step-by-step account that takes you through the actual use of a spreadsheet when solving the type of problems you have encountered in this chapter. Go to the instructor's website, www.pearsoned.co.uk/wall

Chapter 5

Probability and probability distributions

Introduction

Decision making in the growth stage of the product life cycle will invariably require estimates by the organisation of the probability of specified events occurring or failing to occur. What is the probability that Wembley Stadium will be over 60% full for a particular concert? This is a key question for decision making by the event's organiser if, say, 60% of capacity is the break-even attendance for the concert.

Organisations will wish to use probabilities to estimate the 'expected values' in terms of revenue, cost or profit of the many different decision paths available to them for further growing their business. In this chapter the context of our study of probability is an events management company, Stage-it, which is an established company with considerable experience in managing major leisure, sport, cultural and personal events (such as weddings and special family occasions). It has developed considerable expertise in the planning and implementation of such events, including event design, audio-visual production, budget drafting, cash flow management, procurement, scheduling, logistics, health and safety, risk management and public relations. However, it sees a major growth opportunity in adding the management of music festivals and concerts to its portfolio of activities.

The box below gives some reasons why Stage-it wishes to become more involved with the management and production of live music and festivals.

Live music concerts and festivals

With so much concern about lost revenues from illegal downloading, one area in which music revenues are growing is live performances. In 2012 sponsored tours and product endorsement by artists was up 4% in the United Kingdom on the previous year and with the international success of artists such as Adele, the United Kingdom is now the only country outside the United States that sells more of its music around the world than it pays artists from other countries. Revenues from live concerts grew by around 3% in the United Kingdom in 2012 and the same was true for live musical shows in London, which attracted audiences of over 14 million, yielding revenues of over £530 million, some 4% up on the previous year.

Stage-it has identified similar rapid growth potential in the organisation and management of live festivals. As many as 715 festivals took place in the United Kingdom in 2012, many involving music. However, it has been estimated that most festivals only break even when

(continued)

they reach around 80% of capacity and only make significant profits when they reach 90% of capacity or more, as with the Glastonbury and Isle of Wight festivals.

Stage-it is therefore well aware that effective risk management will require its decision making to be underpinned by a realistic assessment and understanding of the probabilities associated with its various events.

Clearly, Stage-it will need to be aware of how to use the full range of techniques to evaluate the probabilities that apply to the existing events it has managed and to the new areas in which it is seeking to grow. This is particularly important since Stage-it is seeking to grow by not only managing these large events for a specified sum, but also by co-producing selected events in which it shares in both the costs (and risks) of production and in any profits that result from a successful event.

In this chapter we look at the basis for calculating the probabilities with which particular events, or combinations of events, might be expected to occur. In fact probabilities are the basis for many economic and business decisions. For example, *insurance* against all kinds of possible future events is only possible because actuaries have worked out, often using past data, the probabilities of those events occurring. These probabilities then determine the *insurance premiums* to be charged to cover the expected value of potential payouts by the insurance company. Of course if circumstances change, and with them the associated probabilities of such events occurring, then insurance premiums will have to rise or fall. The greater likelihood of burglary has, for instance, caused a rise in premiums for insuring house contents against theft.

Spreadsheets

The questions and activities in the Break-Out Boxes use spreadsheets which can be found on the student's website, www.pearsoned.co.uk/wall. Many of the Worked Examples, Self-Check Questions and Review Questions are set out for you as an Excel spreadsheet on the student's website and these questions are marked with an asterisk (*).

Learning objectives

When you have read this chapter you should be able to:

- apply the 'AND' rule to independent events but the 'OR' rule to mutually exclusive events, and use Venn diagrams to solve problems;

- use 'decision tree' analysis to show all the probabilities in complex situations, often involving conditional probabilities;

- identify situations in which probability calculations can aid the decision-making process, as in the case of 'game theory' and expected values (EVs);

- work out the probabilities of particular events occurring when these follow a *normal* distribution and the 'confidence intervals' within which a particular value might lie;

- use and interpret the probability (Z) tables associated with the normal distribution;

- be familiar with the binomial and Poisson distributions, and be able to work out the probabilities of events occurring when they follow such distributions.

5.1   Probability calculations

5.1.1   Experimental probability

This can be found by performing an *experiment* many times and keeping an accurate record of the results. The *experimental probability* of a particular event happening can then be worked out as follows:

$$\text{Experimental probability} = \frac{\text{number of times the event has happened}}{\text{total number of possible occurrences}}$$

Example

When a normal dice was rolled 100 times, the number 5 was actually rolled 19 times. This gives an experimental probability ratio of $\frac{19}{100} = 0.19$

Did you know?

Experimental probabilities are worked out for all types of 'hazards'. For example, the 'risk' of dying from occupational exposure to asbestos has been worked out as 3 per 1,000 persons exposed. Actuaries work out experimental probabilities all the time in order to calculate insurance premiums for road accidents by age and other personal characteristics. Of course experimental probabilities can sometimes be very different to the theoretical probabilities (see below) that you might have expected and they may be influenced by legal, financial, cultural and many other factors. For example, 'whiplash' claims involving car-related injuries are over 75% of all bodily injury claims in the United Kingdom, but only 5% of such claims in France, 8% in Finland and less than 30% in Spain and Switzerland. It has been pointed out that a change in the United Kingdom law in 2004 provided new financial incentives for individuals and their solicitors to make such claims (e.g. since 2004 12% of any successful claim for bodily injuries has gone directly to the solicitor).

5.1.2   Theoretical probability

This is found by considering *equally likely* events. The theoretical probability is found by using the following ratio.

$$\text{Theoretical probability} = \frac{\text{number of ways an event can occur}}{\text{total number of different equally likely events that can occur}}$$

Examples

1. Rolling a dice and getting an even number has theoretical probability $\frac{3}{6} = \frac{1}{2}$

2. Rolling a dice and getting a number 5 has theoretical probability $\frac{1}{6} = 0.17$ (2 d.p.)

Of course if an event is *impossible*, then its theoretical probability is 0. On the other hand if the event is *certain*, then its theoretical probability is 1.

Notice that if we know the theoretical probability of an event occurring, then we also know the theoretical probability of it *not* occurring.

If the probability of an event occurring is, say, p then the probability of the event *not* occurring is $1 - p$.

Examples

1. The theoretical probability of rolling a 5 on a dice $= \dfrac{1}{6}$

2. The theoretical probability of *not* rolling a 5 on a dice $= 1 - \dfrac{1}{6} = \dfrac{5}{6}$

PAUSE FOR THOUGHT 5.1

Can you give an example of how Stage-it might use each of the following in its decision making?

    Experimental probability

    Theoretical probability

Stage-it has been asked to co-develop an event that will incorporate a 'mini-casino' available to visitors. It wants to work out the probabilities for players being successful in various games in order to work out the cash prizes it should offer.

5.1.3 Mutually exclusive events: OR rule

If one event excludes the possibility of another event happening, then we say that the two events are *mutually exclusive*.

Example

- tossing a coin and getting a head and a tail;
- rolling a dice once and getting a 2 and a 3.

Events that are mutually exclusive can have their probabilities *added* to find the probability of one **OR** the other happening.

OR rule: mutually exclusive events

For two mutually exclusive events, A and B, the probability of A OR B occurring can be written as:

$$P(A) \text{ OR } P(B) = P(A) + P(B)$$

Example

If I roll a dice what is the probability that I will roll a 3 or 4?

Probability of rolling a 3 $= \dfrac{1}{6}$

Probability of rolling a 4 $= \dfrac{1}{6}$

The probability of rolling a 3 OR a 4 $= \dfrac{1}{6} + \dfrac{1}{6} = \dfrac{2}{6} = \dfrac{1}{3}$

Worked example 5.1

Stage-it wishes to use its expertise in calculating experimental probabilities to work out likely future changes in its own share price (and therefore ability to borrow). Analysing data on changes in Stage-it's own share price over the past two years gives the following experimental probabilities for 'events' A to E.

A Share price rises *more than* 15%: $P(A) = 0.20$

B Share price rises *less than* 15%: $P(B) = 0.30$

C Share price remains unchanged: $P(C) = 0.10$

D Share price falls *less than* 15%: $P(D) = 0.25$

E Share price falls *more than* 15%: $P(E) = 0.15$

Find

1. the probability that Stage-it's share price will rise;

2. the probability that Stage-it's share price will not rise;

3. the probability that Stage-it's share price will fall.

Solution

The events A to E are mutually exclusive; if one happens the others do not.

1. $P(A \text{ or } B) = P(A) + P(B) = 0.2 + 0.3 = 0.5$

2. $1 - P(A \text{ or } B) = 1 - 0.5 = 0.5$

3. $P(D \text{ or } E) = P(D) + P(E) = 0.25 + 0.15 = 0.40$

PAUSE FOR THOUGHT 5.2

Can you identify three different situations involving mutually exclusive events that might be of interest to Stage-it and for which it would therefore need to calculate the probability using the OR rule?

Self-check questions 5.1

Q1. Write down the theoretical probabilities that Stage-it would apply to outcomes from the following events in its gaming division:

(a) rolling a dice and getting a 2;

(b) rolling a dice and not getting a 3;

(continued)

(c) rolling a dice and getting an odd number;

(d) rolling a dice and getting a 2 or a 3;

(e) drawing an ace from a pack of cards;

(f) drawing a card from a pack of cards and not getting a diamond;

(g) rolling a dice and getting a number less than 7.

Q2. The following probabilities are relevant decisions for Stage-it's gaming division. Two unbiased dice are thrown. Their scores are added to make a total between 2 and 12.

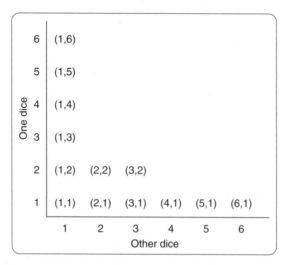

Figure 5.1 Theoretical probability

(a) There are 36 possible totals as indicated in Figure 5.1. Complete the table.

(b) Write down the theoretical probability of throwing a total of:

    (i)   2;

    (ii)   3;

    (iii) 4;

    (iv) 6;

    (v)   7;

    (vi) 8;

    (vii) 10;

    (viii) 12.

(c) What is the theoretical probability of not getting a total of 7?

Q3. Stage-it bids for two contracts, A and B. The probability that it will obtain contract A is 0.3, but 0.5 that it will obtain contract B. What is the probability that it will obtain either contract A or contract B?

Note: Answers to Self-Check Questions can be found on the instructor's website, www.pearsoned.co.uk/wall

Did you know?

The United Kingdom is an exporter of back-stage expertise in theatre and music events, particularly to emerging economies seeking to establish a global reputation. Royal Opera House technicians have been brought in to advise staff at the new Mariinsky Theatre in St Petersburg,

(continued)

Russia, and the new Opera House in Muscat, Oman. China has sent its backstage team for the National Centre for Performing Arts in Beijing to London to take a specially developed training course in stage management.

5.2 Venn diagrams: events not mutually exclusive

Sometimes events can occur at the same time, so that they are *not* mutually exclusive. In solving this type of problem it can be helpful to make use of a Venn diagram.

Suppose, for example, that we have a pack of 52 cards and that event A is drawing a club and event B is drawing a picture card. We now want to work out the probability of a card drawn at random being *either* a club or a picture card – that is, P(A OR B). A pack of 52 cards will have 13 clubs and 12 picture cards.

In this case we *cannot* use the OR rule for mutually exclusive events since here a club could itself be a picture card – that is, events A and B are *not* mutually exclusive. Of the 13 club cards in the pack, the jack, queen and king of clubs are picture cards. There is therefore a danger of double counting if we use the conventional OR rule for mutually exclusive events. The correct answer here is:

$$P(A \text{ OR } B) = \frac{13}{52} + \frac{12}{52} - \frac{3}{52} = \frac{22}{52}$$

OR rule: non-mutually exclusive events

$$P(A \text{ OR } B) = P(A) + P(B) - P(AB)$$

The Venn diagram (Figure 5.2) can be useful in solving problems involving events that are *not* mutually exclusive – that is, that 'overlap' in some way.

We can note the following from Figure 5.2.

- The area of the rectangle corresponds to *all* the possible events in the sample, here the 52 different cards that could be drawn from the pack.
- The circle A corresponds to the 13 club cards.
- The circle B corresponds to the 12 picture cards.
- The *overlap* between the two circles corresponds to the fact that 3 of the club cards can themselves be picture cards.

When completing a Venn diagram it is essential that you first consider the *area of overlap* before going any further. Therefore enter the 3 in the area of overlap in Figure 5.2, then 10 in the remainder of the circle A, representing club cards, and 9 in the remainder

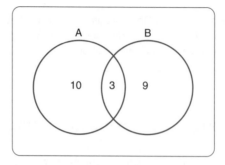

Figure 5.2 Venn diagram for a pack of cards, where A = club, B = picture card

of the circle B, representing picture cards. The required probability that a card drawn at random from the pack is a club OR a picture is obtained by adding up these numbers, namely 10 + 3 + 9 = 22, and then dividing by the total sample of 52 to obtain the result (22 ÷ 52) already outlined.

Self-check question 5.2

Stage-it usually recruits 25 management trainees per annum. In 2012, 140 applications were received and of these:

78 had previous work experience;

43 had passed a vocational exam;

21 had both work experience and had passed a vocational exam (and had been included in the above figures).

(a) Use a Venn diagram to illustrate this situation.

(b) What is the probability that an applicant selected at random by Stage-it had previous work experience or had passed a vocational exam?

Note: Answers to Self-Check Questions can be found on the instructor's website, www.pearsoned.co.uk/wall

---

PAUSE FOR THOUGHT 5.3

Can you suggest any situations in which a Venn diagram might be useful for Stage-it in its decision making?

5.3   Independent events: AND rule

If *one* event has no effect on another event then we say that the events are **independent**. To find the probability of BOTH events happening (one event **AND** then the other) we *multiply* their probabilities.

Example

From a normal pack of cards, what is the probability of drawing an ace, putting it back and then drawing a king?

- Probability of drawing an ace $= \dfrac{4}{52} = \dfrac{1}{13}$

- Probability of drawing a king $= \dfrac{4}{52} = \dfrac{1}{13}$

Since we have independent events, we multiply their individual probabilities,

i.e. $\dfrac{1}{13} \times \dfrac{1}{13} = \dfrac{1}{169}$

Events that are independent can have their probabilities *multiplied* to find the probability of one AND the other happening.

AND rule

For two independent events, A and B, the probability of A AND B occurring can be written as:

$$P(A) \text{ AND } P(B) = P(A) \times P(B)$$

Worked example 5.2

Stage-it is responsible for the electric lighting at an event it is organising. The electrical specialists used by Stage-it have taken one component from each of three separate boxes, and each box has 100 electrical components in it. However, Stage-it is informed later that some faulty items were contained in the boxes. The first box had six faulty items, the second eight and the third five. One component was taken from each box. What is the probability that:

(a) all three components are faulty;

(b) all three components are good (not faulty)?

Solution

Selecting a component from each box is an independent event. Let us call the selection of a component from the respective boxes events A, B and C.

(a) Here we let P represent the probability of selecting a *faulty* component.

$$P(A \text{ AND } B \text{ AND } C) = P(A) \times P(B) \times P(C)$$
$$= 0.06 \times 0.08 \times 0.05$$
$$P(A \text{ AND } B \text{ AND } C) = 0.000240$$

In other words, the probability of selecting three faulty components is 0.024% or 0.000240 as a decimal.

(b) Here we let P represent the probability of selecting a *good* component

$$P(A \text{ AND } B \text{ AND } C) = P(A) \times P(B) \times P(C)$$
$$= 0.94 \times 0.92 \times 0.95$$
$$P(A \text{ AND } B \text{ AND } C) = 0.82156$$

In other words, the probability of selecting three good components is 82.156% or 0.82156 as a decimal.

Self-check questions 5.3

Q1. Stage-it has organised an event that involves five separate companies. The probability of any one company failing to complete its task is estimated at 0.03. What is the probability of all five companies successfully completing their designated tasks (i.e. of none failing to complete their task)?

Q2. Stage-it requires floral decorations in a major event it is organising and has ordered seeds in good time to produce the blue flowers it requires. In a given batch of seeds, the probability of a seed germinating is 0.95. The probability of a blue flower coming from any one of the germinating seeds is 0.4. What is the probability that any one seed will result in a blue flower?

Q3. Two companies have been employed by Stage-it to work on the sound system for a concert. The probability that Company A gets everything right is $\frac{3}{4}$, while the probability that Company B gets everything right is $\frac{9}{10}$. What is the probability that

(a) both companies get everything right;

(b) both companies get everything wrong?

Note: Answers to Self-Check Questions can be found on the instructor's website, www.pearsoned.co.uk/wall

PAUSE FOR THOUGHT 5.4

Can you identify three different situations involving independent events which might be of interest to Stage-it and for which it would therefore need to calculate the probability using the AND rule?

5.4   Dependent events: conditional probability

Here we look at situations in which the probability of an event occurring depends in part on whether or not other events have already occurred. We call this *conditional probability*.

Some events are neither mutually exclusive nor independent. However, if they *do* happen, they influence the probability of other, subsequent, events happening. For example, if Stage-it uses an inexperienced company for lighting or sound for a major concert, then the probability of mishaps occurring on the night will be higher than if it had selected a more experienced company with a proven track record. In other words, we are looking at *dependent* events involving situations of conditional probability.

It will help to become familiar with some terminology.

5.4.1   Conditional probability

$P(A)$ = probability of event A

$P(B/A)$ = probability of event B, given that event A has already occurred

$P(C/AB)$ = probability of event C, given that events A and B have already occurred

The contrast between *independent* events (AND rule) and *dependent* events (conditional probability) can be illustrated in the following example, which involves drawing coloured balls from a bag. When we *replace* the ball selected on the first draw before we draw the second ball, then the second draw is *independent* of the first. However, when we *do not replace* the first ball before we draw the second ball, then the second draw is *dependent* on the first.

Worked example 5.3

A bag contains 40 balls, of which 16 are red and 24 are blue. Three balls are drawn separately from the bag. What is the probability of drawing three red balls

(a) when each ball drawn is *replaced* before the next draw;

(b) when each ball drawn is *not replaced* before the next draw?

Solution

(a) Here we have replacement so that we can treat the events as being independent. It follows that the AND rule applies. Because of replacement the probabilities of selecting a particular colour of ball on each draw remain the same.

Let A = getting a red ball on first draw

Let B = getting a red ball on second draw

Let C = getting a red ball on third draw

$$P(ABC) = P(A) \times P(B) \times P(C)$$

where $P(A) = P(B) = P(C) = \dfrac{16}{40} = 0.4$

So $P(ABC) = 0.4 \times 0.4 \times 0.4$

$$= 0.064$$

In other words, with replacement, there is a 6.4% or 0.064 probability of selecting three successive red balls from the bag.

(b) Here we do *not* have replacement, so the probabilities of selecting subsequent red balls are *dependent* on whether a previous red ball has been selected.

$$P(ABC) = \frac{16}{40} \times \frac{15}{39} \times \frac{14}{38} = \frac{3,360}{59,280} = 0.057 \text{ (to 3 d.p.)}$$

In other words, without replacement, there is a 5.7% or 0.057 probability of selecting three successive red balls from the bag.

Worked example 5.4

Forty workers at the head office of Stage-it can be classified as follows:

	Clerical grade	Administrative grade
Male	4	6
Female	22	8

(a) If a worker is selected at random from head office, what is the probability that the worker will be in the administrative grade?

Worked
example
5.4
(cont'd)

(b) If the worker selected is female, what is the probability that she will be in the administrative grade?

(c) If the worker selected is male, what is the probability that he will be in the administrative grade?

(d) If the worker selected is in the administrative grade, what is the probability of the worker being male?

Solution

(a) P(admin. grade) $= \dfrac{14}{40} = 0.35$

(b) We can work this out as $\dfrac{8}{30} = 0.267$ (to 3 d.p.) since of the 30 female workers only 8 are in the administrative grade.

(c) We can work this out as $\dfrac{6}{10} = 0.6$ since of the 10 male workers 6 are in the administrative grade.

(d) We can work this out as $\dfrac{6}{14} = 0.429$ (to 3 d.p.) since of the 14 administrative grade workers 6 are male.

5.4.2 Decision trees and conditional probability

It is often helpful to use a decision tree to visualise a problem involving probability. When we can clearly see *all* the possibilities in a given situation it makes it much easier to calculate the relevant probabilities. Although decision trees can be used in any situation, they are particularly helpful when solving problems involving conditional probability.

Worked
example
5.5

A bag contains five blue marbles, three yellow marbles and two white marbles. Two marbles are then drawn from the bag, the first marble *not* being replaced before the second marble is drawn.

What is the probability that

(a) both marbles are the same colour;

(b) both marbles are a different colour;

(c) at least one marble is blue?

The decision tree (Figure 5.3) helps us see all the possibilities involved in this problem.

Notice that to find the probability of an event involving any two outcomes occurring (e.g. blue marble AND blue marble, BB) we *multiply* the probabilities.

So P(BB) = P(B) × P(B/B)

The probability of two blues is the probability of the first marble being blue × the probability of the second marble being blue given that the first is blue.

i.e. P(BB) $= \dfrac{5}{10} \times \dfrac{4}{9} = \dfrac{20}{90} = \dfrac{2}{9}$

Worked
example
5.5
(cont'd)

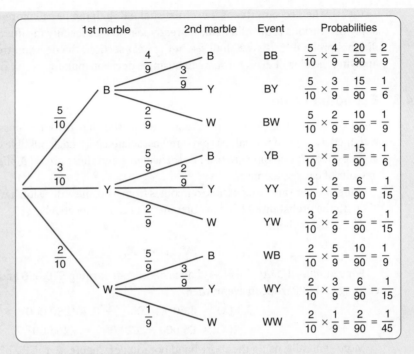

Figure 5.3 Using a decision tree

However, when we calculate solutions to (a), (b) or (c) below which involve either one OR more events occurring, we add the probabilities.

Solution

(a) Both marbles having the same colour can be achieved in three different ways, either two blues OR two yellows OR two whites.

i.e. P(both marbles same colour) = P(BB) + P(YY) + P(WW)

$$= \frac{2}{9} + \frac{1}{15} + \frac{1}{45} = \frac{14}{45}$$

(b) Both marbles having a different colour will have the probability of 1 *minus* the probability they both have the same colour.

i.e. P(both marbles different colour) = 1 − P(both marbles same colour)

$$= 1 - \frac{14}{45} = \frac{31}{45}$$

(c) The probability of at least one marble being blue can be achieved in five possible ways:

P(BB) OR P(BY) OR P(BW) OR P(YB) OR P(WB)

$$\frac{2}{9} \quad + \quad \frac{1}{6} \quad + \quad \frac{1}{9} \quad + \quad \frac{1}{6} \quad + \quad \frac{1}{9}$$

i.e. P(at least one marble blue) $= \dfrac{20 + 15 + 10 + 15 + 10}{90} = \dfrac{70}{90} = \dfrac{7}{9}$

Clearly the decision tree is a useful visual aid, helping us see more clearly how we can apply the various probability rules already learned, especially in situations involving conditional probability. As we shall see in the next section, the decision tree is also helpful in applying the idea of *expected value* to business decision making.

5.4.3 Expected value

The expected value (EV) of a particular event that has different possible outcomes is a weighted average of the values (pay-offs) associated with each possible outcome. The probabilities of each outcome are used as the weights and these are *multiplied* by the respective pay-offs of each outcome.

Suppose there are two possible outcomes from a business decision having pay-offs X_1 and X_2, with the probabilities of each outcome p_1 and p_2 respectively.

The EV(X) is then:

$$EV(X) = p_1X_1 + p_2X_2$$

For example, if there is a 60% chance of Stage-it earning £10,000 and a 40% chance of it earning £50,000 from an event, then:

$$E(X) = 0.60(£10,000) + 0.40(£50,000)$$
$$\text{i.e. } E(X) = £6,000 + £20,000 = £26,000$$

More generally, using the short-hand notation of Chapter 2, the EV of a particular course of action over n possible outcomes can be defined as:

Formulae for expected value

$$EV = \sum_{i=1}^{n} p_i \cdot X_i$$

where p_i = probability of ith outcome

X_i = value of ith outcome

and $\sum_{i=1}^{n} p_i = 1$

This last condition merely states that we have covered all possible outcomes, so the sum of their probabilities must be 1.

Did you know?

The EV of the benefits from reducing the lead content in petrol by 1 gram per gallon in the United States has been estimated at over $1 billion per annum. This calculation involved estimating the probabilities of certain health and economic benefits occurring (e.g. reduced adult blood pressure, raised children's IQs, greater fuel economy, etc.) and then placing a monetary value on each of these benefits.

Worked example 5.6	A fair dice is thrown and, for a £1 stake, the gambler is promised £1.80 if the result is a head, but only £0.10 if the result is a tail. What is the EV to the gambler of each throw?

Let p_1 = the probability of head (0.5)

p_2 = the probability of tail (0.5)

X_1 = the 'pay-off' of a head (£1.80)

X_2 = the 'pay-off' of a tail (£0.10)

Solution

$$EV = \sum_{i=1}^{2} p_i \cdot X_i$$

i.e. $EV = p_1 X_1 + p_2 X_2$

$EV = 0.5 \times £1.80 + 0.5 \times £0.10$

$EV = £0.90 + £0.05$

$EV = £0.95$

The gambler can therefore 'expect' to lose 5 pence on each throw of the dice, though they might be lucky and get more heads than tails on the early throws of the dice, and thereby win by 'quitting while they are ahead'.

On the other hand the individual *offering* the gamble can 'expect' to make a profit (revenue – cost) of £0.05 on each throw (£1.00 − £0.95).

Clearly, the greater the number of 'trials' – throws of the dice in our example – the more likely it will be that the *theoretical probabilities* (see p. 137) will apply rather than the *experimental probabilities* (see p. 137) of a 'lucky' or 'unlucky' run.

5.4.4 Expected value and decision trees

We can use this idea of EV in the decision tree analysis already presented (p. 146). As we have seen, a decision tree is a diagram that can usefully represent a series of choices and their possible outcomes.

- Where the outcome is *pure chance*, then the overall probability of 1 will be divided *equally* between all the possible outcomes (e.g. 0.5 for each of two pure chance outcomes).

- Where the outcome is *uncertain* but where some outcomes are more likely than others, then the decision maker may assign *probabilities* to each possible outcome. The sum of these probabilities over all possible outcomes must, of course, be equal to 1.

The sequence of decisions and outcomes is represented graphically as the branches of a 'tree' (see Figure 5.4) which represents a situation in which Stage-it must make decisions on alternative pricing and advertising strategies. At every point that a decision must be made or an outcome must occur (*node*), the tree branches out further until all the possible outcomes have been displayed.

- *Boxes* (decision nodes) are usually used to indicate situations in which the decision maker consciously selects a particular course of action (strategy) and where the outcome of that action is 'certain'. Branches coming out of these boxes simply indicate the alternative decisions or strategies that might be taken, each of which has a probability of 1 once selected.

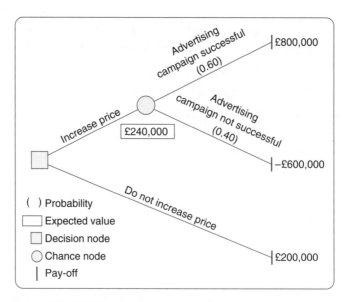

Figure 5.4 Decision tree

- *Circles* (chance nodes) are usually used to indicate situations reflecting a 'state of nature' – that is, situations whose outcomes are *not* entirely under the conscious control of the decision maker. Branches coming out of such circles show the various possibilities that might occur, together with estimates of their probability of occurrence.

- *Pay-offs* are the valuations placed at the end of particular branches emanating from chance nodes. They are the values that management allocates to that event or outcome should it actually occur, and are often denoted by a straight (vertical) line at the end of the branch.

In Figure 5.4, at the *decision node* box, Stage-it, the decision maker, must decide between a strategy of increasing the price or keeping the price unchanged. If this latter strategy is pursued, only one profit outcome is possible which is evaluated at £200,000. If the former strategy (increasing price) is pursued, then the decision maker intends to support the policy change by an active advertising campaign. However, the outcome of such an advertising campaign is not entirely under the control of the decision maker. Stage-it estimates that there is a 60% (0.60) chance of the campaign being a success and a 40% (0.40) chance of it being a failure. These two branches are therefore shown as emanating from a *chance node*, indicated by a circle. Stage-it estimates profits of £800,000 should the advertising campaign (allied to a price increase) be successful, but losses of £600,000 should it fail.

5.4.5 Backward induction

Which branch Stage-it should choose in order to maximise the expected profit can easily be determined. The process of solving this problem is called *backward induction*. This requires us to begin at the right-hand side of the decision tree, where the profit figures are located. The first step is to calculate the *expected profit* when the firm is situated at the chance node immediately to the left of these pay-off figures.

Because there is a 0.60 probability that the branch culminating in a profit of £800,000 will occur, and a 0.40 probability that the branch culminating in a loss of £600,000 will occur, the EV of profit when situated at this chance node is:

$$\text{EV (profit)} = 0.60\ (£800{,}000) + 0.40\ (-£600{,}000) = £240{,}000$$

This number is written below the chance node in question to show that this is the expected profit when located at that node.

Moving further to the left along the decision tree, it is clear that Stage-it has a choice of two branches, one of which leads to an expected profit of £240,000, the other of which leads to an expected profit of £200,000. If Stage-it wants to maximise expected profit, it should choose the former branch. In other words, it should increase its price and accompany this with an advertising campaign.

Worked example 5.7

Stage-it faces a choice between two policy options. One is to make a certain annual profit of £100,000 from interest on a sum of money left on deposit in a bank. The second is to invest that same sum of money in co-producing a major rock concert in the capital city.

If Stage-it goes ahead with the rock concert, there is a 70% probability that a major competitor, Perform Inc, will react by introducing a similar concert and a 30% probability that it will not.

Should Stage-it decide to go ahead with the rock concert it can choose a high price (HP), a medium price (MP) or a low price (LP) scenario for tickets.

How much profit Stage-it *estimates* that it will make depends on a number of factors:

1. whether or not Perform Inc reacts with a similar product;

2. what strategy Stage-it selects in regard to price;

3. what counter-strategy Perform Inc selects in regard to price.

Stage-it calculates the following table to represent the estimated profits (in present value terms) from the different possible outcomes. Stage-it has assigned various probabilities to each possible outcome.

Competition	Stage-it's price strategy	Perform Inc's price response	Probability	Stage-it's profit (£)
Yes	HP	HP	0.6	150,000
Yes	HP	MP	0.3	100,000
Yes	HP	LP	0.1	90,000
Yes	MP	HP	0.3	120,000
Yes	MP	MP	0.5	100,000
Yes	MP	LP	0.2	60,000
Yes	LP	HP	0.0	250,000
Yes	LP	MP	0.4	150,000
Yes	LP	LP	0.6	100,000
No	HP		–	600,000
No	MP		–	300,000
No	LP		–	200,000

Worked
example
5.7
(cont'd)

Question

Construct a decision tree and use it to suggest whether Stage-it should invest in the rock concert or leave its funds to earn interest in the bank.

Solution

Figure 5.5 presents the decision tree for this problem.

Using the technique of *backward induction* we begin our solutions at the right-hand side and work leftwards, back to the initial decision node (box 4). However, we can see that there are two 'earlier' decision nodes (boxes 1 and 2) and four chance nodes (circles HP, MP, LP and 3). The pay-offs are listed at the end of the branches furthest to the right.

At decision box 1, Stage-it must choose between a high price (HP), medium price (MP) and low price (LP) strategy. Its choice will depend on the EV (shown underneath each

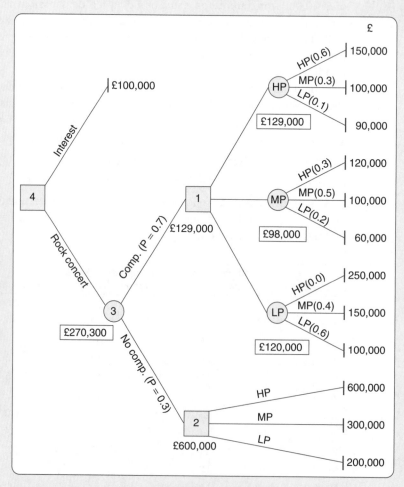

Figure 5.5 Decision tree: rock concert problem

chance node) of each pricing strategy, which in turn depends on the probabilities of the price responses of Perform Inc and the pay-offs estimated for each response.

Using our earlier EV formula:

$$EV = \sum_{i=1}^{n} p_i X_i$$

With all values in £000s we can say:

EV (Stage-it, HP strategy) = 0.6 (150) + 0.3 (100) + 0.1 (90)

$$= 90 + 30 + 9$$

i.e. EV (HP) = £129 (000)

EV (Stage-it, MP strategy) = 0.3 (120) + 0.5 (100) + 0.2 (60)

$$= 36 + 50 + 12$$

i.e. **EV (MP)** = **£98 (000)**

EV (Stage-it, LP strategy) = 0.0 (250) + 0.4 (150) + 0.6 (100)

i.e. **EV (LP)** = **£120 (000)**

At decision node 1, Stage-it will select the strategy with the highest expected profit pay-off, that is, a higher price (HP) strategy (in the event of competition from Perform Inc), yielding £129,000 in expected profit.

At decision node 2, Stage-it has no probabilities to contend with since the pay-offs listed are *not* associated with the possible reactions of Perform Inc. Here it can select the higher price (HP) strategy (in the event of no competition from Perform Inc) yielding £600,000 in expected profit.

However, there are probabilities associated with whether or not Perform Inc will react with a new product of its own. Therefore we must take these into account in working out the EV at chance node 3.

EV (rock concert) = 0.7 (129) + 0.3 (600)

$$= 90.3 + 180$$

i.e. EV (rock concert) = £270.3 (000) = £270,300

At the initial decision box (4) we can see that, based on our expectations, there will be greater profit from investing the available money in the rock concert than from leaving the money earning interest in the bank.

An approach such as that in Worked Example 5.7 is often said to be using different *scenarios* – that is, the evaluation of different possible outcomes for various policy initiatives. Of course if the *probabilities* were to change, for any reasons, or the expected pay-offs were to change, then any initial decision must be re-evaluated in the light of these new circumstances.

Did you know?

Stage-it is aware that the probabilities of at least 'breaking even' from any major co-production are changing over time. For example, the costs of staging a live show running on a daily basis have more than trebled over the past 20 years. As a result there has been a 50% reduction in the probability of breaking even over a continuous run of six months for the show.

Self-check questions 5.4

Q1. In a game show developed by Stage-it, contestants must select from a box with 20 tickets, only 6 of which receive a prize. If three tickets are drawn consecutively from the box, what is the probability of all three tickets being winning tickets
  (a) if there is replacement;
  (b) if there is no replacement?

Q2. Use a decision tree to help solve this problem for another game at a Stage-it event. Two cards are dealt out to a player from a full pack (without replacement). What is the probability of
  (a) both being an ace;
  (b) one of them being an ace;
  (c) neither of them being an ace?

Q3. A machine used by Stage-it is found to have produced 5 defective tickets in every batch of 200 tickets.
  (a) What is the probability of a ticket selected at random from the batch of 200 tickets being defective?
  (b) If 3,000 tickets are produced per week, how many defective tickets would you expect?

Q4. Stage-it is considering introducing a new computer system for one of its branch offices. The company can lease a small, medium or large computer system. Stage-it estimates that if the economy continues to expand over the next year the extra profits from each system will be £100,000, £150,000 and £200,000 respectively. If the economy slows down the extra profits generated will be £60,000, £20,000 and a loss of £20,000 respectively. It is estimated that the probability of continued expansion is 0.4 and of a slowdown is 0.6. Construct a decision tree diagram to represent this problem and use the EV approach to recommend one of the computer systems.

Q5. Stage-it has developed a new online training programme for events managers and is considering either test marketing it at a cost of £65,000 or abandoning it. If the training programme is abandoned (at any stage) Stage-it can recoup £20,000 from the sale of specialist equipment used in developing the training material. The probability of a favourable result from the test market is estimated at 0.65 and an unfavourable result as 0.35. If the test market is unfavourable the project will be abandoned. A favourable test market could be followed either by abandonment of the project or by development. It is estimated that the extra profits generated will depend on the response of established rival firms in events management: if there is no response to produce a competitor online training programme then profits will be £250,000; on the other hand if rivals do respond and develop a similar product then losses of £90,000 will be incurred. The probability of rivals responding is 0.3 and of not responding is 0.7. Illustrate this problem with a decision tree diagram and use it to advise Stage-it.

Note: Answers to Self-Check Questions can be found on the instructor's website, www.pearsoned.co.uk/wall

5.5 Game theory and expected value

EV can be expressed in many forms: in a currency unit (e.g. £), in volume (e.g. tonnes) or in percentages (e.g. percentage of market share). The example below shows how Stage-it can use probabilities and their associated EVs to guide its decision making when it is attempting to take the actions and reactions of its competitors into account.

Suppose Stage-it is considering two possible policies in order to raise its market share: a 20% price cut for its tickets or a 10% increase in advertising expenditure. Whatever initial policy Stage-it adopts, it anticipates that its rival, Perform Inc, will react by using either a price cut or extra advertising to defend its market share.

Stage-it now uses its knowledge of the market and assigns probabilities to evaluate the market share it can expect for each initial policy decision and each possible reaction by Perform Inc. The outcomes expected by Stage-it are summarised in the pay-off matrix in Table 5.1.

If Stage-it cuts price and Perform Inc responds with a price cut, Stage-it receives 60% of the market. However, if Perform Inc responds with extra advertising, Stage-it receives 70% of the market. The 'worst' outcome for Stage-it (60% of the market) will occur if Perform Inc responds with a price cut.

If Stage-it uses extra advertising, then the 'worst' outcome for Stage-it (50% of the market) will again occur if Perform Inc responds with a price cut.

We will assume that both players adopt a *maxi-min* decision rule – that is, always selecting the policy that results in the best of the worst possible outcomes.

Solution

Stage-it will select the price-cut policy since this gives it 60% market share rather than 50% – that is, the best of these 'worst possible' outcomes for Stage-it.

Table 5.1 Stage-it pay-off matrix (% market shares)

		Perform Inc strategies	
		Price cut	Extra advertising
Stage-it strategies	Price cut	60*[†]	70[†]
	Extra advertising	50*	55

* 'Worst' outcome for Stage-it of each Stage-it strategy.

† 'Worst' outcome for Perform Inc of each Perform Inc strategy.

Worked example 5.8

Using Table 5.1 above what policy would you expect Perform Inc to follow if it also uses the maxi-min decision rule? Assume that Stage-it and Perform Inc have 100% of the market between them and that Perform Inc has made the same evaluation of outcomes as has Stage-it in Table 5.1.

Solution

If Perform Inc adopts the same maxi-min decision rule as Stage-it, and has made the same evaluation of outcomes as Stage-it, it also will adopt a price-cut policy. For instance, if Perform Inc adopts a price-cut policy, its 'worst' outcome will occur if Stage-it responds

Worked example 5.8 (cont'd)

with a price cut: Perform Inc then gets 40% of the market (100% – 60%), rather than 50% if Stage-it responds with extra advertising. If Perform Inc adopts extra advertising, its 'worst' outcome will again occur if Stage-it responds with a price cut: Perform Inc then receives 30% rather than 45%.

The best of the 'worst possible' outcomes for Perform Inc occurs if Perform Inc adopts a price cut, which gives it 40% of the market rather than 30%.

In this particular game we have a *stable equilibrium*, without any resort to collusion. Both firms initially cut price, then accept the respective market shares that fulfil their maxi-min targets – that is, 60% to Stage-it, 40% to Perform Inc.

In other words, they are both rather cautious, each assuming the rival will react in the worst possible way for itself to any policy initiative. It then selects the best of these worst possible outcomes.

Worked example 5.9

Stage-it and Perform Inc are two rival firms and each must choose whether to charge relatively high or relatively low prices for its products. Market research suggests the pay-off matrix (profits) shown in Table 5.2. For simplicity we assume that both firms evaluate the pay-off matrix as shown in this table.

Table 5.2 Pay-off matrix showing profits in £millions for Stage-it and Perform Inc

		Perform Inc strategies	
		Low price	High price
Stage-it strategies	Low price	(a) Stage-it 200 Perform Inc 200	(c) Stage-it 40 Perform Inc 260
	High price	(b) Stage-it 260 Perform Inc 140	(d) Stage-it 100 Perform Inc 100

Using the maxi-min decision rule identify:

(a) Stage-it's maxi-min strategy;

(b) Perform Inc's maxi-min strategy;

(c) the likely outcome of the game.

Solution

Pay-off matrices invariably have some outcomes that are worse than others. The maxi-min decision rule is to adopt the policy option that gives the 'best of the worst' of these outcomes.

(a) Stage-it's maxi-min strategy.

Stage-it looks at its policies and asks 'what is the worst that can happen?'

- For Stage-it's low price policy, the worst that could happen would be for Perform Inc to charge a high price and reduce Stage-it's profits to £40 million (cell c).

Worked example 5.9 (cont'd)

- For Stage-it's high price policy, the worst that could happen would be for Perform Inc to charge a high price, giving Stage-it £100 million profit (cell d).
- The best of these 'worst possible outcomes' is £100 million; thus Stage-it's maxi-min strategy would be to charge the higher price.

(b) Perform Inc's maxi-min strategy:

Perform Inc looks at its policies and asks 'what is the worst that can happen?'

- Perform Inc's low price policy gives £140 million (cell b) as the worst possible outcome.
- Perform Inc's high price policy gives £100 million (cell d) as the worst possible outcome.
- The best of these 'worst possible outcomes' is £140 million; thus Perform Inc's maxi-min policy would be to charge a low price.

(c) Likely outcomes of the game.

Cell (b) would be the outcome of Stage-it and Perform Inc both adopting a maxi-min strategy. Stage-it would be pleasantly surprised by doing better than expected (£260 million compared to £100 million) and Perform Inc would do as expected (£140 million). This could therefore be a stable equilibrium, with neither firm seeking to change its policies.

The term 'dominant strategy' is sometimes used in game theory to refer to situations in which a firm is able to identify one policy option as being best for it, regardless of the reactions of any rivals. In Table 5.2 Stage-it would identify 'high price' as the policy option that corresponds to a 'dominant strategy', since this gives Stage-it the highest profit whether or not Perform Inc reacts with low price (£260 million, £200 million) or high price (£100 million, £40 million).

Self-check question 5.5

Look carefully at Table 5.3 for a market share game.
(a) Which strategy would Stage-it follow if it uses a maxi-min approach to the game?
(b) Would the strategy change if Stage-it uses a mini-max approach to the game (worst of the best possible outcomes)?

Table 5.3 Stage-it pay-off matrix (market share game)

		Perform Inc strategies	
		Price cut	Extra advertising
Stage-it strategies	**Price cut**	50%	60%
	Extra advertising	40%	70%

Note: Answers to Self-Check Questions can be found on the instructor's website, www.pearsoned.co.uk/wall

PAUSE FOR THOUGHT 5.5

Can you construct a pay-off matrix for Perform Inc using the data in Table 5.3 when only the two firms control the market and Perform Inc evaluates pay-offs in the same way as Stage-it?

5.6   The normal distribution

We noted in Chapter 2 (p. 46) that the normal distribution is perfectly symmetrical ('bell' shaped), with all three measures of central location, namely arithmetic mean, median and mode, being the same value for some variable X. If we call this arithmetic mean value the Greek letter μ ('mew'), then we know that since this is also the median value, 50% of the distribution will lie either side of μ. We can of course express such percentages as *decimals*, with the whole distribution underneath the normal curve expressed as 1 and with 0.5 of the distribution then lying either side of μ.

Indeed the symmetry of any normal distribution around μ will allow us to calculate probabilities involving the distribution of the variable X around μ. We can do this by calculating the standard deviation (σ) for the variable X. This measure of dispersion (see Chapter 2) can then be used to calculate probabilities for any normal distribution. For example, as shown in Figure 5.6, we know that 68.26% of all the observations will lie within one standard deviation of the mean; 95.44% of the observations will lie within two standard deviations of the mean; and 99.74% of the observations will lie within three standard deviations of the mean.

PAUSE FOR THOUGHT 5.6

Can you suggest three different types of distribution you might expect to be normal or close to normal?

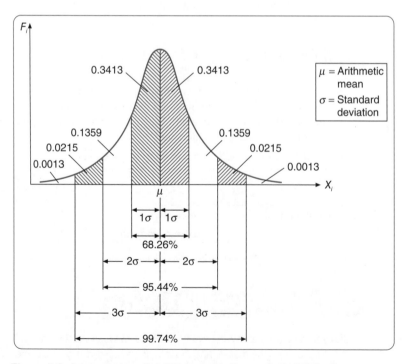

Figure 5.6 Areas and probabilities under the normal distribution

We use the term **confidence intervals** to refer to those ranges of values from the arithmetic mean (μ) expressed in terms of the standard deviation (σ), within which we can expect a particular value of the variable X to lie. We return to consider confidence intervals further in Chapter 6 (p. 190).

5.6.1 Standard normal distribution

The calculation of probabilities under any normal distribution can be taken a step further by transforming the values of the variable X_i into the numbers of standard deviations (σ) from the mean (μ). The resulting distribution is often referred to as the **standard normal distribution** and the transformation that brings it about is often called the **Z score** or **Z statistic**.

$$Z = \frac{X - \mu}{\sigma} = \frac{\text{value of variable} \;-\; \text{arithmetic mean}}{\text{standard deviation}}$$

In other words, the Z statistic simply calculates the number of standard deviations of a particular observation from the arithmetic mean. If the distribution of the variable X is normal, then the distribution of the Z statistic will also be normal, as shown in Figure 5.7.

A table giving the area shaded in Figure 5.7 for any value of the Z statistic is presented in full in Appendix 2 (p. 344). To help you become familiar with using the full Z table, a small section of that table is shown below (Table 5.4).

For example, for a Z score of $+1.0$ we will have 0.1587 (15.87%) of the distribution to the *right* of that Z score.

Of course, since the Z statistic is normally distributed, a Z score of -1.0 will give us an equivalent area, but this time to the *left* of that Z score.

In other words, if the particular value for X is one standard deviation above (or below) the mean for a normally distributed variable, then we can expect 0.1587 (15.87%) of the distribution to be above (or below) that value.

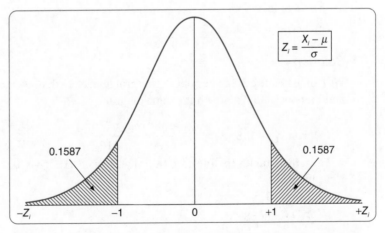

Figure 5.7 The standard normal (Z) distribution: mean 0, standard deviation 1

Table 5.4 *Z* scores and probabilities

Z	.00	.01	.02	.03	.04	.05	.06	.07	.08	.09
1.0	.1587	.1562	.1539	.1515	.1492	.1469	.1446	.1423	.1401	.1379
1.1	.1357	.1335	.1314	.1292	.1271	.1251	.1230	.1210	.1190	.1170
1.2	.1151	.1131	.1112	.1093	.1075	.1056	.1038	.1020	.1003	.0985
1.3	.0968	.0951	.0934	.0918	.0901	.0885	.0869	.0853	.0838	.0823
1.4	.0808	.0793	.0778	.0764	.0749	.0735	.0721	.0708	.0694	.0681

> If $Z = +$, then area is in right-hand tail
> If $Z = -$, then area is in left-hand tail

Note that the mean of the standard normal (Z) distribution is a Z score of zero. In other words, when the value of X is the mean (μ) itself, then we are zero standard deviations from the mean, so the Z score is zero. It therefore follows that for $Z = 0$, there will be 0.5 (50%) of the distribution to the right, and 0.5 (50%) to the left.

If the Z score is found to be $+1.15$, then go *down* the Z column to the 1.1 row and *across* the 1.1 row to the position underneath the 0.05 column. We read off the value 0.1251, which tells us that 0.1251 or 12.51% of the distribution is in the *right-hand tail*. Of course had the Z score been -1.15, then 0.1251 or 12.51% of the distribution would have been in the *left-hand tail*.

Check that for $Z = +1.38$ you would read 0.0838 (8.38%) in the right-hand tail, and for $Z = -1.42$ you would read 0.0778 (7.78%) in the left-hand tail.

Worked example 5.10

Suppose Stage-it is told that attendance at a conference it is managing has a normal distribution with a mean of 100 and a standard deviation of 10. Suppose that Stage-it wants to find the probability of X (the attendance) being:

(a) 115 or more;

(b) 75 or less;

(c) between 75 and 115.

Solution

We can use Figure 5.8 to help solve this problem. Note that we show both the variable X and its associated Z score on the same diagram.

(a) For $X_1 = 115$, $Z_1 = \dfrac{X_1 - \mu}{\sigma} = \dfrac{115 - 100}{10} = +1.5$

From the Z tables (p. 344), we find that $Z_1 = +1.5$ gives 0.0668 as the area in the right-hand tail.

i.e. $Z_1 = +1.5$

$P_1 = 0.0668$

$P_1 = 6.68\%$

Worked
example
5.10
(cont'd)

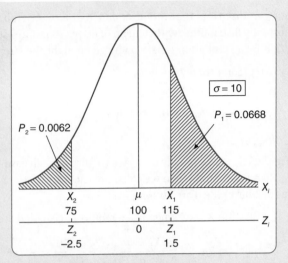

Figure 5.8 Probabilities for attendance at the conference

There is a 6.68% chance of X_i being 115 or more.

(b) For $X_2 = 75$, $Z_2 = \dfrac{X_2 - \mu}{\sigma} = \dfrac{75 - 100}{10} = -2.5$

From the Z tables (p. 344), we find that $Z_2 = -2.5$ gives 0.0062 as the area in the left-hand tail.

i.e. $Z_2 = -2.5$

$P_2 = 0.0062$

$P_2 = 0.62\%$

There is a 0.62% (i.e. less than 1% chance) of X being 75 or less.

(c) The whole area beneath the Z curve is 1.00, so the area between $X_2 = 75$ and $X_1 = 115$ is $1.00 - (0.0062 + 0.0668) = 1 - 0.0730 = 0.9270$.

In other words, there is a 92.7% chance of X being between 75 and 115.

In solving problems of this kind it is always helpful to draw a sketch diagram to indicate what has been given in the question and what needs to be found, as in Figure 5.8 above. Sometimes we will need to make use of the fact that the area to each side of the mean under the normal curve is 0.50 (50%). You will see in Worked Example 5.11 that sometimes we must subtract the area in the respective tails of the distribution from 0.50 in order to obtain the area required. Note also that whenever we seek to find an area that extends across the mean (μ), then it is helpful to solve for each side of the mean separately before combining the result.

Worked example 5.11

Stage-it discovers that the attendance at a night club it is managing is thought to be normally distributed, with a mean of 80 persons and a standard deviation of 12 persons. What is the probability that on any given night the attendance is

(a) greater than 74 persons;

(b) fewer than 83 persons;

(c) between 70 and 85 persons?

Solution

Figure 5.9 represents the areas we require in each case.

Remember that when we calculate the Z score, the Z tables (p. 344) give us the area in the *tails* of the distribution.

(a) To find $X > 74$ means we require the shaded areas A_1 and A_2 in Figure 5.9A.

$$\text{For } X_1 = 74, \; Z_1 = \frac{X_1 - \mu}{\sigma} = \frac{74 - 80}{12} = -0.5$$

$$Z_1 = -0.5$$

$$P_1 = 0.3085$$

$$A_1 = 0.5000 - 0.3085 = 0.1915$$

$$A_2 = 0.5000$$

$$A_1 + A_2 = 0.6915$$

There is a 0.6915 (69.15%) probability that the attendance will be greater than 74 persons.

(b) To find $X < 83$ means we require the shaded areas A_1 and A_2 in Figure 5.9B.

$$\text{For } X_1 = 83, \; Z_1 = \frac{X_1 - \mu}{\sigma} = \frac{83 - 80}{12}$$

$$Z_1 = +0.25$$

$$P_1 = 0.4013$$

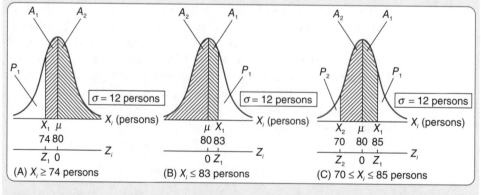

Figure 5.9 The areas required are shaded (A_1 and A_2); the areas given in the Z tables are unshaded (P_1 and P_2)

Worked
example
5.11
(cont'd)

$$A_1 = 0.5000 - 0.4013 = 0.0987$$

$$A_2 = 0.5000$$

$$A_1 + A_2 = 0.5987$$

There is a 0.5987 (59.87%) probability that the attendance will be less than 83 persons.

(c) To find $70 < X < 85$ persons we require the shaded areas A_1 and A_2 in Figure 5.9C.

For $X_1 = 85$, $Z_1 = \dfrac{X_1 - \mu}{\sigma} = \dfrac{85 - 80}{12} = \dfrac{+5}{12} = +0.42$ (rounded)

$$Z_1 = +0.42$$

$$P_1 = 0.3372$$

$$A_1 = 0.5000 - 0.3372 = 0.1628$$

$$A_1 = 0.1628$$

For $X_2 = 70$, $Z_2 = \dfrac{X_2 - \mu}{\sigma} = \dfrac{70 - 80}{12} = \dfrac{-10}{12} = -0.83$

$$Z_2 = -0.83$$

$$P_2 = 0.2033$$

$$A_2 = 0.5000 - 0.2033$$

$$A_2 = 0.2967$$

$$A_1 + A_2 = \mathbf{0.4595}$$

There is a 0.4595 (45.95%) probability that the attendance will be between 70 and 85 persons.

BREAK-OUT BOX 5.1

Using the normal distribution

The spreadsheet provides data on the ages and incomes of 5,000 people attending a major music event on a given night. If we assume that the data is normally distributed, we can find various probabilities involving the age and income of people attending the music event, which can be important marketing information.

Using Chapter5_Example_1 Excel spreadsheet answer the following questions.

(a) What is the probability of someone attending the music event being under 45 years of age?

(b) What is the probability of someone attending the music event having an annual income of more than £55,000?

You will see instructions on the spreadsheet on how to respond to these questions.

When you have responded to these questions for the data on one particular night, you can press the button identified and find data for attending the musical event on another night.

5.6.2 Finding the variable value when probability is known

So far we have known the *specific values* of the variable X and found the probabilities with which these values might occur. Here we reverse the process. Suppose we know the *probabilities* with which specific values of the variable X might occur, how can we then find these values of X? Worked Example 5.12 shows how we go about solving such problems.

Worked example 5.12	The life of a specialised piece of audio equipment used by Stage-it in major concerts is normally distributed with mean 60 hours and standard deviation 30 minutes. If 2.5% (0.025) of such equipment last for more than X_1 hours, find the value of X_1.

Solution

In a question like this, do make sure that you express all values in the *same unit*, here hours or minutes. If we use hours, then the standard deviation is 0.5 hours, as shown in Figure 5.10.

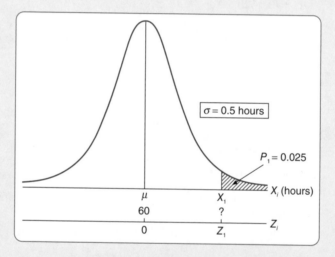

Figure 5.10 Probability known, value of variable unknown

$$P_1 = 0.025$$

We can therefore look in the *body* of the Z tables (p. 344), to find the Z value (Z_1) which would give us the probability in the right-hand tail of 0.025.

$$Z_1 = +1.96$$

We know that

$$Z_1 = \frac{X_1 - \mu}{\sigma}$$

i.e. $+1.96 = \dfrac{X_1 - 60}{0.5}$

$+1.96\,(0.5) + 60 = X_1$

$60.98 = X_1$

In other words, we would expect 2.5% (0.025) of the specialised audio equipment to last more than 60.98 hours.

Note: if the left-hand tail had been involved then the calculations would have used a *negative* value for Z. You can check this yourself by finding the number of hours (X_2) for which 2.5% (0.025) of the components last *less than* X_2 hours. Check that your answer is 59.02 hours and that -1.96 was used in your calculation.

Self-check questions 5.6

Q1. Find the area beneath the (normal) curve over the following values for the Z score. Draw diagrams in each case and use the Z tables (p. 344).

(a) $Z_1 = 0$ and $Z_2 = 0.2$
(b) $Z_1 = 0.5$ and $Z_2 = 1.0$
(c) $Z_1 = 0.95$ and $Z_2 = 2.55$
(d) $Z_1 = 1.55$ and $Z_2 = (+)$ infinity
(e) $Z_1 = -1.5$ and $Z_2 = 0$
(f) $Z_1 = -1.85$ and $Z_2 = -1.05$
(g) $Z_1 = -1.55$ and $Z_2 = (-)$ infinity

Q2. Attendances at rock concerts in a stadium are normally distributed with mean 20,000 persons and standard deviation 4,000 persons. For a future event to be managed by Stage-it, what is the probability that

(a) more than 28,000 persons will attend;
(b) fewer than 14,000 persons will attend;
(c) between 17,000 and 25,000 persons will attend?

Q3. Use the same data as in the previous question.

(a) If there is a 5% (0.05) probability that more than a certain number of people (X_1) will attend, what is the value of X_1?
(b) If there is a 10% (0.10) probability that fewer than X_2 people will attend, what is the value of X_2?

Note: Answers to Self-Check Questions can be found on the instructor's website, www.pearsoned.co.uk/wall

5.7 The binomial distribution

The **binomial distribution** can be used to describe the likely outcome of events for discrete variables that

(a) have only two possible outcomes; and

(b) are independent.

Suppose we are conducting a questionnaire. The *binomial distribution* might be used to analyse the results if the only two responses to a question are 'yes' or 'no' *and* if the response to one question (e.g. 'yes') does not influence the likely response to any other question (i.e. 'yes' or 'no').

> ## Binomial distribution
>
> Put rather more formally, the *binomial distribution* occurs when there are n independent trials (or tests) with the probability of 'success' or 'failure' in each trial (or test) being constant.
>
> Let p = the probability of 'success'
>
> Let q = the probability of 'failure'
>
> then $q = 1 - p$
>
> n = number of trials
>
> r = number of successes (or failures) to be found

For example, if we toss an unbiased coin 10 times, we might wish to find the probability of getting 4 heads! Here $n = 10, r = 4, p$ (head) $= 0.5, q$ (tail) $= 0.5$ and $q = 1 - p$.

The probability of obtaining r 'successes' in 'n' trials (tests) is found using a formula that is rather complicated, but fortunately the information we need to solve such problems can be expressed in a table from which we can calculate the relevant probabilities.

5.7.1 Cumulative binomial tables

You can find a fuller version of Table 5.5 in Appendix 3, 'Cumulative binomial probabilities'. Here we present an extract from this table that we can use to show how we solve the earlier problem of calculating the probability of getting 4 heads from 10 tosses of an unbiased coin.

Because the table shows *cumulative* binomial probabilities, it tells us the probability of getting *r or more* successes out of n trials in a binomial situation.

Where there are blanks in the table – for instance, for $n = 10$ with $r = 6$ and $p = 0.05$ – this simply means that the probability of such an outcome is so small that it would not show up in a table that is only presented to four decimal places.

It will be useful to solve our earlier problem to see how this cumulative binomial table works.

Table 5.5 Cumulative binominal probabilities (n = 10)

	p = 0.05	0.1	0.15	0.2	0.25	0.3	0.35	0.4	0.45	0.5
$r = 0$	1.0000	1.0000	1.0000	1.0000	1.0000	1.0000	1.0000	1.0000	1.0000	1.0000
1	0.4013	0.6513	0.8030	0.8926	0.9437	0.9717	0.9866	0.9940	0.9975	0.9991
2	0.0862	0.2639	0.4556	0.6242	0.7560	0.8506	0.9141	0.9537	0.9768	0.9893
3	0.0116	0.0702	0.1797	0.3222	0.4744	0.6171	0.7384	0.8328	0.9005	0.9454
4	0.0011	0.0128	0.0499	0.1209	0.2241	0.3503	0.4862	0.6178	0.7340	0.8282
5	0.0001	0.0016	0.0098	0.0328	0.0781	0.1502	0.2485	0.3670	0.4956	0.6231
6		0.0001	0.0013	0.0064	0.0197	0.0473	0.0949	0.1663	0.2616	0.3770
7			0.0001	0.0009	0.0035	0.0105	0.0260	0.0548	0.1020	0.1719
8				0.0001	0.0004	0.0015	0.0048	0.0123	0.0274	0.0547
9						0.0001	0.0005	0.0017	0.0045	0.0108
10								0.0001	0.0003	0.0010

Worked example 5.13

Use the cumulative binomial probabilities table to find the probability of getting 4 heads from 10 tosses of an unbiased coin.

Solution

We have $n = 10$, $p = 0.5$, and $r = 4$ heads.

Using the block of the tables shown above for $n=10$, we will be under the column $p = 0.5$ and we go down that column to $r = 4$, giving 0.8282. But this is a cumulative binomial distribution table and gives us the probability of getting *four or more* heads. However, the next line tells us the probability of getting *five or more* heads, when $n = 10$ and $p = 0.5$, which is 0.6231.

So we can easily calculate the probability of getting exactly four heads as:

$$0.8282 - 0.6231 = 0.2051$$

In other words, the probability of getting exactly 4 heads from 10 tosses of an unbiased coin is 0.2051 (or 20.51%).

Worked example 5.14

Stage-it uses lighting equipment and finds that 10% of that equipment is defective. A small batch of 10 items is taken from the supplier of the equipment. Find the probability of getting two defective items in the sample.

Solution

We can still use the extract from the cumulative binomial probabilities table (i.e. Table 5.5 above).

Here $n = 10$, $p = 0.1$, $r = 2$, $q = 0.9$

P(2 or more defective items) $= 0.2639$

P(3 or more defective items) $= 0.0702$

P(exactly 2 defective items) $= 0.2639 - 0.0702$

$= 0.1937$ (or 19.37%)

5.7.2 Normal approximation to the binomial distribution

Using the cumulative binomial probabilities table to calculate the probabilities for a given number of 'successes' to occur is obviously time consuming. It is therefore useful to note that if n is large and $p > 0.1$ then we can solve calculations using the *normal distribution* considered earlier (p. 344). The Z statistic is calculated as before:

$$Z = \frac{X - \mu}{\sigma}$$

However, when we are using the normal distribution to solve, as an *approximation*, binomial-type problems, we must express μ and σ in particular ways.

For a binomial distribution

$$\mu = np$$

$$\sigma = \sqrt{npq}$$

where p = probability of 'success'

q = probability of 'failure'

n = number of trials

> Generally speaking, as a 'rule of thumb' we can use the normal approximation to the binomial distribution when $np > 5$, and $p > 0.1$

Continuity correction

Whereas the binomial distribution represents *discrete* data, the normal distribution represents *continuous* data. Strictly speaking, whenever we are approximating a discrete variable with a continuous one, we should use a continuity correction.

The idea behind the continuity correction is illustrated in Figure 5.11. The curve, representing the continuous distribution, cuts through the blocks of the histogram representing the discrete distribution.

Clearly some areas, such as A, are *included* under the continuous distribution, while other areas, such as B, are excluded under the continuous distribution. Overall these areas will tend to cancel each other out. However, since each block of the discrete (binomial) distribution represents a whole number, such as the number of 'successes', it can be regarded as extending from 0.5 above that whole number.

Thus, in Figure 5.11, the block representing 30 'successes' extends from 29.5 to 30.5. It follows that to find the area, and therefore the probability, for a series of outcomes, it will be necessary to go from 0.5 below the lowest whole number (integer) to 0.5 above the highest whole number (integer).

- In Figure 5.11, to find the probability of between, say, 26 and 30 'successes', we must find the area under the normal curve from 25.5 to 30.5.

$$P(26 \text{ to } 30) = P(25.5 \text{ to } 30.5)$$

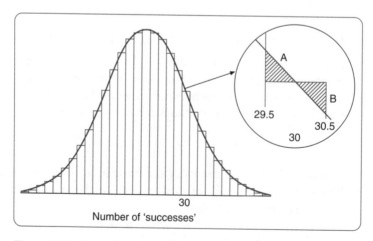

Figure 5.11 Normal approximation to the binomial distribution

- In Figure 5.11, to find the probability of, say, 30 or more 'successes', we must find the area under the normal curve to the right of 29.5.

$$P(30 \text{ or more}) = P(29.5 \text{ or more})$$

Continuity correction

To adjust *discrete* data to *continuous* data, find the probability from 0.5 below the lowest whole number (integer) to 0.5 above the highest whole number (integer).

Worked example 5.15

Past data suggests to Stage-it that for every 100 telephone enquiries at the reception desk of a hotel it is managing, only some 20 bookings are made. Find the probability that from the next 100 enquiries received, the hotel will receive more than 30 bookings.

Solution

This is a binomial situation as each enquiry leads to only one of two outcomes, booking (success) or non-booking (failure). There is an established or fixed probability ($p = 0.2$) of any enquiry leading to a booking, based on past experience.

However, because n is large ($n = 100$) and p is > 0.1 ($p = 0.2$), then we can use the Normal Approximation to the Binomial Theorem (see Figure 5.12). Note that with the continuity correction, X_1 will be 29.5 rather than 30.

$$p = 0.2$$

$$q = 0.8$$

$$\mu = np = 100\ (0.2) = 20$$

$$\sigma = \sqrt{npq} = \sqrt{100(0.2)(0.8)} = 4$$

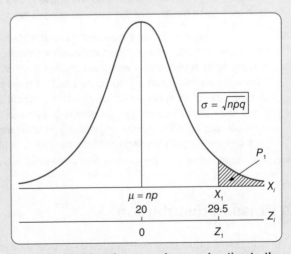

Figure 5.12 Using the normal approximation to the binomial distribution

Worked example 5.15 (cont'd)

$$Z_1 = \frac{X_1 - np}{\sqrt{npq}} = \frac{29.5 - 20}{4} = +2.38$$

$$Z_1 = +2.38$$

Using the Z tables (p. 345)

$$P_1 = 0.0087$$

There is a 0.0087 (0.87%) probability of the next 100 hotel enquiries yielding more than 30 bookings.

Clearly this is a much quicker method than finding P(31), P(32) … P(100) using the conventional formula for the binomial distribution presented on p. 167.

Self-check questions 5.7

Q1. Stage-it finds that the probability that an invoice contains an error is 5% (0.05). If an audit of 10 invoices is taken, what is the probability of finding fewer than 6 incorrect invoices? Solve this using Table 5.5 above or the fuller cumulative binomial probabilities table in Appendix 3 (p. 346).

Q2. From the previous hotel booking problem for Stage-it calculate the probability that the next 100 enquiries will yield

    (a) 25 or more bookings;

    (b) 16 or more bookings;

    (c) fewer than 14 bookings.

Q3. Suppose that 10% of all houses in a district have burglar alarms. A random sample of 121 houses is selected. Use the normal approximation to find the probability that

    (a) exactly 14 of the houses have alarms;

    (b) fewer than 10 houses have alarms;

    (c) from 7 to 11 inclusive of the selected houses have alarms;

    (d) from 9 to 14 inclusive of the selected houses have alarms.

Q4. An airline offers all 180 passengers on the London/Madrid flight a lunch choice of chicken kiev or beef in beer. As passengers choose once the flight is in progress, there is no way of knowing in advance how many will choose beef on any particular flight. The airline does not want to disappoint customers but, at the same, wants to avoid food waste and the cost of carrying excessive meals. Historical evidence suggests that 65% of passengers choose chicken when offered the choice. What is the probability that, on any particular flight, the number of passengers choosing chicken will be more than 125? (Hint: Use the normal approximation to the binomial to evaluate.)

Note: Answers to Self-Check Questions can be found on the instructor's website, www.pearsoned.co.uk/wall

5.8   The Poisson distribution

The Poisson distribution may be regarded as a special case of the binomial distribution. As with the binomial distribution, the Poisson distribution can be used when there are only two possible outcomes, 'success' (p) or 'failure' (q) and these events are independent. The Poisson distribution is usually used where n is very large but p is very small, and where the mean (np)

Table 5.6 Cumulative Poisson probabilities

	$\mu = 1.1$	1.2	1.3	1.4	1.5	1.6	1.7	1.8	1.9	2.0
$r = 0$	1.0000	1.0000	1.0000	1.0000	1.0000	1.0000	1.0000	1.0000	1.0000	1.0000
1	0.6671	0.6988	0.7275	0.7534	0.7769	0.7981	0.8173	0.8347	0.8504	0.8647
2	0.3010	0.3374	0.3732	0.4082	0.4422	0.4751	0.5068	0.5372	0.5663	0.5940
3	0.0996	0.1205	0.1429	0.1665	0.1912	0.2166	0.2428	0.2694	0.2963	0.3233
4	0.0257	0.0338	0.0431	0.0537	0.0656	0.0788	0.0932	0.1087	0.1253	0.1429
5	0.0054	0.0077	0.0107	0.0143	0.0186	0.0237	0.0296	0.0364	0.0441	0.0527
6	0.0010	0.0015	0.0022	0.0032	0.0045	0.0060	0.0080	0.0104	0.0132	0.0166
7	0.0001	0.0003	0.0004	0.0006	0.0009	0.0013	0.0019	0.0026	0.0034	0.0045
8			0.0001	0.0001	0.0002	0.0003	0.0004	0.0006	0.0008	0.0011
9							0.0001	0.0001	0.0002	0.0002

is constant and typically <5. As p is very small ($p < 0.1$ and often much less), the chance of the event occurring is extremely low. The Poisson distribution is therefore typically used for unlikely events such as accidents, strikes and so on.

The Poisson distribution is also used to solve problems when events tend to occur at random, such as incoming telephone calls, passenger arrivals at a terminal and so on.

This time we can use the cumulative Poisson table. Table 5.6 presents an extract from the fuller table presented in Appendix 4 (p. 347). This table is *cumulative* in that it gives the probabilities of *r or more* 'successes'.

Worked example 5.16

Suppose we require the probability of fewer than three faulty calls occurring in a single day when they typically occur at random at the mean rate of two per day on a telephone line.

Solution

We use the table for $r = 3$ *or more* for the purposes of the cumulative tables. So for $\mu = np = 2$, $r = 3$ we read off the value 0.3233 from the cumulative tables. The probability of *fewer than three* faulty calls is, of course, 1 – probability of *3 or more* faulty calls – that is, $1 - 0.3233 = 0.6767$.

5.8.1 Normal approximation to the Poisson distribution

If the Poisson distribution is appropriate *except* that $\mu(=np) > 30$ (instead of $\mu = <5$) then the **normal approximation to the Poisson distribution** can be used. The Z statistic is calculated as before and the Z tables of Appendix 2 (p. 344) can be used to find probabilities in the respective tails of this distribution.

$$Z = \frac{X - \mu}{\sigma}$$

where $\mu = np$

$$\sigma = \sqrt{np(1 - p)}$$

i.e. $$Z = \frac{X - np}{\sqrt{np(1 - p)}}$$

Note: the continuity correction when adjusting discrete data to continuous data (see p. 168) will also apply here.

5.8.2 Choosing the probability distribution

Figure 5.13 will give you some guidance on when to use the binomial or Poisson distributions, or the normal approximations to these distributions.

Of course the flow chart only applies to variables that are discrete (take on fixed values), that can take one of two possible outcomes (p, q) and that occur independently.

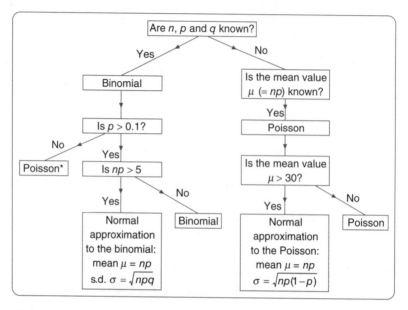

Figure 5.13 Selecting the distribution to use (discrete variable, two outcomes, each independent)

*Note: *Poisson is used here as an approximation to the binomial.*

Self-check questions 5.8

Q1. Suppose $n = 1,000$ and $p = 0.0002$. Use the Poisson distribution to find:
 (a) $P(X = 0)$
 (b) $P(X = 4)$
 (c) $P(X > 1)$
 (d) $P(X \leq 4)$

 mean value $\mu = np = 1000 \times 0.0002 = 0.2$

Q2. The average number of trips per family to amusement parks managed by Stage-it is Poisson distributed with a mean of 0.7 trips per year. What is the probability of randomly selecting a family and finding that

 (a) the family did not make a trip to an amusement park last year;
 (b) the family took two or more trips last year;
 (c) the family took three or fewer trips over a three year period;
 (d) the family took exactly four trips over a six year period?

(continued)

Q3. The reception desk in a hotel usually receives four guests per five minute period. Assuming that the conditions for a Poisson distribution hold, find:

(a) the probability that over a five minute period, exactly four guests will arrive;

(b) the probability that more than two people will arrive;

(c) the probability that exactly six people will arrive over a 10 minute period.

Note: Answers to Self-Check Questions can be found on the instructor's website, www.pearsoned.co.uk/wall

REVIEW QUESTIONS

R5.1. A supplier of light bulbs to Stage-it has packed 169 into a container, but 43 are defective. Stage-it follows its usual practice of trying a sample of six light bulbs before purchasing a crate. What is the probability that five or more (out of the six) will work?

R5.2. An insurance company estimates that, at a large musical event, one person in every 50 insured people is likely to make a claim. The company has recently sold 1,600 insurance policies relating to the musical event.

(a) How many claims can the company expect?

(b) If the typical claim is for £750 what is the minimum (ignore all other costs) the company must charge for each policy in order to break even?

R5.3. The probability that a record shop will sell at most 8 copies of a CD of the music event each day is 0.60 and the probability that it will sell 9 to 12 copies of the CD each day is 0.35. What is the probability of

(a) at least 9 sales;

(b) at most 12 sales;

(c) more than 12 sales?

R5.4. A sample of 4 items is selected from a batch of electric light bulbs for Stage-it lighting that has been found to contain 8 defective bulbs and 24 bulbs without defects. What is the probability that

(a) all four bulbs will be defective (assume replacement);

(b) all four bulbs will not be defective (again assume replacement)?

(c) How would your answers to (a) and (b) alter if there was no replacement?

R5.5. A market research company has studied the quality of service provided by 100 music-related retailers in the London region. The findings are summarised below:

	Good service	Poor service
High-street chain	40	24
Independent retailer	26	10

(a) If a music retailer is selected at random, what is the probability that the retailer gives good service?

(b) If a music retailer is selected at random, what is the probability that the retailer selected is an independent retailer and gives good service?

(c) What is the probability that a music retailer that is part of a high-street chain will give poor service?

R5.6. A sales representative of Stage-it is selling videos of the music event and finds that the probability of making a sale on the first visit to a new client is 0.5. On the second visit the probability of making a sale is 0.6 if a sale was made on the first visit and 0.4 if no sale was made on the first visit. Use a decision tree diagram to work out the probability of just one sale resulting from the two visits.

R5.7. A company is contracted by Stage-it to finish a £100,000 project relating to the music event by 31 December. If it does not complete on time a penalty of £8,000 per month or part of a month is incurred. The company estimates that there is only a 40% chance of completing on time and that the project might be one, two, three or even four months late with equal probability. Sub-contractors can be hired by the firm at a cost of £18,000.

If the sub-contractors are hired then the probability that the company completes on time is doubled.

If the project is still late it will only be one or two months late with equal probability.

Draw a decision tree to represent the problem and analyse using the EV technique.

R5.8. This question is based on the following scenario for Stage-it and the data in the box below. Stage-it is fully aware of the importance of probabilities for the outcomes of the events it is managing or co-producing. It has agreed to finance and co-produce a major music event to be run on three successive nights in London. The event is to take place in a 60,000 seater stadium in London and Stage-it has used its previous experience of managing similar events to devise the following probabilities and EVs.

Stage-it is also aware that rival organisers sometimes stage competing events within 50 miles, and should this occur the various probabilities and EVs will be affected. All values relate to a single night's running of the event.

Some of the details, probabilities and EVs of the event are outlined below.

> Capacity: 60,000 people
>
> Break-even: 75% of capacity
>
> Profit: £15 per attendee beyond break-even
>
> Losses: £5 per attendee below break-even
>
> Full capacity (*no competitor reaction*): probability 0.6
>
> Break-even capacity (*no competitor reaction*): 0.8
>
> Full capacity (*competitor reaction*): probability 0.4
>
> Break-even capacity (*competitor reaction*): 0.6
>
> Mean attendance of past music events in venue: 48,000 people
>
> Standard deviation of past music events in venue: 3,000 people
>
> Abandon event: penalty cost £50,000

Questions

(a)   What is the EV for profit if there is a full capacity attendance on a single night?

(b)   What is the EV for profit if there is break-even attendance on a single night?

(c)   If the distribution of attendances is normal, with mean attendance 48,000 people and standard deviation of 3,000 people, what is the probability of

    (i)   an attendance of 51,000 people or more;

    (ii)   an attendance of 55,000 people or more;

(iii) an attendance of 45,000 people or fewer;

(iv) an attendance of 42,000 people or fewer;

(v) an attendance between 39,000 people and 51,000 people?

(d) What is the 95% confidence interval for attendance at the music event?

Note: Answers to Review Questions can be found on the instructor's website, www.pearsoned.co.uk/wall

Further practice

You can find more questions (with solutions) on probability and probability distributions on the instructor's website, www.pearsoned.co.uk/wall.

Spreadsheets: video guide

You can also find a step-by-step account that takes you through the actual use of a spreadsheet when solving the type of problems you have encountered in this chapter. Go to the instructor's website, www.pearsoned.co.uk/wall.

Chapter 6

Sampling and tests of hypotheses

Introduction

Chapter 5 introduced the normal distribution and the Z statistic. In this chapter we continue to apply these ideas, but in the context of sampling. Most firms would find it either impractical or too expensive to survey *all* their customers or to carefully examine every item that flows from their production line. Instead they usually resort to selecting a *sample* from the whole group or, as it is often called, the *population*. Of course here the term 'population' can refer to all the items under consideration as well as referring to all the people.

The car industry in general, and the production of electric cars in particular, provide the context for the growth strategies of Electrofit in this chapter. Electrofit is an established component supply company in the motor vehicle sector which produces high-technology electronic components. It believes strongly in the future of the electronic car, seeing the success of 'hybrid' cars that run on both petrol and electric batteries as just a stage in the process towards the eventual dominance of wholly electric cars. Electrofit is therefore spending considerable R&D resources on developing and adapting electronic components for use in both hybrid and electronic cars.

Of relevance to Electrofit's growth strategy is the fact that in the European Union a legally binding regulation on maximum emissions of CO_2 and other greenhouse gases by new vehicles comes into force in 2015. This sets a maximum emission of 130 g of CO_2 per km travelled by new cars by 2015, falling to 95 g per km in 2020. Nor is CO_2 the only pollutant from conventional petrol engines to face tighter regulations. By 2014 NOX (nitrous oxide) emissions from EU diesel cars will have to be 84% below the limits set as recently as 2000. China, in response to weeks and months of heavy air pollution in Beijing and other major cities in 2013, introduced similar restrictions to those in the European Union for emissions of CO_2, NOX and other pollutants from petrol and diesel cars, which are to be tightened further in 2016.

The box below provides some useful insights into why Electrofit is focusing on the electric car for future growth, though it also identifies some risk factors in this growth strategy.

Electric cars: the future

China provides a useful case study for seeing why environmentally friendly electric cars are seen by many in the motor vehicles sector as having major market potential. In 2009 the Chinese government boldly announced that by 2015 it would sell 500,000 all-electric vehicles (i.e. ones that can't use petrol at all) and by 2020 it would sell 5 million such vehicles per year. To encourage Chinese consumers, substantial subsidies have been offered to those who purchase all-electric cars – for example, over £8,000 per vehicle in Shenzhen. There is, however, some way to go before the full potential of the electric car is realised! In 2013 the lack of charging stations was still seen as a major issue, with less than one third of the target number of charging stations installed in China in 2013. Nevertheless Chinese car firms such as SAIC, Great Wall, Chery and BYD have all entered into joint ventures with US, EU and other car companies to produce both the hybrids and all-electric cars for the Chinese and global markets.

Nor is the situation more encouraging in the United States for the all-electric car! President Obama has set a target for 1 million electric cars on American roads by 2015, but by 2013 only 50,000 were actually running. Similarly Germany has set a target for 1 million such cars by 2020, but only 3,000 were sold in 2012/13.

Nissan became the first car maker to invest in electric vehicle charging points, based on its own forecasts for the future of electric cars. Nissan has developed a compact and fast-charging device, giving the batteries in its Leaf and Zoe electric cars an 80% charge in only 30 minutes.

The term *statistical inference* is often used to refer to the many procedures discussed in this chapter whereby attributes are ascribed by Electrofit to the 'population' based on the results of its sample investigations.

Spreadsheets

The questions and activities in the Break-Out Boxes use spreadsheets which can be found on the student's website, www.pearsoned.co.uk/wall. Many of the Worked Examples, Self-Check Questions and Review Questions are set out for you as an Excel spreadsheet on the student's website and these questions are marked with an asterisk (*).

Learning objectives

When you have read this chapter you should be able to:

- appreciate the key features of the different types of sample;
- understand the properties of the distribution of sample means;
- apply the 'Z' score and tables to the distribution of sample means drawn from a normal population;
- explain the relevance of the Central Limit Theorem to the distribution of sample means drawn from a skewed population;
- calculate confidence intervals for either the population mean or the sample mean;
- test hypotheses using one- and two-tailed tests and various levels of significance;
- know when and how to use the student t-distribution and the chi-squared distribution.

6.1   Types of sample

Different types of sample may be used, depending in part on the characteristics or attributes of the 'populations' to be sampled and the objectives of those undertaking the sample. Here we briefly review some of the key features of the various types of sample.

6.1.1   Random sampling

A random sample is used when the intention is to give each item in the 'population' as much chance of being selected in the sample as every other item. A common way to conduct random sampling is to list all the 'members' or items in the population (the *sampling frame*) and then to use random number tables (merely a collection of random digits) or computer-generated random numbers to help select the sample. Such procedures avoid various types of 'bias' which might creep into the selection of items to be included in the sample when undertaken by humans. Even the selection of numbers by individuals might be influenced by unconscious preferences for odd numbers, even numbers and so on.

The key objective of random sampling is to obtain a sample that fairly reflects the population as a whole. Random sampling is more likely to be used when the population itself is relatively homogeneous – that is, when it is composed of items of broadly the same type. Of course there may be considerable practical difficulties in actually locating and interviewing each 'member' of the population that has been randomly selected. For example, if the chosen adult is not at home or otherwise available a researcher may have to return or seek to contact that individual on another occasion – another member of the household will not be acceptable.

Stages in random sampling

There are a number of stages involved in random sampling.

- Number each of the cases in your sampling frame with a unique number. The first case is numbered 0, the second 1 and so on.
- Select cases using your random numbers until your actual sample size is reached.
- Select your *first* random number at random (e.g. close your eyes and pick a number from your random number table). In the extract from the random number table below, suppose you picked 55 to begin with.
- Starting with this number (55), you read off the random numbers that follow (here the next is 10) and keep on going until you reach your sample size:
  - If you come across a number *already used*, move on and simply ignore it, as you need different cases in your sample.
  - If you come across a number *outside your sampling frame* (e.g. your sample frame is 71 cases and you come across the number 72 in the random number table), ignore it and move on.

Features of random sampling

- Each item selected has an equal chance of being drawn.
- It is usually adopted when the population is largely homogeneous, that is, when it is difficult to distinguish between items.

- Implementation often involves the use of random number tables or of computer-generated random numbers.
- Selection is unbiased.
- A major drawback is that a population listing (sampling frame) is required and the chosen items need to be located, then questioned or measured.

Worked example 6.1

Electrofit has 71 garages (the sampling frame) to which it supplies electric car batteries. It wants to obtain information on consumer experience of purchasing its electric batteries and therefore asks you to select a random sample of 12 garages which you will then visit in order to conduct an in-depth questionnaire.

Electrofit gives you a named list of these 71 garages which is your sampling frame. You give each garage a number, starting at 00 and finishing at 70 (i.e. 71 numbers).

(a) Use the extract from the random number table below (Table 6.1) to select a random sample of 12 garages from Electrofit's sample frame of 71 named garages, starting with the number 55. Identify the 12 numbers that will be in your random sample.

(b) What would each random number included in your sample size of 12 represent?

(c) What is the benefit of this random sampling process?

Table 6.1 Random number table

78	41	11	62	72	18	66	69	58	71	31	90	51	36	78	09	41	00
70	50	58	19	68	26	75	69	04	00	25	29	16	72	35	73	55	85
32	78	14	47	01	**55**	10	91	83	21	13	32	59	53	03	38	79	32
71	60	20	53	86	78	50	57	42	30	73	48	68	09	16	35	21	87
35	30	15	57	99	96	33	25	56	43	65	67	51	45	37	99	54	89
09	08	05	41	66	54	01	49	97	34	38	85	85	23	34	62	60	58
02	59	34	51	98	71	31	54	28	85	23	84	49	07	33	71	17	88
20	13	44	15	22	95												

Solution

(a) You start with the number 55 in the extract from the random number table. Remember that the highest random number in your sampling frame is 70, representing the 71 garages altogether in your 'population' as you gave the first garage the number 00. You select the next 11 garages to be included in your sample after this number 55, remembering to ignore numbers higher than 70.

$$10, 21, 13, 32, 59, 53, 03, 38, 32, 60, 20, 50$$

Note: we ignored 53 the second time it appeared.

(b) It would represent the name of each of the 12 garages to be included in your random sample.

(c) Every garage in the sampling frame had the same chance, from the outset of the process, to be included in your sample.

To find a more extensive random number table see Appendix 7 (p. 352).

PAUSE FOR THOUGHT 6.1

Can you identity three well-known products for which a random sampling procedure might be considered appropriate for testing customer responses?

The random sampling procedure will also be seen to be important when we wish to apply the Central Limit Theorem to test various theories (hypotheses) based on sample information (see p. 187).

6.1.2 Stratified random sampling

Of course there will be times when we might prefer a *non-random* sampling procedure. Such a non-random procedure might, for example, be preferred when the population is *segmented* or *heterogeneous* – that is, when it contains very different sub-sets of items or subjects. If, say, 40% of all garages have annual revenue over £x and 15% have annual revenue below £y, then we might wish our sample of garages to exactly mirror such proportions, rather than give every garage an equal chance of selection. This is the basis of stratified random sampling.

Here you divide the sampling frame for your 'population' into one or more groupings (or strata) that have similar characteristics. You do this because you recognise that there are distinct and different groupings within a 'population'. A random sample can then be drawn from each stratum – which is why the term used is 'stratified random sampling'.

Dividing the population into a series of relevant strata gives you the opportunity to ensure that your overall sample is representative of your population. For example, if 30% of your population of garages have annual revenue above £450,000 per annum, then you can make sure that 30% of your *overall* sample includes the garages (randomly) selected from this higher revenue stratum.

The steps involves in stratified random sampling include:

● identifying the sampling frame to include all the cases for your population;

● choosing the variable or variables to identify your different strata (e.g. level of annual revenue) within the sampling frame;

● splitting the sampling frame for your population into these strata;

● numbering each of the cases within each strata with a unique number, starting from zero, as before;

● selecting a random sample from each of these strata as before;

● developing an *overall* sample from these various random samples that reflects the proportions of the various strata in the sampling frame. So if the sample size is 100, and 30% of the garages in the overall sampling frame (population) have annual revenues over £450,000, then 30 of the garages randomly selected from this stratum should be included in your *overall* sample of size 100.

Did you know?

It costs five times as much to recruit a new customer via marketing strategies that use sample surveys of new products, new designs and so on as it does to provide excellent customer service and retain an existing customer.

Note that the intention here is still to obtain a representative sample, but one that 'fairly' reflects a population that itself is heterogeneous. We might say that such a sample is free from 'selective bias', since the proportion of any identified attribute in the sample is merely a reflection of its contribution to the population as a whole.

Worked example 6.2

Electrofit has identified two strata for the garages selling its electric batteries: those with annual revenues below £450,000 and those with annual revenues above £450,000. It has found that different types of purchaser characterise the customers for each of these two strata. Some 30% of the garages selling Electrofit's batteries have annual revenues above £450,000 – that is, 21 out of the 71 garages in its sampling frame. The numbers 00–20 are given to these named garages in the sampling frame, and the numbers 21–70 are given to the 50 out of 71 named garages having annual revenue at or below £450,000.

(a) Starting at number 55, use the extract from the random number table (see Table 6.1, p. 179) to select a random sample of six garages having annual revenue above £450,000. Identify the six numbers.

(b) Starting at number 55, use Table 6.1 to select a random sample of 14 garages having annual revenue at or below £450,000. Identify the 14 numbers.

(c) What are the numbers to be included in your overall sample?

(d) What is the benefit of this stratified random sampling approach?

Solution

(a) 10,   13,   03,   20,   09,   16

(b) 21,   32,   59,   53,   38,   60,   50
     57,   42,   30,   48,   68,   35,   33

Note: we ignored numbers 32, 53, 21, 35, 30 and 57 when they appeared a second time.

(c) Actually the numbers already presented in (a) and (b) would themselves be the overall sample, as the 6 randomly selected numbers in stratum 1 (over £450,000 revenue per annum) and the 14 randomly selected numbers in stratum 2 (at or below £450,000 revenue per annum) are in the 'correct' proportions of 30% and 70% respectively.

(d) The benefit is that we have an overall sample that reflects the different segments (strata) in the correct proportions to their overall contribution but gives every case in each of these strata the same chance of being selected (random sampling).

Features of stratified random sampling

- This is used when the population has a number of identifiable attributes and a complete sampling frame is available for the population.
- Populations stratified in this way are known as heterogeneous.
- The overall composition of the sample must reflect the attributes present in the population – for example, the actual proportions of low, middle and high income earners.
- Individuals or items within each stratum will still be selected randomly, giving them all the same chance of being included in the overall sample.

- The overall sample will include cases from these random samples for each stratum in proportion to the contribution of the various strata to the total sample frame.

- A stratified sample is free from selective bias, since it reflects the proportions of any given attribute present in the population as a whole.

6.1.3 Probability and non-probability sampling

So far we have considered techniques that require a complete list of all the members of the total population (sampling frame), from which the sample is then selected at random, so that each member of the population has the same chance of being included in the sample. These techniques are often called 'probability sampling' since we know the chance or probability of each member of the population being selected.

However, it may not be possible to obtain a full listing of the 'population' from which you are sampling! Without a sampling frame you will not be able to use probability sampling. Fortunately there are a variety of 'non-probability' sampling techniques we can use, as outlined in Table 6.2.

6.1.4 Quota sampling

The use of quota sampling is widespread in market research. Here the intention is often to deliberately introduce selective bias into the samples, in the sense that attributes of the members or items selected will represent the choice of the sampler rather than the attributes of the population as a whole. In this sense there is no attempt to seek a representative or unbiased sample from the population. For example, if a firm sells most of its product to those with incomes over £x, then the sample may contain 80% of such adults even if they only comprise, say, 40% of the population. Nor is there usually any attempt to use random sampling *within* the quotas selected, as often happens within the different strata in stratified random sampling. It is often left to the discretion of interviewers and so on to include specified numbers (quotas) of subjects possessing given attributes within the sample. To do so accurately may be costly, requiring highly trained interviewers.

Table 6.2 Types of sampling

Probability sampling	Non-probability sampling
Simple random sampling	Quota sampling
Stratified random sampling	Purposive sampling
	Snowball sampling
	Self-selection sampling
	Convenience sampling

Did you know?

Whether using probability or non-probability samples, the rapidly changing age distribution must be taken into account when seeking to represent the 'population' of potential consumers for many products. It has been estimated that one third of all babies born in 2013 in the United Kingdom will live to 100 years or more and that the 14,500 people in the United

(continued)

Kingdom currently aged 100 years or over will rise to 110,000 people by 2034. In 2013 in the United Kingdom the female life expectancy at birth was 82.1 years, compared to 78.1 years for males. However, increases in longevity are a global phenomenon, with a sharp increase from the global average of 48 years in 1950 to 60 years in 1980 and just over 70 years in 2013.

Features of quota sampling

- This is widely used in market research.
- A sample includes a specified number or quota of subjects with given attributes.
- Interviewers must be highly trained as they are often responsible for identification and selection of respondents.
- A 'biased' sample therefore results, but one that may be useful in representing the customers seen as most likely to purchase the firm's products.

PAUSE FOR THOUGHT 6.2

Can you identify three well-known products for which a quota sampling procedure might be considered appropriate for testing consumer responses?

6.1.5 Purposive sampling

This is the most widely used form of non-probability sampling, and is often used for selecting a small sample involving 'qualitative' data – for example, consumers to be interviewed or individuals to be invited to join a focus group.

The selection criteria to be used in 'purposive sampling' can vary, depending on the reasons for your sample.

Extreme case

For example, you may wish your sample to reflect extremes of opinion, so you only choose people from groups known to be very positive or very negative in regard to a particular issue, to help illustrate the wide range of viewpoints.

Typical case

For example, you want your sample to be broadly representative of the population, but not strictly statistically representative. In other words, judgement will be required by those taking the sample.

6.1.6 Snowball sampling

This refers to non-probability sampling in which the first sample member helps to identify other sample members. It is often used when it is difficult to identify all the members of your population – that is, your sampling frame. Having found one person who can be identified as being in your intended population, they may help you to find others who are also members of that population. This approach may be used in a situation where members of a population are difficult to access – for example, chief executive officers (CEOs) of major companies. However, starting with one CEO, they may be able to use their networks to arrange access for you to interview other CEO colleagues.

6.1.7 Self-selection samples

This refers to non-probability sampling in which possible sample members are asked to identify themselves. For example, you might use an advert to ask people with specified characteristics or circumstances to contact you, the researcher, to be part of your sample for a specified purpose.

6.1.8 Convenience sampling

This refers to non-probability sampling in which the sample members are chosen because of the ease or convenience of accessing them, rather than because of their being particularly appropriate to the research.

Self-check question 6.1

As a researcher for Electrofit you have been asked to draw up a sampling frame that includes the 20 major purchasers of a specific electronic component. You give these the numbers 00 to 19. You now want to create a random sample of six of these for an in-depth survey; closing your eyes you pick out the number 09 on the first row of Table 6.1 (p. 179) as your starting point.

(a) Identify the numbers you will include in your random sample of six.

(b) If you now extend your random sample to 10 (still starting at number 09 on the first line of Table 6.1) identify the extra 4 numbers to include in your random sample.

(c) You are now asked to construct a random stratified sample, with two separate groups (strata). Group 1 only include purchasers who spend £100,000 or less per year on your electronic components. Some twelve purchasers come into this category. Group 2 only includes purchasers who spend over £100,000 per year on your electronic components. Some eight purchasers come into this category.

(d) Using Table 6.1, outline how you would select your stratified random sample.

(e) If you start at number 62 in the first row of Table 6.1, what numbers would be included in your sample for each of these groups (strata)?

(f) How would you ensure that your overall sample is appropriate for this sampling approach?

Note: Answers to Self-Check Questions can be found on the instructor's website, www.pearsoned.co.uk/wall

---

PAUSE FOR THOUGHT 6.3

How might Electrofit use sampling if it wishes to find out the level of satisfaction of the major purchasers of its electronic components?

Did you know?

A critical factor in the growth of the all-electric (and hybrid) car is the availability of charging points. In May 2012 Oxford installed a further 60 charging points, becoming the world's leading city in terms of the number of charging points per person. With 2,381 people per charging point, it surpassed Amsterdam (4,029) and Paris (4,813). There is still much to do in

(continued)

this respect, as data for Dublin (8,000), London (11,927) and Barcelona (23,685) makes only too clear! Until recently most electric cars had a range of around 100 miles before requiring a recharge, although the most recent hybrid models (electric plus petrol), such as the Ampera produced by Vauxhall, have a range of 360 miles or more thanks to a small petrol-fuelled generator that supplies electricity to the wheels after the battery has run out.

6.2   Distribution of sample means

We explored the properties of a normal distribution in Chapter 5 and how we could calculate probabilities using the Z statistic, which tells us the number of standard deviations of an observation from the arithmetic mean of the population. Here we only have data on the *samples* we take from the population.

However, we can say that if the distribution of the population (X) is normal then the distribution of the arithmetic means ($\bar{X}$) of samples of size n taken from that population will also be normal (see Figure 6.1). The new distribution will have the same arithmetic mean μ but a different standard deviation. We call this the standard error (SE) and it can be found by dividing the standard deviation of the population (σ) by the square root of the sample size (i.e. $\sqrt{n}$).

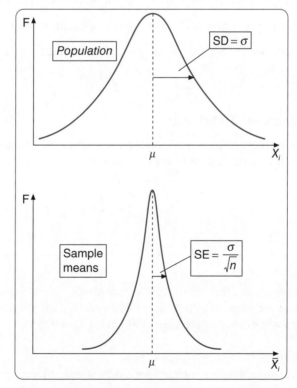

Figure 6.1 Distribution of population for variable X_i and for the means $\bar{X}_i$ of samples of size n drawn from that population

> **Standard error (SE) = standard deviation of distribution of sample means**
>
> $$SE = \frac{\sigma}{\sqrt{n}}$$

Note: Where the *population* standard deviation (σ) is not available, the *sample* standard deviation (s) is often used as an approximation.

> i.e. $SE = \dfrac{s}{\sqrt{n}}$

Of course if the sample were, say, of size 1 then we would be back to the population X and there would be no difference between SD and SE (SD $=$ SE $= \sigma/\sqrt{1} = \sigma$).

However, if the samples were of a size greater than 1, then the samples themselves would tend to *average out* any extreme values of X, so that the distribution of sample means ($\bar{X}$) could be expected to have a smaller dispersion around the population mean (μ) than would the distribution of each item of the population. The *larger* the sample size n, the smaller this dispersion of $\bar{X}$ around μ is likely to be. For example, samples of size 36 taken from the population (X) give an SE for the distribution of sample means ($\bar{X}$) of $\dfrac{\mu}{\sqrt{36}}$ which is *smaller* than the SE had the samples taken from the population only been of size 4, giving $SE = \dfrac{\mu}{\sqrt{4}}$.

6.2.1 Using the *Z* statistic

Because the distribution of sample means is *normal*, we can still use the Z statistic. However, note that we now calculate the Z statistic as:

> $$Z = \frac{\bar{X} - \mu}{\dfrac{\sigma}{\sqrt{n}}}$$

Worked example 6.3

A production line of Electrofit makes electronic components that are normally distributed with a mean weight (μ) of 200 g and a standard deviation (σ) of 9 g. What is the probability of a sample of 36 units having a (sample) mean weight ($\bar{X}$) of 203 g or more?

Solution

Drawing a diagram such as Figure 6.2 can help in solving this type of problem.

$$\mu = 200 \text{ g}$$
$$\sigma = 9 \text{ g}$$

Worked example 6.3 (cont'd)

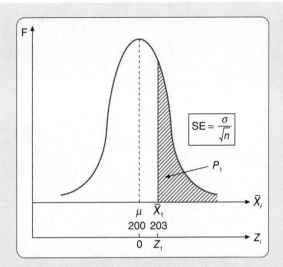

Figure 6.2 Solving Worked Example 6.3

$n =$ sample size $= 36$

$$SE = \frac{\sigma}{\sqrt{n}} = \frac{9}{\sqrt{36}} = 1.5$$

$$Z_1 = \frac{\bar{X} - \mu}{\sigma/\sqrt{n}} = \frac{203 - 200}{1.5} = +2$$

Using the Z tables (Appendix 2, p. 345)

$P_1 = 0.0228$

In other words, there is a 2.28% probability of the sample mean weight of the electronic component being 203 g or more.

6.2.2 Central Limit Theorem

Even if the population is *not* normally distributed, the Central Limit Theorem tells us that if sampling is random and the sample size (n) is > 32, then the distribution of the sample means can be regarded as approximately normally distributed, with mean μ and standard error $\dfrac{\sigma}{\sqrt{n}}$ as shown in Figure 6.3.

We can therefore still use our Z statistic for calculating probabilities for the distribution of sample means even when the population is not itself normally distributed. All we need to do is use a random sampling procedure and make sure that our sample size is large enough (at least 32).

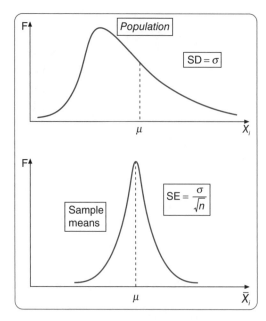

Figure 6.3 Central Limit Theorem: population skewed, but distribution of sample means (Xi) normal, with same mean (μ) and SE $= \dfrac{\sigma}{\sqrt{n}}$

Worked example 6.4

The output of an electronic component has a mean thickness of 4 cm and a standard deviation of 1 cm. If a random sample of 100 components is taken, what is the probability of the sample mean having a thickness of between 3.9 cm and 4.2 cm?

Solution

The Central Limit Theorem applies as random sampling has been adopted and $n > 32$. The distribution of sample means ($\bar{X}$) is therefore normal with mean (μ) = 4 cm and

standard error $\dfrac{\sigma}{\sqrt{n}} = \dfrac{1}{\sqrt{100}} = 0.1$ cm.

Drawing a diagram such as Figure 6.4 can help in solving this type of problem.

$$Z_1 = \frac{\bar{X}_1 - \mu}{\sigma/\sqrt{n}} = \frac{3.9 - 4.0}{0.1} = -1$$

$$P_1 = 0.1587$$

$$A_1 = 0.5000 - 0.1587$$

$$A_1 = \mathbf{0.3413}$$

$$Z_2 = \frac{\bar{X}_2 - \mu}{\sigma/\sqrt{n}} = \frac{4.2 - 4.0}{0.1} = +2$$

Worked example 6.4 (cont'd)

$$P_2 = 0.0228$$

$$A_2 = 0.5000 - 0.0228$$

$$A_2 = \mathbf{0.4772}$$

$$A_1 + A_2 = \mathbf{0.8185}$$

That is, there is an 81.85% chance of the sample mean of 100 components having a thickness of between 3.9 cm and 4.2 cm.

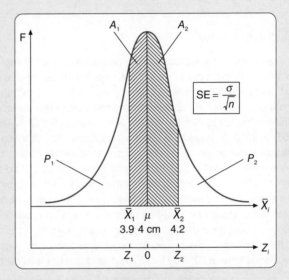

Figure 6.4 Solving Worked Example 6.4

Self-check questions 6.2

Q1. It is thought that the monthly cost of transport to and from work for Electrofit employees is normally distributed with mean £100 a month and standard deviation £10. What is the probability that a *sample* of 100 employees will give a sample mean of:
(a) less than £98 a month;
(b) more than £103 a month?

Q2. A departmental manager at Electrofit believes that the average value of a large population of invoices is £10 with a standard deviation of £2. What is the probability that a *sample* of 36 invoices selected at random will give a sample mean:
(a) below £9.50;
(b) above £10.75;
(c) above £11?

(continued)

Q3. An automatic machine used by Electrofit produces electric batteries with a mean net weight of 340 g and a standard deviation of 8 g, with the weight of the electric car an important factor in fuel efficiency. What is the probability that a *sample* of 64 electric batteries selected at random will have a sample mean:

(a) above 340.75 g;

(b) below 338.5 g;

(c) between 339 g and 342 g?

Note: Answers to Self-Check Questions can be found on the instructor's website, www. pearsoned.co.uk/wall

Did you know?

Chinese wholly owned car making plants have been losing market share in recent years to joint-venture car making plants in China. The latter involve the Chinese car makers paying extensive royalties for technical know-how and the more advanced components used to produce Ford, Hyundai, Volkswagen and other non-Chinese brands. In the past few years Chinese brands have fallen from a 30% share of the Chinese car market in 2009 to less than 26% in 2013. In seeking to test the hypothesis that Chinese cars are less well built and less reliable than foreign joint-venture cars produced in China, two well-regarded Chinese cars were compared with their joint-venture equivalents. A Sedan from Geely and an SUV from Great Wall were road tested against their joint-venture competitors and stripped down by specialist engineers to examine their build quality. Sampling the bodywork and other components from the Chinese and joint-venture cars, it was concluded that while the bodywork was of similar quality, the individual components and the overall build of the Chinese brands fell short of the specifications achieved by the joint-venture competitors, though the gap has narrowed over time. A poll in 2013 by McKinsey found that Chinese car buyers were of the same opinion.

6.3   Confidence intervals

A confidence interval is a range of values within which we can have a certain level of 'confidence' (usually 95% or 99%) that a particular value of a variable will lie. In the context of sampling, we are usually interested in one of two possible *types* of confidence interval.

6.3.1   Confidence interval for the sample mean

This is the range of values around the population mean (μ) within which we can be 95% or 99% confident that a particular sample mean ($\overline{X}$) will lie.

95% confidence interval

In terms of Figure 6.5, we wish to find the values for $\overline{X}_1$ and $\overline{X}_2$, which are 47.5% (0.475) either side of the population mean (μ).

Of course this will imply 2.5% (0.025) in each tail of the distribution for $\overline{X}_i$.

We have already seen (p. 164) how we calculate the Z_1 and Z_2 scores (+1.96 and −1.96 respectively) which will give us 0.025 in each tail. We can then use our formula for the Z statistic (as applied to the distribution of sample means) to calculate $\overline{X}_1$ and $\overline{X}_2$.

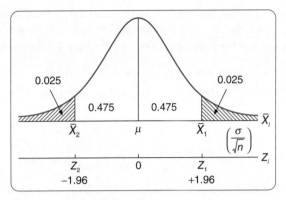

Figure 6.5 Finding the 95% confidence interval for the sample mean ($\bar{X}_i$)

$$Z_1 = \frac{\bar{X}_1 - \mu}{\sigma/\sqrt{n}}$$

i.e. $$1.96 = \frac{\bar{X}_1 - \mu}{\sigma/\sqrt{n}}$$

$$+1.96(\sigma/\sqrt{n}) = \bar{X}_1 - \mu$$

$$\mu + 1.96(\sigma/\sqrt{n}) = \bar{X}_1$$

We can use the same procedure for finding Z_2, except that we insert -1.96 for the Z_2 score. You should then be able to show that:

$$\mu - 1.96(\sigma/\sqrt{n}) = \bar{X}_2$$

The end values of the confidence interval are called the confidence limits. Here $\bar{X}_1$ and $\bar{X}_2$ are the confidence limits for the 95% confidence interval.

In general, the 95% confidence interval for the sample mean can be written as follows.

95% confidence interval for sample mean

$$\bar{X} = \mu \pm 1.96\left(\frac{\sigma}{\sqrt{n}}\right)$$

i.e. $$\bar{X} = \mu \pm 1.96 \, \text{SE}$$

In other words, we can be 95% confident that a single sample mean ($\bar{X}$) will lie within 1.96 standard errors (SE) of the population mean (μ).

99% confidence interval

The approach here is exactly the same as above except that we wish to find the values for the distribution of sample means, namely $\bar{X}_1$ and $\bar{X}_2$, which are 49.5% (0.495) either side of the population mean (μ). Of course this will imply 0.5% (0.005) in each tail of the distribution for $\bar{X}$.

As we shall see in Figure 6.6B below, the only difference will be that our Z_1 and Z_2 scores respectively will be $+2.58$ and -2.58 in order to give 0.005 in each tail.

In general the 99% confidence interval for the sample mean can be written as follows.

99% confidence interval for sample mean

$$\bar{X} = \mu \pm 2.58\left(\frac{\sigma}{\sqrt{n}}\right)$$

i.e.
$$\bar{X} = \mu \pm 2.58 \; SE$$

In other words, we can be 99% confident that a single sample mean ($\bar{X}$) will lie within 2.58 standard errors (SE) of the population mean (μ).

The end values of this 99% confidence interval, $\bar{X}_1$ and $\bar{X}_2$, will be the 99% confidence limits.

Worked example 6.5

A large number of random samples of size 100 are taken from the production line for glass panels which is thought to produce panels with mean thickness 4 cm and standard deviation 1 cm.

Find (a) the 95% and (b) the 99% confidence intervals and associated confidence limits for the sample mean.

Solution

$$\bar{X} = \mu \pm 1.96\left(\frac{\sigma}{\sqrt{n}}\right)$$

(a) $\bar{X} = 4 \pm 1.96\left(\dfrac{\sigma}{\sqrt{100}}\right)$

$\bar{X} = 4 \pm 1.96\,(0.1)$

$\bar{X} = 4 \pm 0.196$

$\bar{X} = 4.196$ and 3.804

The 95% confidence interval is 3.804 cm. to 4.196 cm.

In terms of Figure 6.6A the confidence limits are:

$$\bar{X}_1 = 4.196 \text{ cm.}$$

$$\bar{X}_2 = 3.804 \text{ cm.}$$

(b) $\bar{X} = \mu \pm 2.58\left(\dfrac{\sigma}{\sqrt{n}}\right)$

Note: if you check the Z tables in Appendix 2 (p. 345) you will see that 2.575 is strictly the Z score giving 0.005 in each tail. Rounding up the 5 to the third decimal place gives 2.58.

Worked
example
6.5
(cont'd)

$$\bar{X} = 4 \pm 2.58\left(\frac{1}{\sqrt{100}}\right)$$

$$\bar{X} = 4 \pm 2.58\,(0.1)$$

$$\bar{X} = 4 \pm 0.258$$

The 99% confidence interval is 3.742 cm. to 4.258 cm.

In terms of Figure 6.6B the confidence limits are:

$$\bar{X}_1 = 4.258 \text{ cm.}$$

$$\bar{X}_2 = 3.742 \text{ cm.}$$

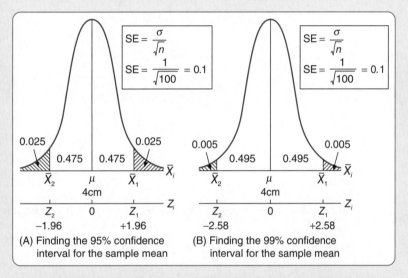

(A) Finding the 95% confidence
interval for the sample mean

(B) Finding the 99% confidence
interval for the sample mean

Figure 6.6 Finding the 95% and 99% confidence intervals for the sample mean

PAUSE FOR THOUGHT 6.4

Can you suggest why the use of confidence intervals for the sample mean might be helpful to Electrofit for quality control purposes?

6.3.2 Confidence interval for the population mean

This is the range of values around the *sample mean* $(\bar{X})$ within which we can be 95% or 99% certain that the *population mean* (μ) will lie.

The previous analysis applies here except that in this case we are likely to be given information about a particular *sample* and asked to find the ranges of values within which we might expect to find the population mean (μ).

It may be that instead of being given information about the *population standard deviation* (σ) we are only given information about the *sample standard deviation* (s). However, we have already noted (p. 186) that we can use s as an approximation to σ in calculating the standard error for the distribution of sample means.

$$\text{i.e. SE} = \frac{\sigma}{\sqrt{n}} = \frac{s}{\sqrt{n}}$$

We have seen that the Z statistic for the distribution of sample means is:

$$\pm Z = \frac{\overline{X} - \mu}{\dfrac{s}{\sqrt{n}}}$$

$$\text{i.e. } \pm Z\left(\frac{s}{\sqrt{n}}\right) = \overline{X} - \mu$$

$$\mu = \overline{X} \pm Z\left(\frac{s}{\sqrt{n}}\right)$$

All we have done is re-arrange the terms to have μ on the left-hand side this time instead of $\overline{X}$.

As before:

95% and 99% confidence intervals for population mean

$\mu = \overline{X} \pm 1.96\left(\dfrac{s}{\sqrt{n}}\right)$ for a 95% confidence interval.

$\mu = \overline{X} \pm 2.58\left(\dfrac{s}{\sqrt{n}}\right)$ for a 99% confidence interval.

Worked example 6.6

Estimate (a) the 95% and (b) the 99% confidence intervals and associated confidence limits for the *population mean* when Electrofit is using the following *sample data*.

Sample mean ($\overline{X}$) = 950 kg

Sample standard deviation (s) = 15 kg

Sample size (n) = 36

Solution

(a)   95% confidence interval and confidence limits for μ

➡

Worked example 6.6 (cont'd)

$$\mu = \bar{X} \pm 1.96\left(\frac{s}{\sqrt{n}}\right)$$

$$\mu = 950 \pm 1.96\left(\frac{15}{\sqrt{36}}\right)$$

$$\mu = 950 \pm 1.96\,(2.5)$$

$$\mu = 950 \pm 4.9$$

$$\mu = 945.1 \text{ kg to } 954.9 \text{ kg}$$

In other words, we can be 95% confident that the population mean (μ) will lie in the interval between 945.1 kg and 954.9 kg, given the sample data provided. These values are the 95% confidence limits for the population mean.

(b)　99% confidence interval and confidence limits for μ

$$\mu = \bar{X} \pm 2.58\left(\frac{s}{\sqrt{n}}\right)$$

$$\mu = 950 \pm 2.58\left(\frac{15}{\sqrt{36}}\right)$$

$$\mu = 950 \pm 2.58\,(2.5)$$

$$\mu = 950 \pm 6.45$$

$$\mu = 943.55 \text{ kg to } 956.45 \text{ kg}$$

We can be 99% confident that the population mean (μ) will lie in the interval between 943.55 kg and 956.45 kg, given the sample data. These values are the 99% confidence limits for the population mean.

BREAK-OUT BOX 6.1

Finding confidence intervals for the population mean

In the Excel sheet Chapter6_Example_1 you will find data on the cost of delivering a sample of 52 consignments of parts to Electrofit to be used for producing electronic components. It is believed that the costs are normally distributed.

Using the sample data you are asked to find the following values for the 'population'.
(a)　Find the 95% confidence interval for the population mean.
(b)　Find the 99% confidence interval for the population mean.

You will need to find the sample mean and the sample standard deviation using the spreadsheet. You can then use the formula to calculate the 95% and 99% confidence intervals and write them down on the spreadsheet. You can then check your answers by pressing the appropriate button.

You can also find a new set of sample data of 52 consignments for practice.

Self-check questions 6.3

Q1. The management of a branch of Electrofit claims that the average weekly earnings of its employees is £550 with a standard deviation of £120. A random sample of 144 employees is taken. Calculate the 95% and 99% confidence intervals for the *sample* mean.

Q2. A random sample of 64 previous purchasers of electric cars was selected and the average expenditure per week on running the car was found to be £61.50 with a (sample) standard deviation of £13.00. Calculate the 95% and 99% confidence intervals for the *population* mean.

Note: Answers to Self-Check Questions can be found on the instructor's website, www.pearsoned.co.uk/wall

---

6.4   Tests of hypotheses: principles and practice

We can use our work on the distribution of sample means and the Central Limit Theorem for testing hypotheses (theories). A hypothesis is an assumption about a situation. We usually want to *test* this assumption against one or more alternative assumptions.

It will be useful at this stage to become familiar with the terminology widely used in this topic area. For simplicity we assume that we are testing a main hypothesis (*null* hypothesis, H_0) against one other hypothesis (*alternative* hypothesis, H_1).

● **Null Hypothesis (H_0):** the hypothesis to be tested.

For example, that the mean thickness of glass panels for the electric car is 4 cm.

$$H_0: \mu = 4 \text{ cm}$$

● **Alternative Hypothesis (H_1):** the hypothesis we wish to accept if we reject the Null Hypothesis.

For example, that the mean thickness of glass panels for the electric car is *not* equal to 4 cm.

$$H_1: \mu \neq 4 \text{ cm}$$

In testing our Null Hypothesis, there are essentially two *types of error* we might wish to avoid.

● **Type 1 error**: rejecting the Null Hypothesis when it is, in fact, true.

● **Type 2 error**: accepting the Null Hypothesis when it is, in fact, false.

Avoiding a Type 1 error is usually the main concern of problems in this topic area. When testing the Null Hypothesis we usually state the *maximum risk* we are willing to take of committing a Type 1 error – that is, of rejecting the Null Hypothesis when it is, in fact, true. This is called the *level of significance* and is typically either 5% (0.05) or 1% (0.01)

Levels of significance

The maximum risk we are willing to take of making a Type 1 error – that is, of rejecting the null hypothesis when it is, in fact, true.

6.4.1 Confidence limits and critical values

If we look back to Figure 6.6 (p. 193) we can usefully illustrate the idea of the level of significance. It is clear that there is a 95% (0.95) chance of any sample mean ($\bar{X}$) lying within 1.96 standard errors (SE) of the true population mean (μ). However, there is still a 5% (0.05) chance of a single sample mean lying *outside* this 95% *confidence interval* even though the population mean really is μ.

Here this 5% (0.05) chance is split evenly to be 2.5% (0.025) in each tail. If the sample mean lies outside the *confidence limits* $\bar{X}_1$ or $\bar{X}_2$ then our decision will be to reject H_0 even though we might be wrong in rejecting H_0. However, the chance of our being wrong is *less than 5%*, since there was a less than 5% chance of actually getting a sample mean $\bar{X}$ outside $\bar{X}_1$ and $\bar{X}_2$ when μ really is the population mean.

These *confidence limits* for the population mean, μ, can therefore be regarded as the *critical values* for tests of hypotheses. In other words, they are the values of $\bar{X}_i$ (or their Z_i equivalents) *outside of which* we are willing to reject the null hypothesis (H_0). In that sense they are the values 'critical' to the decision we are about to take in our test of the null hypothesis (H_0).

> ### Critical values
>
> These are the values of $\bar{X}$ or Z for the sample *outside* of which we are willing to reject the null hypothesis (H_0) at a particular level of significance.

6.4.2 Two- and one-tailed tests

Two-tailed tests

The approach so far has involved a two-tailed test – that is, where we split the risk of being wrong in rejecting the null hypothesis *equally* between each tail of the distribution.

Let us formally set out the Null (H_0) and Alternative (H_1) Hypotheses for a *two-tailed* test. We use our earlier example of thickness of glass panels by way of illustration.

> $$H_0: \mu = 4 \text{ cm}$$
>
> $$H_1: \mu \neq 4 \text{ cm}$$

Since the Alternative Hypothesis (H_1) says $\mu \neq 4$ cm it is clear that we are just as interested in situations where $\mu > 4$ cm as we are in situations where $\mu < 4$ cm.

> ### Two-tailed test
>
> We divide the risk we are willing to take in making a Type 1 error equally between each tail of the distribution.

If we test the Null Hypothesis at a 5% (0.05) level of significance, we place 2.5% (0.025) in each tail. Here we will reject H_0 if we think that $\mu > 4$ cm or if we think that $\mu < 4$ cm.

Acceptance and rejection regions

- The region *within which* we are willing to accept the Null Hypothesis (H_0) we call the *acceptance region*.

- The region *outside which* we are willing to reject the Null Hypothesis (H_0) we call the *rejection region*.

Figure 6.7 displays the acceptance and rejection regions for a two-tailed test, using 5% (0.05) and 1% (0.01) levels of significance.

$\bar{X}_1$ and $\bar{X}_2$ correspond to the **critical values** – that is, the sample means at the boundary between the acceptance and rejection regions for the Null Hypothesis (H_0).

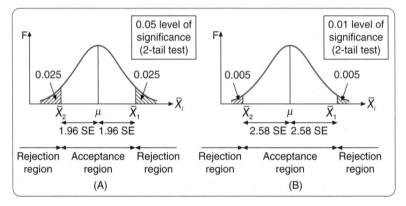

Figure 6.7 Acceptance and rejection regions for the Null Hypothesis (H_0): two-tailed tests at (A) 5% (0.05) and (B) 1% (0.01) levels of significance

Worked example 6.7

Find the critical values for a two-tailed test at the 5% (0.05) level of significance for the earlier example of glass panels, mean (μ)=4 cm, standard error $\left(\dfrac{\sigma}{\sqrt{n}}\right)$ = 0.1 cm.

Solution

$$\mu \pm 1.96 \text{ SE} = \text{critical values}$$

$$4 \pm 1.96 \,(0.1) = \text{critical values}$$

$$3.804 \text{ cm} = \bar{X}_2; 4.196 \text{ cm} = \bar{X}_1$$

We can be 95% certain of getting a sample mean in the *acceptance region* 3.804 cm to 4.196 cm if the true (population) mean is 4 cm.

If, however, we get a sample measurement *outside* these critical values (i.e. in the *rejection region*), then we can reject H_0: $\mu = 4$ cm with less than a 5% (0.05) chance of being wrong. This is because there is a less than 5% (0.05) chance of $\bar{X}$ being outside these critical values if H_0: $\mu = 4$ cm is true.

Find the critical values for a two-tailed test at the 1% (0.01) level of significance for the earlier example of glass panels for electric cars, mean (μ) = 4 cm, standard error $\left(\frac{\sigma}{\sqrt{n}}\right) = 0.1$ cm.

Solution

This time we place half of 1% (0.005) in each tail, giving a Z score of ± 2.58.

$$\mu \pm 2.58 \text{ SE} = \text{critical values}$$
$$4 \pm 2.58\,(0.1) = \text{critical values}$$
$$3.742 \text{ cm} = \bar{X}_2;\ 4.258 \text{ cm} = \bar{X}_1$$

We can be 99% certain of getting a sample mean in the *acceptance region* 3.742 cm to 4.258 cm if the true (population) mean is 4 cm.

If, however, we get a sample measurement *outside* these critical values (i.e. in the *rejection region*), then we can reject H$_0$: $\mu = 4\,cm$ with less than a 1% (0.01) chance of being wrong. This is because there is a less than 1% chance of $\bar{X}$ being outside these critical values if H$_0$: $\mu = 4$ cm is true.

BREAK-OUT BOX 6.2

Testing hypotheses

Automatic example generator

In the Excel sheet Chapter6_Example_2 you will find data on the production line for cars which seeks to provide a given distance between window and door. The size of this gap is important for fitting the Electrofit components during the car assembly process.

The Null Hypothesis is that the mean gap is 2 mm.

The Alternative Hypothesis is that the mean gap is not 2 mm.

You are asked to test the Null Hypothesis at a 5% level of significance.

You will find some guidance on the spreadsheet about what you will need to find from the sample data. You can use this data to test the hypothesis given on the spreadsheet.

When you have done this for the sample data shown on the spreadsheet, you can press the button identified and find another set of sample data to use in testing the hypothesis.

One-tailed test

Here we do *not* split the risk of being wrong in rejecting the Null Hypothesis equally between each tail of the distribution. Here we are only concerned with *one side* (and therefore *one tail*) of the distribution when testing our Null Hypothesis (H$_0$) against an Alternative Hypothesis (H$_1$). We therefore place *all* the risk of making a Type 1 error in one tail.

> #### One-tailed test
>
> We place the risk we are willing to take in making a Type 1 error in one tail of the distribution.

Let us formally set out the Null (H$_0$) and Alternative (H$_1$) Hypotheses for a **one-tailed** test. We again use our earlier example of thickness of glass panels by way of illustration.

Either

$$H_0: \mu = 4 \text{ cm}$$
$$H_1: \mu > 4 \text{ cm}$$

In testing H_0 against H_1 we are only interested in rejecting H_0 (i.e. accepting H_1) if the sample means suggest a true (population) mean *greater than* 4 cm.

Or

$$H_0: \mu = 4 \text{ cm}$$
$$H_1: \mu < 4 \text{ cm}$$

In testing H_0 against H_1 we are only interested in rejecting H_0 (i.e. accepting H_1) if the sample mean suggests a true (population) mean *less than* 4 cm.

Acceptance and rejection regions

Figure 6.8 indicates the relevant acceptance and rejection regions for a one-tailed test at 5% (0.05) and 1% (0.01) levels of significance. Remember, the Z scores are calculated using the Z tables (Appendix 2, p. 344) and are used to give the area in the respective tails.

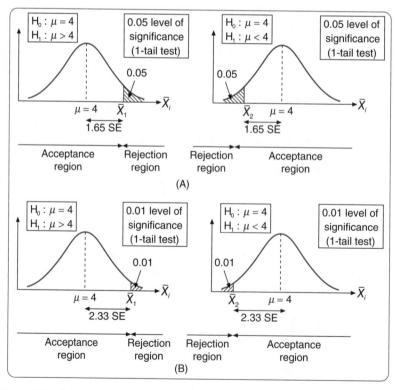

Figure 6.8 Acceptance and rejection regions for the Null Hypotheses (H_0): one-tailed tests at (A) 5% (0.05) and (B) 1% (0.01) levels of significance

Worked example 6.9	Look again at Figure 6.8A (p. 200). Find the critical values for a one-tailed test at the 5% (0.05) level of significance for the earlier example of glass panels, mean $(\mu)=4$ cm, standard error $\left(\dfrac{\sigma}{\sqrt{n}}\right) = 0.1$ cm

Solution

$$\overline{X}_1 = \mu + 1.65 \text{ SE}$$
$$\overline{X}_1 = 4 + 1.65 \,(0.1)$$
$$\overline{X}_1 = 4.165 \text{ cm.}$$
$$\overline{X}_2 = \mu - 1.65 \text{ SE}$$
$$\overline{X}_2 = 4 - 1.65(0.1)$$
$$\overline{X}_2 = 3.835 \text{ cm}$$

If the sample mean $\overline{X}$ lies outside these critical values then we would be outside the acceptance region and in the rejection region.

- For H_0: $\mu = 4$ cm

    H_1: $\mu > 4$ cm

    Reject H_0 if $\overline{X} > 4.165$ cm

- For H_0: $\mu = 4$ cm

    H_1: $\mu < 4$ cm

    Reject H_0 if $\overline{X} < 3.835$ cm

PAUSE FOR THOUGHT 6.5

Can you suggest a number of hypotheses that Electrofit might be interested in testing?

6.4.3 Seven-step plan for tests of hypotheses

In this section we develop a simple seven-step plan for tackling all problems involving tests of hypotheses. This seven-step plan draws on the ideas already presented.

However, before we outline these steps let us select *one* of two alternative approaches to finding critical values.

Critical values: Z scores or sample mean values

As we saw in Figure 6.8 (p. 200), the critical values can be expressed in terms of the *sample means*, $\overline{X}_1$ and $\overline{X}_2$ respectively. However, they can just as easily be expressed in terms of the *Z scores* – that is, the number of standard errors from μ, the population mean.

In Figure 6.9, α (alpha) is the *level of significance* at which the test is conducted. The *Z scores* are shown for the respective *critical values*. These *Z* scores can be said to depend on both the level of significance and on whether the test is one- or two-tailed.

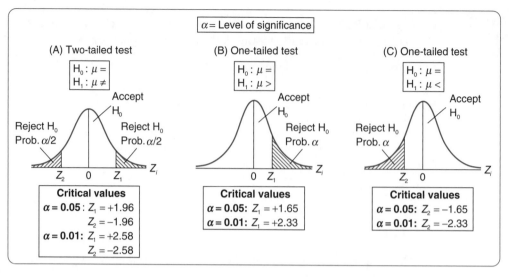

Figure 6.9 Using the Z scores for the critical values: (A) two-tailed test; (B) one-tailed test; (C) one-tailed test

In this approach we calculate the *Z score* using the *sample data* provided. If the *Z* score for the sample data lies *outside* the relevant *Z* critical values, then the decision rule will be to *reject* the Null Hypothesis (H_0).

It will be useful at this stage to go through a worked example before using this to illustrate our seven-step plan for testing hypotheses.

Worked example 6.10

It is thought that the average wage for a branch of Electrofit is £130 a day with a standard deviation of £30. A sample of 100 employees finds the sample average to be £123.

Solution

Test $H_0: \mu = £130$

$H_1: \mu \neq £130$

using a 5% level of significance.

This is a two-tailed test since the alternative hypothesis (H_1) has been expressed as $\neq$.

If the *Z* score if calculated for the sample data and found to be outside the *Z critical value*, then reject H_0.

Drawing a diagram such as Figure 6.10 can help in solving such problems.

Here $\overline{X}_1 = 123$,

gives $Z_1 = \dfrac{\overline{X}_1 - \mu}{\sigma/\sqrt{n}}$

$Z_1 = \dfrac{123 - 130}{30/\sqrt{100}}$

Worked
example
6.10
(cont'd)

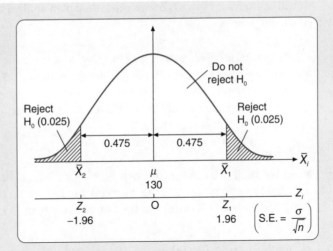

Figure 6.10 Solving Worked Example 6.10

i.e. $Z_1 = \dfrac{123 - 130}{3}$

$Z_1 = \dfrac{-7}{3}$

$Z_1 = -2.33$

Our Z score is *outside* the Z critical value of -1.96, so we reject H_0.

We can now formally set out our seven-*step plan* for testing a hypothesis, using this example to illustrate each step.

Example

Step 1. State hypotheses
$H_0: \mu = £130$
$H_1: \mu \neq £130$

Step 2. State significance level
5% (0.05)
Note: A sketch diagram will usually help here (e.g. Figure 6.9A for $\alpha = 0.05$)

Step 3. State critical values
$Z_1 = +1.96$
$Z_2 = -1.96$

Step 4. Calculate the Z score for the *sample*
$Z = -2.33$

Step 5. Compare this Z sample score with the Z critical values
Here $Z = -2.33$ is *outside*
$Z_2 = 1.96$

Step 6. Come to a conclusion
Reject H_0

Step 7. Put your conclusion in words
The sample evidence does *not* support the Null Hypothesis at a 5% level of significance

It will be useful for you to see this seven-step plan applied to a couple of examples, before trying it out yourself.

Worked example 6.11

A manager of an electric battery charging centre for Electrofit believes the average amount spent per week on recharging batteries to be £25.00 per owner of an electric vehicle. A random sample of 100 owners of electric vehicles found an average expenditure on such supplements of £24.00 with a standard deviation of £4.0. Test the manager's belief at a 5% level of significance.

Solution

Note: We shall use a *two-tailed* test here, since any divergence from £25.00 (above or below) would invalidate the manager's belief. Since only the sample mean (s) is available, we use this instead of the population mean (σ) in calculating the standard error.

Step 1. $H_0: \mu = £25.00$

$H_1: \mu \neq £25.00$

Step 2. 5% (0.05) level of significance

Step 3. Critical values for Z: ± 1.96

Drawing a diagram such as Figure 6.11 can help in solving such problems.

Step 4. For sample data

$$Z = \frac{\overline{X} - \mu}{s/\sqrt{n}} = \frac{24.00 - 25.00}{4.00/\sqrt{100}}$$

$$Z = \frac{-1.00}{4.00/10} = \frac{-1.00}{0.4} = -2.50$$

Step 5. -2.50 is outside -1.96

Step 6. Reject Null Hypothesis (H_0)

Step 7. Evidence does not support the manager's belief that average spending on recharging batteries is £25.00 per week.

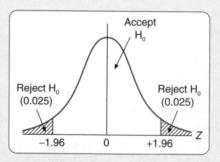

Figure 6.11 Solving Worked Example 6.11

Worked example 6.12

The expected mean diameter of a batch of cables is 2 cm. A quality control inspector of Electrofit takes a sample of 64 cables and finds that the sample has a mean diameter of 1.94 cm and a standard deviation of 0.4 cm. Test whether the manufacturing process is now producing cables with a smaller diameter than previously at a 1% level of significance.

Solution

Note: We shall use a *one-tailed* test here, since our concern is that the manufacturing process is producing *smaller* diameter cables than claimed. Again we use sample standard deviation (s) as an approximation for the population standard deviation (σ). Our test is at the 1% level of significance this time; that is, we are less willing than in Worked Example 6.11 to take the risk of rejecting the Null Hypothesis (H_0) when it is in fact true.

Step 1. H_0: $\mu = 2.00$ cm

H_1: $\mu < 2.00$ cm

Step 2. 1% (0.01) level of significance

Step 3. Critical value for Z: -2.33

Drawing a diagram such as Figure 6.12 can help in solving such problems.

Step 4. For sample data

$$Z = \frac{\bar{X} - \mu}{s/\sqrt{n}} = \frac{1.94 - 2.00}{0.4/\sqrt{64}}$$

$$Z = \frac{-0.06}{0.4/8} = \frac{-0.06}{0.05} = -1.2$$

Step 5. -1.2 is *inside* -1.96

Step 6. Accept Null Hypothesis (H_0)

Step 7. There is insufficient evidence from the sample data to reject the initial hypothesis that the manufacturing process is still producing cables of diameter of 2 cm. We would be taking more risk than we are willing to take if we were to accept the alternative hypothesis that the cables are now being produced with a diameter of less than 2 cm.

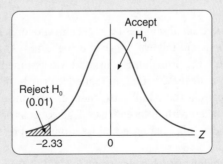

Figure 6.12 Solving Worked Example 6.12

You can now test your familiarity with this *seven step* approach with the following Self-Check Questions. There are also more questions for practice (Review Questions) at the end of this chapter.

PAUSE FOR THOUGHT 6.6

What circumstances might lead Electrofit to apply a lower level of significance for testing various hypotheses?

Self-check questions 6.4

Q1. A firm manufactures light bulbs for some of the electronic components of Electrofit and the sales manager claims that tests have proved that the average life of these bulbs is 1,000 hours. Electrofit wishes to buy some of these light bulbs but before doing so wishes to check that the claim about their average life is correct. It therefore takes a sample of 36 bulbs and tests them and finds that the average life of the bulbs in the sample is 940 hours with a standard deviation of 126 hours. Is the manufacture's claim justified? Test at both a 5% (0.05) and a 1% (0.01) level of significance.

Q2. A manager of a process used to produce electronic components for Electrofit claims that the mean running time of machines is 14 hours a day. A random sample of 64 machines shows that their mean running time is only 13 hours 20 minutes, with a standard deviation of 3 hours. Test the manager's assertion at the 5% significance level.

Note: Keep the units the same throughout (i.e. hours or minutes).

Q3. Electrofit uses a machine that produces electronic components whose lifetimes have a mean of 1,000 hours and a standard deviation of 140 hours. A new technique is now introduced into their production. A *sample* of 49 components gives a mean of 1,040 hours. Has the new technique produced longer-lasting components? Test at a 5% level of significance.

Note: Answers to Self-Check Questions can be found on the instructor's website, www.pearsoned.co.uk/wall

---

6.5   Student *t*-distribution

For repeated *small* samples ($n < 32$) it is no longer accurate to assume that the distribution of sample means follows a *normal* distribution. As a result we can no longer use the *Z* tables to work out the probabilities. Instead, we assume that the distribution of sample means follows the *student t-distribution* (called 't-distribution' for simplicity). This distribution actually changes as the sample size changes. We must therefore apply different probabilities to samples taken with different sizes. The concept of *degrees of freedom* (v) captures this idea, where the number of degrees of freedom is expressed as $v = n - 1$, where n is sample size (see Figure 6.13).

We can illustrate this idea using 2.5% (0.025) in the tail of the *t*-distribution.

v (n − 1)	0.025
1	12.706
2	4.303
5	2.571
10	2.228
30	2.042

Notice that the *critical values* (i.e. number of *standard errors* from the mean) vary depending on the value of v (=$n − 1$). So with a sample size (n) of 3 and v (= $n − 1$) of 2, we must be 4.303 standard error from the mean to get 2.5% (0.025) in either tail. However, with a sample size (n) of 11 and v (= $n − 1$) of 10, we need only be 2.228 standard errors from the mean to get 2.5% (0.025) in either tail.

Drawing a diagram such as Figure 6.14 can help in solving such problems.

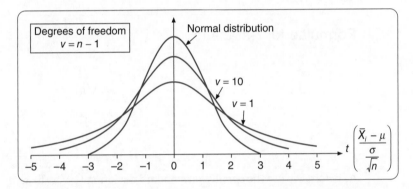

Figure 6.13 Showing how the distribution of sample means $(\overline{X}_i)$ expressed in terms of standard errors (t) takes different shapes depending on the number of degrees of freedom, ($v = n − 1$)

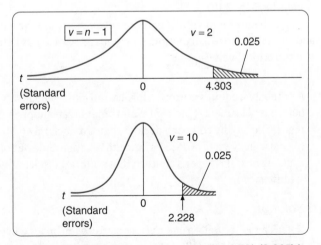

Figure 6.14 Showing how the t score for 2.5% (0.025) in the right-hand tail will vary depending on the number of degrees of freedom, $v = (n − 1)$

6.5.1 Critical values

We express the *critical values* for the *t*-distribution as $t_{\alpha,v}$

where α = level of significance shown in the tables

v = number of degrees of freedom

So for $\alpha = 0.025$, and $v = 3$ in the table above, we can write.

$$t_{\alpha,v} = t_{0.025,\,2} = 4.303$$

and

$$t_{\alpha,v} = t_{0.025,\,10} = 2.228$$

6.5.2 *t*-statistic

We calculate the ***t*-statistic** or ***t*-score** exactly as we did for Z – that is, we find the number of *standard errors* from the mean.

Formulae for *t*-statistic

$$t = \frac{\bar{X} - \mu}{\sigma/\sqrt{n}}$$

$$\text{or } t = \frac{\bar{X} - \mu}{s/\sqrt{n}}$$

As before, we use the *population* standard deviation (σ) or the *sample* standard deviation (s) for calculating t, depending on the information we are given in the question.

6.5.3 *t*-tables

The full *t*-tables to be used in finding the appropriate critical values can be found in Appendix 5 (p. 348).

It will be useful to go through our seven-step plan for a problem involving *small samples* and therefore the *t*-distribution. Our steps are exactly as before, except in the way we calculate the critical values.

Worked example 6.13

A company requires batteries for its transport vehicles that last on average 20,000 km before replacement. Electrofit claims that it can supply batteries that meet this requirement. The buying company decides to test that claim and buys 16 batteries and finds that they last an average of 19,500 km with a standard deviation of 1,200 km. Test Electrofit's claim against the buyer's concern that batteries last less than 20,000 km, at a 5% level of significance.

Solution

Note: This is arguably a *one-tail* test because the buyer will only be worried if the batteries fall *below* the claim of 20,000 km. The sample size is less than 32, so it is a *t*-test example. We use s rather than σ in calculating standard errors.

Worked example 6.13 (cont'd)

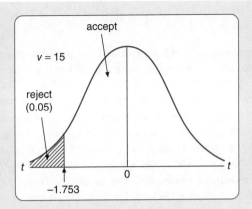

Figure 6.15 Solving Worked Example 6.13

Drawing a diagram such as Figure 6.15 can help in solving such problems.

Step 1. $H_0: \mu = 20{,}000$ km

$H_1: \mu < 20{,}000$ km

Step 2. $\alpha = 0.05$

Step 3. $v = n - 1$

$= 16 - 1$

$= 15$

$t_{0.05,\,15} = -1.753$

Step 4.

$$t = \frac{\bar{X} - \mu}{\sigma/\sqrt{n}} \quad \text{(here } s \text{ for } \sigma \text{)}$$

$$= \frac{19{,}500 - 20{,}000}{1{,}200/\sqrt{16}}$$

$$= \frac{-500}{300} = -1.667$$

Step 5. $-1.667 > -1.753$

Step 6.   Accept H_0

$\mu = 20{,}000$ km

Step 7.   There is insufficient evidence for the buying company to conclude that the batteries perform less well than is claimed.

Self-check questions 6.5

Q1. It is believed that the mean time that owners of electric cars actually use them per week is 18 hours. A random sample of 25 owners of electric cars gives a mean time of 18.6 hours with a standard deviation of 1.02 hours. Test the view that the mean time spent driving electric cars per week is greater than 18 hours at the 5% significance level.

Q2. Suppose we want to test, on the basis of a random sample of eight electric cars, whether the average content of non-biodegradable materials is less than 15%. The sample mean for the electric cars is found to be 14.3% with a sample standard deviation of 0.96%. What conclusion would you come to at the 1% significance level?

Q3. Workers on a production line for Electrofit produce an average of 154 faulty items per shift. A training package has been developed and tested on a random sample of 20 workers. The 20 workers in the sample produce an average of 141 faulty items with a standard deviation of 12 items. The training package will be applied to all workers only if it can be shown that it improves worker performance. Based on the sample should Electrofit proceed with the programme? Test at the 1% level of significance.

Note: Answers to Self-Check Questions can be found on the instructor's website, www.pearsoned.co.uk/wall

6.6 Chi-squared test

The chi-squared (χ^2) test looks not at an *individual* item of data (i.e. a single parameter) but at the *whole* distribution. As a result it is known as a *non-parametric* test, unlike the Z and t-tests which are known as parametric tests, with their focus on a single parameter such as a sample mean which is then compared with an allegedly known value of a parameter from the population.

In non-parametric tests, such as the chi-squared test, the Null Hypothesis (H_0) and Alternative Hypothesis (H_1) are defined in terms of the distribution as a whole. Usually we test:

H_0: the distribution as a whole is evenly (equally) spread.

H_1: the distribution as a whole is *not* evenly (equally) spread.

6.6.1 χ^2 statistic

The χ^2 statistic or score makes use of actually *observed values* (O) which are then contrasted with the *expected values* (E) we should anticipate if the Null Hypothesis (H_0) is in fact true. It is defined as:

$$\chi^2 = \sum_{i=1}^{n}\left[\frac{(O - E)^2}{E}\right]$$

where O = observed values

E = expected values (if Null Hypothesis, H_0, is true)

n = number of observations in the sample

The χ^2 distribution follows the pattern shown in Figure 6.16.

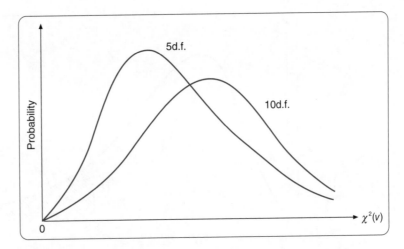

Figure 6.16 χ^2 varies with v, where v is the number of degrees of freedom

Note that, as with the t-distribution, the χ^2 distribution actually changes as the sample size (n) changes. We therefore again make use of the idea of *degrees of freedom* (v) (see p. 206), with the number of degrees of freedom expressed as $v = n - 1$, where n corresponds to the number of observations in the sample.

Of course if the distribution as a whole *is* evenly spread throughout, as our Null Hypothesis (H_0) suggests, then the *observed values* (O) would exactly equal the *expected values* (E). It follows that ($O - E$) in the numerator of the χ^2 statistic will equal zero for every one of the n observations in the sample, and summing the squares of zero will still give us zero for χ^2. In other words, $\chi^2 = 0$ will correspond to a *perfectly evenly spread* distribution. The less evenly spread the distribution, the greater the discrepancy between any observation (O) and its expected value (E), when the latter is calculated on the assumption that the distribution *is* evenly spread (i.e. H_0 is true).

6.6.2 Critical values

The critical values are those values for χ^2 outside of which we are willing to *reject* the Null Hypothesis (H_0) that the distribution is evenly spread. In this case we reject H_0, where the observations (O) are sufficiently different from the expected values (E) we should anticipate if the distribution really is evenly spread.

- As we have already noted, the χ^2 distribution will vary with the *number of degrees of freedom* (v), where $v = n - 1$. It follows that the critical values will therefore vary with v.

- The *level of significance* (α), as before, represents the maximum risk we are willing to take in rejecting the Null Hypothesis (H_0) when it is in fact true.

The critical values for the χ^2 distribution can therefore be expressed as:

$$\chi^2_{\alpha, v}$$

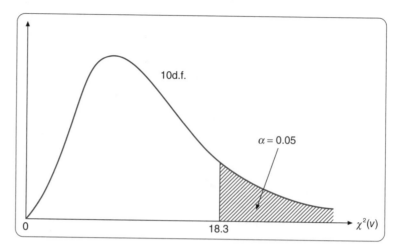

Figure 6.17 Finding the critical value of χ^2

where α = level of significance

$\quad\quad v$ = number of degrees of freedom (n − 1)

All tests involving the χ^2 distribution are one-tailed tests.

Appendix 6 (p. 350) gives a full table of critical values for a given level of significance (α) and a given number of degrees of freedom (v). For example, as shown in Figure 6.17, for a 5% level of significance (α = 0.05) and 10 degrees of freedom (v = 10), we have a critical value of 18.3 for χ^2. In other words, if, from our sample data, we calculate the χ^2 statistic as over 18.3, then we will reject the Null Hypothesis (H_0) that the data is evenly spread. There will then be less than a 5% chance of being wrong in deciding to reject the Null Hypothesis.

<table>
<tr><td>Worked
example
6.14</td><td>Over a year Electrofit experiences 100 computer breakdowns. These are classified into the four time slots indicated below.</td></tr>
</table>

Time of computer breakdowns	Number of breakdowns
9.00 a.m.–11.00 a.m.	22
11.00 a.m.–1.00 p.m.	18
1.00 p.m.–3.00 p.m.	26
3.00 p.m.–5.00 p.m.	34

Test the hypothesis that computer breakdowns are spread evenly through the working day, using a 5% (0.05) level of significance.

Worked
example
6.14
(cont'd)

Solution

We can follow the same seven steps in testing a hypothesis as for the Z and t-distributions.

Step 1. H_0: breakdowns evenly spread

H_1: breakdowns not evenly spread

Step 2. $\alpha = 0.05$

Step 3. $v = n - 1$

$= 4 - 1$

$= 3$

$\chi^2_{0.05,3} = 7.81$

Step 4.   Calculate the χ^2 statistic from the sample data

$$\chi^2 = \sum_{i=1}^{4} \frac{(O - E)^2}{E}$$

O	E	(O − E)	(O − E)²	$\frac{(O - E)^2}{E}$
22	25	−3	9	0.36
18	25	−7	49	1.96
26	25	+1	1	0.04
34	25	+9	81	3.24
				5.60

Note: If H_0 is true, then we expect 25 breakdowns to occur in each of the 4 time periods of 2 hours.

$\chi^2 = 5.60$

Step 5. $5.60 < 7.81$

Step 6.   Accept H_0

Step 7.   Cannot reject H_0 that computer breakdowns are evenly spread over time. In other words, there is not enough evidence to conclude that the computer breakdowns that occur at different times are due to anything other than chance.

6.6.3   Data shown in table or matrix form

Often the data is shown, or can be represented, in table or matrix form. As we shall see from Worked Example 6.15 we follow exactly the same procedures as above, with one difference which relates to calculating the *number of degrees of freedom* (v).

> ## For data in tabular form
>
> $$v = (r - 1) \times (c - 1)$$
>
> where v = number of degrees of freedom
>
> r = number of rows in table
>
> c = number of columns in table

As we shall also see in Worked Example 6.15, we can devise a useful formula for calculating the *expected values* (E) when data is presented in tabular form.

> ## For data in tabular form
>
> $$E = \text{row total} \times \frac{\text{column total}}{\text{grand total}}$$
>
> where E = expected value

Worked example 6.15

A survey of job satisfaction was undertaken for systems analysts and computer programmers employed by a major manufacturer of motor vehicles, including electric cars, at its European headquarters. A questionnaire asked 100 workers of each type whether or not they were satisfied with their job. The results are shown below.

Type of employee	Satisfied	Not satisfied	Totals
Systems analysts	63	37	100
Computer programmers	53	47	100
Totals	116	84	200

Is there a significant relationship between the type of employee and job satisfaction?

Solution

This is a χ^2 test since we are testing the Null Hypothesis (H_0) of no association between type of employee and job satisfaction against the Alternative Hypothesis (H_1) that there is such an association. We are using *observations* from sample data (200 employees) to help test H_0.

If 'everything is in proportion' and there is no association, then H_0 is true. We should then *expect* that the *overall proportion* of satisfied employees should be reflected in the totals for each type of employee claiming to be satisfied. We return to this idea below when working out the 'expected' values (E).

Worked example 6.15 (cont'd)

Sometimes tabular data is given with row and column totals provided. If not, it will help if you insert such row and column totals. Note also that the sum of the respective row and column totals is referred to as the 'grand total', here the 200 employees involved in the survey.

We can follow our usual seven steps, but remember to apply the procedures already mentioned for data in tabular form.

Step 1. H_0: No association between type of employee and job satisfaction (i.e. responses are in proportion)

H_1: Association between type of employee and job satisfaction (i.e. responses are not in proportion)

Step 2. $\alpha = 0.05$ (our choice as not specified in the question)

Step 3. $v = (r - 1) \times (c - 1)$

$v = (2 - 1) \times (2 - 1)$

$v = 1$

Note: when using tabular data, do *not* count the row total or column total when calculating v.

$$\chi^2_{a,v} = \chi^2_{0.05,1} = 3.84$$

Step 4.   Calculate the χ^2 statistic from the sample data.

$$\chi^2 = \sum_{i=1}^{4} \frac{(O - E)^2}{E}$$

where O = observations

E = expected values if H_0

(no association) is true.

Here we can apply our formula to work out expected values.

$$E = \text{row total} \times \frac{\text{column total}}{\text{grand total}}$$

$$E \text{ (systems analysts satisfied)} = 100 \times \frac{116}{200} = 58$$

$$E \text{ (systems analysts not satisfied)} = 100 \times \frac{84}{200} = 42$$

$$E \text{ (computer programmers satisfied)} = 100 \times \frac{116}{200} = 58$$

$$E \text{ (computer programmers not satisfied)} = 100 \times \frac{84}{200} = 42$$

Worked example 6.15 (cont'd)

The formula simply helps us impose the *overall proportions* of satisfied/not satisfied on the totals for systems analysts and computer programmers respectively. The resulting values tell us what to expect if the Null Hypothesis H_0 (no association) is true.

We can express our table of expected values (E) as

	Expected values	
	Satisfied	**Not satisfied**
Systems analysts	58	42
Computer programmers	58	42

We can now calculate χ^2, as follows.

O	E	$(O - E)$	$(O - E)^2$	$\dfrac{(O - E)^2}{E}$
63	58	+5	25	$25/58 = 0.431$
37	42	−5	25	$25/42 = 0.596$
53	58	−5	25	$25/58 = 0.431$
47	42	+5	25	$25/42 = \underline{0.596}$
				2.054

$$\chi^2 = 2.054$$

Step 5. $2.054 < 3.84$

Step 6.   Accept H_0

Step 7.   No association between type of employee and job satisfaction. There is not enough evidence to conclude that these different types of employees have different views as to job satisfaction.

Self-check question 6.6

Using the following observations recorded by a researcher, check if the assumption of no relation between lung disease and asbestos exposure in brake-pad production can be accepted at the 5% level of significance.

Observation table

	Recorded asbestos exposure	No recorded asbestos exposure	Totals
Lung disease	200	200	400
No lung disease	150	450	600
Totals	350	650	1,000

Note: Answers to Self-Check Questions can be found on the instructor's website, www.pearsoned.co.uk/wall

REVIEW QUESTIONS

R6.1. The manageress of a restaurant at Electrofit headquarters claims that her weekly turnover is £3,130 with a standard deviation of £115 per week. If the turnover is normally distributed and a random sample of 25 weekly turnover figures is recorded, what is the probability that the sample mean will be
   (a) less than £3,100;
   (b) greater than £3,190;
   (c) between £3,110 and £3,180?

R6.2. The mean salary of graduates employed by Electrofit, one year after graduating, is £18,500 with a standard deviation of £1,500. What is the probability that a sample of 49 of these had a mean salary of at least £21,000?

R6.3. A sample of 49 observations is taken from a normal population. The sample mean is 58, and the standard deviation of the sample is 10. Determine the 95% and the 99% confidence interval for the population mean.

R6.4. The Durable Components Company supplies Electrofit with recharging plugs for electric vehicles. The plugs need to withstand certain pressures. A sample of 64 plugs is taken from the production line and tested for the pressure they can withstand before they distort. The test results from the sample of 64 plugs suggest an average pressure of 39.8 Pascals before distortion with a standard deviation of 6 Pascals.
   (a) Construct a 99% confidence interval for the population mean.
   (b) Construct a 90% confidence interval for the population mean.
   (c) How large should the sample be if the company want a 99% confidence interval for the population mean with a margin of error of 2 Pascals of pressure?

R6.5. A car manufacturer states that its new model does 32.5 miles per gallon (mpg). A recent independent study of 50 of the new cars showed a mean mpg of only 30.4 with a standard deviation of 5.3 mpg. Test the view that the manufacturer's claim is too high using a 1% level of significance.

R6.6. The expected life of a car engine in an electric car is claimed to be 90,000 miles. A sample of 190 electric cars gives a mean life of 96,700 miles with a standard deviation of 37,500 miles. Test whether the electric cars are lasting longer than expected at the 1% level of significance.

R6.7. A machine used by Electrofit is set to cut metal rods to a length of 8.75 cm. It is felt by the operator that the rods are too short. The hypothesis is to be tested at the 1% significance level from the following sample of rods: 9.0, 8.5, 8.7, 8.4, 8.6, 8.3, 8.5 and 8.8. What conclusion can be drawn on the basis of the sample?

R6.8. A mail order firm that is used by Electrofit to sell electronic components claims that new procedures enable it to dispatch orders more quickly than previously. Records show that the previous average delay was 20 days. A random sample of 16 orders using the new procedure shows a delay time of 18 days with a sample standard deviation of 2.5 days. Is the claim made for the new procedures supported at the 5% level?

R6.9. A recruitment agency used by Electrofit to staff its Cambridge headquarters claims that four-bedroom detached houses near the Cambridge Science Park can be rented for £1,500 per calendar month (pcm) on average. A random sample of 20 houses gives a mean rental of £1,700 pcm for this type of property with a sample standard deviation of £290 pcm. Test the agency's claim at the 10% significance level.

Note: Answers to Review Questions can be found on the instructor's website, www.pearsoned.co.uk/wall

Further practice

You can find more questions (with solutions) on sampling and tests of hypotheses on the instructor's website, www.pearsoned.co.uk/wall.

Spreadsheets: video guide

You can also find a step-by-step account that takes you through the actual use of a spreadsheet when solving the type of problems you have encountered in this chapter. Go to the instructor's website, www.pearsoned.co.uk/wall.

PART THREE

Maturity stage of product life cycle

A number of quantitative techniques can be used to 'model' the future trajectory of key variables of interest to the business, whether on the demand or supply side. Such techniques are, of course, important throughout the product life cycle, but are particularly so when seeking to extract further efficiencies or additional sources of revenue as the product approaches its maturity stage, with other competitors present and active in the key markets. A whole range of initiatives for identifying the level of output and appropriate prices for maximising revenue or profit, subject to various constraints, or for minimising costs, will be reviewed and evaluated.

Chapter 7 uses the highly competitive retail sector to review the application of *linear* (straight line) models. The retail sector is facing many challenges, not least those stemming from technical change (e.g. online shopping) and from constrained high-street demand (e.g. national austerity programmes!). Linear models are first used to identify 'break-even' situations in which the minimum level of output or activity is identified that must be reached if all costs are to be covered. Attention then turns to finding solutions to situations in which maximum or minimum values are important to the business. The technique of linear programming is applied to identify price, output or factor input decisions that will help maximise profit or revenue, or minimise costs.

Chapter 8 reviews the use of *non-linear* models to evaluate business decision making in the 'media' sector, in which established businesses such as publishing, newspapers and terrestrial television are under constant challenge from both technical change and innovative new entrants to these established markets. We review various techniques to help the business find *turning points*, whether maxima or minima, when non-linear relationships exist between the variables to be modelled.

Chapter 9 explores the contribution of a management consultancy firm that uses data analysis techniques to plan projects for completion within specified time and cost constraints. The projects may involve infrastructure (e.g. stadia), events (e.g. Olympic Games) or processes (e.g. constructing integrated supply chains that may extend beyond national boundaries). While project planning is important at all stages of the product life cycle, including start-up, the effective management of larger and more complex projects requires appropriate project management techniques, which are especially important for large, more mature businesses.

Chapter 7

Business modelling
Linear relationships

Introduction

In the first part of this chapter we concentrate on how the retail sector can use straight line (*linear*) relationships to resolve various business-related problems. In the next chapter we move on to *non-linear* relationships and their application.

We have already noted some of the characteristics of linear relationships involving intercept and gradient in Chapter 4 when we calculated the simple linear least squares line and used it for forecasting. The characteristics of linear relationships are also considered in more detail in Appendix 1 (p. 334). Here we assume that the key relationships for revenue, cost and profit can, for all practical purposes, be regarded as linear. We then use this assumption to find the volume or value of output that will be required to break even and to cover all costs, whether for an individual retailer or for a manager of a product range in a superstore such as Tesco or Sainsbury's. We also use our linear assumption to find the volume or value of output that will maximise revenue or profit, or minimise costs, subject to a set of constraints involving the resources available (e.g. land, labour and capital) and the processes in which they are combined.

When we assume relationships to be linear we are, in effect, assuming that everything is *proportional*. For example, in terms of factor input this means that we assume *constant returns* (double input, double output), and so on. Of course in reality most relationships turn out to be non-linear or non-proportional. Nevertheless there is much empirical evidence to suggest that for relatively small changes in output or input, the assumption of a linear or proportional relationship is a close approximation to reality. It is in this sense that the techniques considered in this chapter can be of practical use to businesses such as retail outlets or supermarkets, and we first consider *break-even analysis* before moving on to *linear programming*.

Ocado models an improved performance

Ocado, the online grocery store provides a useful example of how solving equations can help improve business performance. Ocado delivered an average of 123,000 online orders per week in 2012 from its huge automated warehouse in Hatfield, Hertfordshire. Every product placed in every crate for online delivery is the result of software at Ocado solving a mathematical equation, according to its head of investor relations. Even the bag into which a crate packer puts a specific product is the result of solving a calculation by its software package in order to minimise the time spent by each worker in finding a product and then packing that product.

(continued)

221

> Ocado prides itself that its software system helps staff pick between 280 and 700 products an hour depending on the picking system, product and order demand, significantly more than staff picking products from the shelves in Sainsbury's or Tesco's online stores. Ocado's new automated warehouse in Dordon, Warwickshire is even more efficient.

In this chapter we use linear relationships as the basis for the equations in our models, and first consider *break-even analysis* before moving on to *linear programming*, using the retail sector for our applications. We relax this linearity assumption in the next chapter and start to review how businesses in the media sector can use non-linear relationships to identify levels of output, prices or factor input that will maximise revenue or profit, or minimise costs.

Learning objectives

When you have read this chapter you should be able to:

- understand how linear relationships can be used to solve various business-related problems;

- use linear analysis to identify the level of output and sales that the firm must reach if it is to cover all costs – that is, its break-even output – using both graphical and mathematical techniques;

- express certain problems in terms of a linear objective function to be maximised or minimised;

- identify a set of linear constraints that will influence maximisation or minimisation outcomes;

- solve such linear programming problems using both graphical and mathematical techniques;

- apply linear analysis to the solution of business-related problems in the retail sector and more generally.

7.1   Break-even analysis

A widely used application of the linear principle involves *break-even analysis*. The idea here is to find the level of output that the retail store must achieve if it is to 'break even' – that is, to cover all its costs.

7.1.1   Revenue, cost and profit

Check that you are familiar with the following definitions of revenue, cost and profit as these definitions are widely used in break-even analysis.

$$\text{\textbf{Total revenue}} = \text{price} \times \text{quantity sold}$$
$$\text{i.e. TR} = \text{P} \times \text{Q}$$
$$\text{\textbf{Average revenue}} = \text{revenue per unit sold} = \text{price}$$
$$\text{i.e. AR} = \frac{\text{TR}}{\text{Q}} = \text{P}$$
$$\text{\textbf{Total cost}} = \text{total fixed cost} + \text{total variable cost}$$
$$\text{i.e. TC} = \text{TFC} + \text{TVC}$$
$$\text{\textbf{Total profit}} = \text{total revenue} - \text{total cost}$$
$$\text{i.e. TP} = \text{TR} - \text{TC}$$

We look at these definitions in more detail later in this chapter. Here, however, we should notice that at the break-even level of output, total revenue exactly equals total cost so that total profit is zero.

At break-even output

$$\text{TR} = \text{TC}$$
$$\text{where } \text{TC} = \text{TFC} + \text{TVC}$$
$$\text{and } \quad \text{TP} = \text{TR} - \text{TC} = 0$$

Types of cost

Fixed costs

These are costs that *do not* vary with output for the store, and are sometimes called 'overheads'. Costs such as business rates, lighting and heating are often regarded as fixed costs. Fixed costs are incurred before production begins and are unchanged thereafter.

Variable costs

These are costs that *do* vary with output, and are sometimes called 'running costs'. Costs such as wages, raw materials and energy are often regarded as variable costs. For the retail store extra customers and therefore sales output may require more people, both full time and part time, increasing the wage bill. Maybe the store will be open longer, increasing energy costs.

Did you know?

The Poundland story

Identifying the price to charge consumers is no problem for Poundland stores since 'everything sells for £1'. However, identifying the break-even output and turnover is certainly something each store manager must take into account. Established in 1990, Poundland sells over 3,000 quality products and over 1000 well-known brands, across 17 categories including food and drink, health and beauty, household, gardening, DIY, pet, stationery, books, DVDs and toys. Such 'single-price-point' retailing has a long history, with the original Marks and Spencer

(continued)

stores in the 1890s in the United Kingdom charging 1 penny for most items. Poundland has grown rapidly in the United Kingdom and serves over 5 million customers every week, 78% of which are female. The next largest price discount competitor is the 99p stores with 240 stores compared to Poundland with 510 stores. Similar price-point retailing stores have operated in the United States since the 1870s.

Costs and linearity

The linearity assumption underlying break-even analysis is reflected in the cost lines of Figure 7.1A.

In this example the Poundland store apportions its costs as follows:

$$\text{TFC} = £50,000$$

$$\text{AVC} = £0.50 \text{ per item sold}$$

Notice that both TFC and TVC are represented by straight lines with *constant* slopes or gradients.

- slope of TFC = 0
- slope of TVC = AVC = 0.50

You should be familiar with the fact that we obtain the TC line by summing vertically the TFC and TVC lines. The slope of TC will be the same as that for TVC – that is, 0.5.

Note: Since AVC is constant at £0.5 per unit, *marginal cost* (MC) = AVC in this case. In other words, each extra (marginal) unit sold adds £0.5 to TVC, which is the same as the £0.5 AVC per unit.

Revenue and linearity

Figure 7.1B reproduces the cost lines of Figure 7.1A, together with a TR line drawn on the understanding that every item in the Poundland store is sold at a price (AR) of £1.

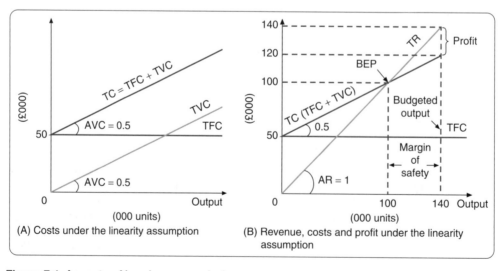

(A) Costs under the linearity assumption

(B) Revenue, costs and profit under the linearity assumption

Figure 7.1 Aspects of break-even analysis

Of course the TR then has a slope (= AR) of 1 and an intercept of 0 (since zero output means zero revenue).

Note: Since price (AR) is constant at £1 per unit, *marginal revenue* (MR) = AR in this case. In other words, each extra (marginal) unit adds £1 to TR, which is the same as the £1 AR per unit.

7.1.2 Break-even point (BEP)

The break-even point **(BEP)** is often defined as that level of output for which all costs are covered;

i.e. where TR = TC so that TP = zero.

In Figure 7.1B we can see that BEP for our Poundland store occurs at a sales output of 100,000 units.

We can use our definitions of revenue, cost and profit to check the BEP outcome we observe in Figure 7.1B.

$$TR = P \times Q = £1 \times 100,000 = £100,000$$

$$TC = TFC + TVC$$

$$TFC = £50,000$$

$$TVC = AVC \times Q$$

$$TVC = £0.5 \times 100,000$$

$$TVC = £50,000$$

$$\text{i.e. } TC = £50,000 + £50,000 = £100,000$$

$$TP = TR - TC$$

$$\text{i.e. } TP = £100,000 - £100,000$$

$$\textbf{TP = £0}$$

The BEP for our Poundland store is indeed 100,000 units.

PAUSE FOR THOUGHT 7.1

In 2013, 3 of the 400 Poundland shops in the United Kingdom responded to competitive pressure from nearby 99p Stores by cutting all their prices to 97p. How would this affect the BEP for Poundland?

Clearly we can solve for BEP either:

a) using graphical analysis;

b) using simple algebra.

Even if we do use graphical analysis, simple algebra can be a useful check on our solution. The following expressions will help our calculations of BEP.

Contribution per unit

This tells the manager of the Poundland store what each unit of sales output is contributing (over and above the variable costs incurred) to the fixed costs already incurred.

Contribution per unit (C/U) = Price (AR) − AVC

We can now express the BEP as:

$$BEP = \frac{TFC}{C/U}$$

In our example:

C/U = £1 − £0.5

C/U = £0.5

$$BEP = \frac{TFC}{C/U} = \frac{£50,000}{£0.5} = 100,000 \text{ units}$$

In other words, the Poundland store must sell 100,000 units if it is to earn sufficient revenue over and above its variable costs to cover the £50,000 of fixed costs already incurred.

Budgeted output

Budgeted output is the level of output the Poundland store intends (budgets) to produce. One would normally expect the budgeted output to be *greater than* the BEP.

Suppose the budgeted output in Figure 7.1B is 140,000 units. At this budgeted output:

TR = P × Q = £1 × 140,000 = £140,000

TC = TFC + TVC

= £50,000 + (140,000 × £0.5)

= £50,000 + £70,000 = £120,000

TP = TR − TC

TP = £140,000 − £120,000

TP = £20,000 at budgeted output

In other words, at a budgeted output of 140,000 units, the Poundland store can expect to earn a TP of £20,000, as can be seen in Figure 7.1B.

Margin of safety

The Poundland store will usually seek to operate with some *margin of safety*, here defined as the difference between budgeted (intended) output and the break-even output.

Margin of safety = Budgeted output − Break-even output

In Figure 7.1B

Margin of safety $= 140{,}000 - 100{,}000$

Margin of safety $= 40{,}000$ units

The margin of safety is often expressed as a *percentage of the budgeted output*.

$$\text{Margin of safety (\%)} = \frac{\text{Budgeted output} - \text{BEP}}{\text{Budgeted output}} \times 100$$

i.e. Margin of safety $= \dfrac{40{,}000}{140{,}000} \times 100$

Margin of safety $= 28.6\%$

This tells us that the output of the Poundland store can fall by as much as 28.6% below its budgeted output and still break even or better.

In other words, the margin of safety is a useful measure of risk. The larger the margin of safety, the lower the risk of indebtedness should unexpected events cause the Poundland store to fall short of the budgeted output.

Break-even analysis can also be used to compare different situations ('scenarios') facing the retail manager of a small Tesco store, as in the Worked Example below.

Worked example 7.1

A small, town-centre retail outlet of Tesco sells a product that has a variable cost of £3 a unit. Fixed costs are £10,000 per month. The store manager estimates that if the price is set at £5 a unit, the sales volume will be 10,000 units per month; whereas if the price is reduced to £4 a unit, the sales volume will rise to 15,000 per month.

(a) Draw a break-even chart covering each of the possible sales prices, and state the budgeted profits, the BEPs and the margins of safety.

(b) Compare the two possible situations. Consider the assumptions and limitations of your analysis.

Solution

Figure 7.2 presents a break-even chart showing how the TR line and budgeted output vary depending on the price set.

Price $= £5$

Budgeted profit (at 10,000 units per month) $= \text{TR} - \text{TC}$

$$\text{TR} = £5 \times 10{,}000 = £50{,}000$$

$$\text{TC} = \text{TFC} + \text{TVC} = £10{,}000 + (£3 \times 10{,}000)$$

i.e. Budgeted profit $= £50{,}000 - £40{,}000 = £10{,}000$ per month

$\text{C/U} = \text{Price} - \text{AVC}$

$= £5 - £3$

$\text{C/U} = £2$

Worked
example
7.1
(cont'd)

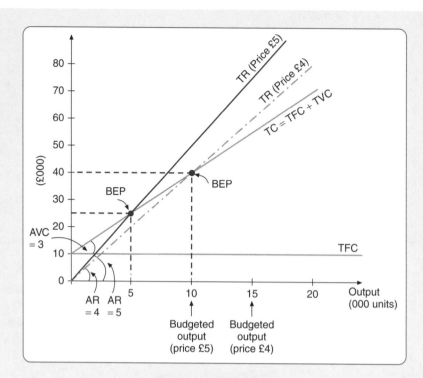

Figure 7.2 Break-even analysis under different price scenarios

$$\text{BEP} = \frac{\text{Total Fixed Cost}}{\text{Contribution per unit}}$$

$$\text{BEP} = \frac{£10,000}{£2}$$

BEP = 5,000 units per month

Margin of safety = budgeted output − BEP

$$= 10,000 - 5,000$$

Margin of safety = 5,000 units

As a percentage:

$$\text{Margin of safety} = \frac{\text{budgeted output} - \text{BEP}}{\text{budgeted output}} \times 100$$

$$= \frac{10,000 - 5,000}{10,000} \times 100$$

Margin of safety = 50%

In summary, for £5 price scenario:

Budgeted profit = £10,000 per month

BEP = 5,000 units per month

Worked
example
7.1
(cont'd)

Margin of safety (%) = 50%

Price = £4

Budgeted profit (at 15,000 units) = TR − TC

$$TR = £4 \times 15{,}000 = £60{,}000$$

$$TC = TFC + TVC = £10{,}000 + (£3 \times 15{,}000) = £55{,}000$$

$$\text{Budgeted profit} = £60{,}000 − £55{,}000$$

Budgeted profit = £5,000 per month

$$C/U = \text{price} − AVC$$

$$= £4 − £3$$

C/U = £1

$$BEP = \frac{TFC}{C/U}$$

$$BEP = \frac{£10{,}000}{£1}$$

BEP = 10,000 units per month

Margin of safety = budgeted output − BEP

$$= 15{,}000 − 10{,}000$$

Margin of safety = 5,000 units

As a percentage:

$$\text{Margin of safety} = \frac{\text{Budgeted output} − BEP}{\text{budgeted output}} \times 100$$

$$= \frac{15{,}000 − 10{,}000}{15{,}000} \times 100$$

Margin of safety = 33.3%

In summary for £4 price scenario:

$$\text{Budgeted profit} = £5{,}000 \text{ per month}$$

$$BEP = 10{,}000 \text{ units per month}$$

Margin of safety = 33.3%

The £5 price scenario would appear to be the most attractive for the retail outlet of Tesco. Setting a price of £5 would give it a higher budgeted profit, a lower BEP and a higher margin of safety, than would setting a price of £4. The £5 price would seem to be both more profitable and less risky for the retail outlet than the £4 price. As well as an extra £5,000 in expected profit, the firm would need to produce and sell 5,000 fewer units in order to break even. The margin of safety reinforces this aspect of reduced risk, in that at a price of £5 the firm could experience a fall in its sales of up to 50% below its budgeted (expected) output before losses would actually be incurred. In contrast, at a £4 price the retail outlet could only see sales fall 33.3% below expectation before losses would actually be incurred.

PAUSE FOR THOUGHT 7.2

Can you find the new BEP and margin of safety at each price if a sudden rise in rates increases the fixed costs to £20(000) in Figure 7.2?

- Of course all this break-even analysis is based on the linearity assumption. This may *not* actually be valid in practice. For example, the assumption that variable cost per unit (AVC) is constant at all levels of sales output may be unrealistic. If various economies of scale occur, then AVC might *fall* as sales output increases, raising contribution per unit (price – AVC) at the £4 price scenario with its higher budgeted output. In this case the TVC and TC curves would cease to be a straight line (linear).

- Further, the TR curves may not be linear in practice! In order to sell more output it may be that the firm may have to *reduce price*. It may therefore make little sense to draw a TR curve as a straight line with a constant slope representing a given and unchanged price as output varies.

For these and other reasons the break-even analysis may be over-simple. Nevertheless the linearity assumption may have some validity for relatively small changes in output, which is often the most likely result of policy changes by a firm.

Did you know?

A 2013 study by Mintel found that over one third of British diners frequently use vouchers when eating out, and as many as 17% say they will only eat at certain restaurant chains if vouchers or some other price discount is available. Popular voucher websites such as LivingSocial and DiscountVouchers identify a wide range of casual dining chains as running regular voucher offers, such as Pizza Hut, Carluccio's, YO! Sushi and Browns. Estimates suggest that the vouchers can, in effect, represent as much as a 20% discount on the price offered, pivoting downwards and to the right the TR lines in Figure 7.2 (p. 229). Together with an average annual rise of 5% in food costs in recent years, any significant reduction in the actual 'price' received via the use of vouchers will result in significant increases in the BEP for these casual dining chains.

Source: Adapted from Vouchers Likely to Remain on the Menu. *The Financial Times*, 01/02/2013 (Thompson, C.), *The Financial Times*, © The Financial Times Limited. All Rights Reserved.

In the previous Worked Example we compared two different price scenarios. Of course we could equally compare two different cost scenarios, as in Self-Check Questions 7.1 and 7.2 below.

Self-check questions 7.1

Q1. A retail store expects to sell 8,000 units of its product each year at a price of £4 a unit, a variable cost of £2 a unit and fixed costs of £15,000. New technology reduces variable costs to £1.50 a unit of sales but raises fixed costs to £20,000. Budgeted output remains unchanged at 8,000 units per year and price unchanged at £4 a unit.

(a) Draw a break-even chart to compare the situation before and after technical change. Which break-even solution might the retail store prefer? Explain your reasoning.

(b) Consider the assumptions and limitations of your analysis.

Q2. Tesco makes its own kitchen units in regional workshops to sell in its superstores with a projected selling price of £600. The variable costs per unit in a particular workshop are estimated at £200. The fixed costs are £12,000 for the time period in question.

(a) Find the break-even output.

(b) If budgeted output is 60 units over the time period, estimate the profit earned and the margin of safety.

(c) Suppose a new, more capital-intensive manufacturing process is introduced, with a higher fixed cost of £25,000 but a lower variable cost of £100 per unit. Would you recommend adopting the new process if your budgeted output remains at 60 units? Explain your reasoning.

Q3. The costs of producing and selling a particular own-brand item of furniture in a John Lewis superstore are as follows:

Material per unit	£100
Labour per unit	£70
Other variable costs per unit	£30

The fixed overhead cost in the furniture assembly factory of John Lewis is £40,000 for the time period in question, here per month. The John Lewis superstore estimates it can sell 500 items of furniture per month at a price of £300 per item.

(a) Calculate the budgeted profit, BEP and margin of safety.

(b) If the superstore estimates it could raise price to £400 and sell 300 items of furniture per month, what would you recommend? Explain your reasoning.

(c) If the superstore retains the pricing strategy in (a) but finds a new, more capital-intensive process that raises fixed costs to £60,000 per time period but reduces variable costs to £150 per unit (item of furniture), what would you recommend? Explain your reasoning.

Note: Answers to Self-Check Questions can be found on the instructor's website, www.pearsoned.co.uk/wall

In this chapter we concentrate on straight line (linear) relationships and their application to resolve various business-related problems. We now review a further application of our linearity assumption, this time involving linear programming.

7.2 Linear programming

Linear programming involves the use of straight line relationships to maximise or minimise some function, usually called the 'objective function'.

7.2.1 Deriving the objective function

We shall use the letter Z to relate to the objective function. Suppose we are faced with the following problem.

> A large retailer that specialises in bathroom accessories has its own factory which can produce two types of its own-brand bathroom cabinet for sale, namely Basic (B) and Deluxe (D). The estimated profit per unit is £10 Basic and £15 Deluxe. How much of each type of bathroom cabinet should the firm produce in order to maximise total profit?

The objective function (Z) is here a total profit function, and the intention is to maximise that function. We can express this as:

$$\text{maximise } Z = 10B + 15D$$

$$\text{where } Z = \text{total profit in } £$$

Every unit of the Basic product (B) adds £10 to total profit (Z); every unit of the Deluxe product (D) adds £15 to total profit (Z).

We can graph this objective function, Z, as shown in Figure 7.3.

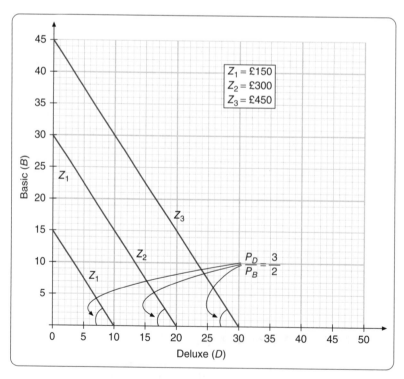

Figure 7.3 Graphing the objective function (Z) where $Z = 10B + 15D$ and all values are £

The objective function in this example is a line of constant profit, sometimes called an isoprofit line (iso = constant). It shows the different combinations of output of the two products, B and D, which yield a particular level of profit.

From Figure 7.3 we can note the following:

- Z_1 shows the different combinations of output of B and D yielding £150 profit; for example, £150 profit could be obtained from 10D and 0B, or 15B and 0D, or any combination of outputs shown on the Z_1 line (e.g. 7.5B and 5D).

- Z_2 shows the different combinations of output of B and D yielding £300 profit; for example, £300 profit could be obtained from 20D and 0B, or 30B and 0D, or any combination of outputs shown on the Z_2 line (e.g. 15B and 10D).

- Z_3 shows the different combinations of output of B and D yielding £450 profit; for example, £450 profit could be obtained from 30D and 0B, or 45B and 0D, or any combination of outputs shown on the Z_3 line (e.g. 22.5B and 15D).

We can note the following properties from graphing the objective function, Z.

- The *slope* of the objective function, Z, is given by the relative profitability of the two products.

$$\text{Slope of } Z = \frac{\text{profitability of } D}{\text{profitability of } B} = \frac{P_D}{P_B} = \frac{15}{10} = \frac{3}{2}$$

- The *position* of the objective function, Z, is given by the total profitability from producing the two products.

Notice in Figure 7.3 that successively higher values for Z, the objective function, are obtained by shifting the Z line outwards from the origin and parallel to itself.

The further the Z line is from the origin, the greater its value.

Did you know?

The need for retail outlets in the high streets of Britain or the shopping malls of the United States to have a well-defined objective function and to maximise the returns on all their activities has never been greater than it is today! The proportion of empty retail outlets in British high streets has risen dramatically from 3% in 2008 to 14% in 2013. Indeed the government-appointed Portas Review in 2012 had argued that only a fundamental diversification of the traditional British high street to incorporate multi-functional activities such as learning, health and well-being, and housing could prevent its progressive decline in favour of online and out-of-town shopping. Nor are the shopping malls of the United States faring any better, with the US property group Savills predicting that around 15% of the US's 1,300 largest enclosed malls will close within five years. Such reports suggest that, as in Britain, only if malls are reconfigured with additional healthcare, education, entertainment and other services can their continued viability be assured and the 200 million square feet reduction in malls experienced in the United States between 2007 and 2013 be reversed!

7.2.2 Deriving the structural constraints

Of course the seller of bathroom cabinets will only be interested in combinations of output that are *feasible* – that is, that can actually be produced for selling in the retail outlet given the resources available for producing them. For example, the factory is only likely to have limited amounts of, say, land, labour and capital equipment available for the production process of bathroom cabinets. In other words, the seller of bathroom cabinets must seek to maximise (or minimise) its objective function (here profit) subject to a set of constraints that reflect both the limited resources available and the production processes that determine the amounts in which those resources must be combined.

Suppose the factory producing the bathroom cabinets must allocate a certain amount of labour and capital between the Basic (B) and Deluxe (D) products. If it uses more resources for one type of product, then fewer will be available for the other type of product. Suppose the situation is as follows.

> The factory producing bathroom cabinets has 60 hours of labour available per day and 100 units of capital. Each unit of Basic product (B) requires 2 hours of labour and 4 units of capital. Each unit of Deluxe product (D) requires 4 hours of labour and 5 units of capital.

We can summarise the structural constraints facing the factory by using inequalities.

$$2B + 4D \leq 60 \ldots \textbf{labour constraint}$$

$$4B + 5D \leq 100 \ldots \textbf{capital constraint}$$

In other words, the *feasible* combinations of products B and D must involve using less than or equal to the 60 hours of labour actually available in total. Similarly, the *feasible* combinations of products B and D must involve using less than or equal to the 100 units of capital actually available in total.

We can graph these *inequalities*, as in Figure 7.4. The constraint lines we draw for labour and capital correspond to the equals sign in each inequality.

The labour constraint line

For example, if we use *all* our 60 hours of labour available per day on the Basic product (B) we can produce 30 units of B, but 0D ($30 \times 2 + 0 \times 4 = 60$). At the other extreme, if we use *all* our 60 hours of labour available per day on the Deluxe product (D), we can produce 15 units of D, but 0B ($15 \times 4 + 0 \times 2 = 60$). The labour constraint line between these two extremes represents all other combinations of B and D which use *all* our labour resources when we produce some of each product – for example, 20B, 5D ($20 \times 2 + 5 \times 4 = 60$) or 10B, 10D ($10 \times 2 + 10 \times 4 = 60$) and so on.

Notice that it is feasible to produce any combination *on or inside* the labour constraint line. A point inside the line such as 10B and 5D is certainly feasible, but will only use up 40 hours of labour ($10 \times 2 + 5 \times 4$), which is less than the 60 hours available. Any point inside the labour constraint line corresponds to using less than the total labour available.

Notice also that it is not feasible to produce any combination *outside* the labour constraint line. A point outside the line such as 20B, 10D would use up 80 hours of labour ($20 \times 2 + 10 \times 4$), which is more than the 60 hours available.

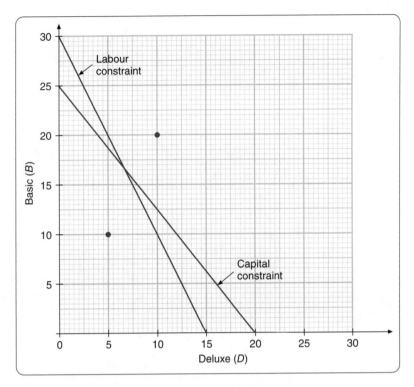

Figure 7.4 Graphing the constraints as equalities

In summary, with regard to the labour constraint line, we can say:

- combinations of products *on* the constraint line use up *all* the resources available and are feasible;
- combinations of products *inside* the constraint line use up *less than* the total resources available and are feasible;
- combinations of products *outside* the constraint line use up *more than* the total resources available and are not feasible.

The capital constraint line

We can repeat this reasoning and draw the capital constraint line, as in Figure 7.4. This shows that if our firm uses *all* its 100 units of capital per day it can produce the combinations of products B and D *on* the capital constraint line: for example, 25B, 0D ($25 \times 4 + 0 \times 5 = 100$), or 12.5B, 10D ($12.5 \times 4 + 10 \times 5 = 100$), or 0B, 20D ($0 \times 4 + 20 \times 5 = 100$).

Feasible region

The feasible region of production for the firm corresponds to those combinations of products B and D that meet *all* the production constraints faced by the firm, in this case both labour and capital constraints.

In Figure 7.5, the feasible region is shaded and corresponds to area 0VWX. All combinations of product on or inside this area are feasible.

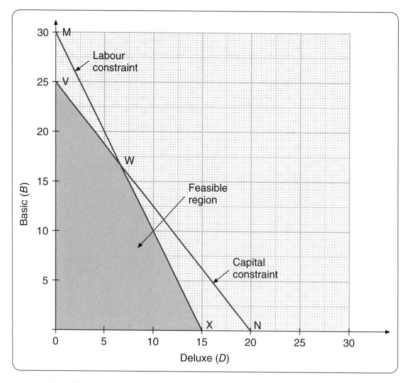

Figure 7.5 The feasible region of production – that is, area 0VWX

Non-negative constraints

In linear programming it is usual to limit the analysis to zero or positive outputs (here of B and D) only. These non-negative constraints are expressed as:

$$B \geq 0, \ D \geq 0$$

If we put all the parts of the linear programme involving Basic (B) and Deluxe (D) products together, we have the following problem.

$$\text{Maximise } Z = 10B + 15D \dots \text{objective function}$$

Subject to:

$$2B + 4D \leq 60 \dots \text{labour constraint}$$

$$4B + 5D \leq 100 \dots \text{capital constraint}$$

$$B \geq 0, \ D \geq 0 \dots \text{non-negative constraints}$$

7.3   Solving the linear programme: maximisation

A solution to a linear programme involving *maximisation* is to find the value of the straight line representing Z (the objective function) which is furthest from the origin but still feasible. We have noted (p. 232) that as the objective function moves further from the origin it increases in value. However, only combinations of product that can actually be produced (i.e. that are *feasible*) are of interest to the firm. The maximisation solution must therefore involve a *tangency* (just touching) between the objective function of Figure 7.3 and the feasible region of Figure 7.5.

Did you know?

The resources available for superstores such as Tesco to make it feasible for them to provide a wider range of goods and services directly in their stores, even if produced off-site, are continuing to increase. In 2013 Tesco acquired the Euphorium Bakery, Harris and Hoole coffee shop and Giraffe restaurant chains with a view to providing these extra service activities within its superstores (each operating as a standalone retail unit), thereby attracting new customers. Tesco is also using its own resources to refurbish its superstores, with more wooden features and furnishings and increased heating to make the shopping experience more attractive.

7.3.1   Corner point solutions

Because all relationships are *linear*, any tangency between the objective function and the feasible region must occur at one (or more) of the corner points. In terms of Figure 7.5, the tangency solution must occur at one of the corner points, V, W or X, or along segment VW or segment WX (i.e. involving two corner points in each of these cases). In any event, if we find the value of the objective function at each and every corner point in the feasible region, we must have found the maximum value for Z.

Let us illustrate this idea by solving for Z at each of the corner points in Figure 7.5.

Value of Z at corner point V

We know, from Figure 7.5, that the co-ordinates of corner point V are 0D and 25B. We can find the value of Z at this corner point by substituting these co-ordinates directly into the Z function.

$$Z_v = 10B + 15D$$

$$Z_v = 10\,(25) + 15\,(0)$$

$$Z_v = £250$$

Value of Z at corner point X

Similarly, we know from Figure 7.5 that the co-ordinates of corner point X are 15D and 0B. We can therefore find the value of Z at this corner point by substituting these co-ordinates directly into the Z function.

$$Z_x = 10B + 15D$$

$$Z_x = 10(0) + 15(15)$$

$$Z_x = £225$$

Value of Z at corner point W

The value of Z at corner point W requires a little more effort to solve! We have two options:

(a) Draw a *precise graph* so that we can read off the co-ordinates at which the two constraints (labour and capital) intersect.

(b) Use simple *simultaneous equations* (see Appendix 1, p. 331) to solve for the co-ordinates at W.

This can easily be done since two constraint lines, each represented by an equation, have the *same value* in B and D at the point of intersection.

If we use approach (b), we can say that these two equations must solve simultaneously.

(1) ... $2B + 4D = 60$ ... labour constraint

(2) ... $4B + 5D = 100$ ... capital constraint

Here we can multiply equation (1) by 2 and then subtract the two equations, thereby eliminating B.

(1) × 2 ... $4B + 8D = 120$

(2) ... $4B + 5D = 100$

Subtracting $3D = 20$

$$D = \frac{20}{3} = 6\tfrac{2}{3}$$

We can now substitute this value for D into either equation, and solve for B.

From (1) $2B + 4(6\frac{2}{3}) = 60$

$$2B + 26\frac{2}{3} = 60$$

$$2B = 60 - 26\frac{2}{3}$$

$$2B = 33\frac{1}{3}$$

$$B = 16\frac{2}{3}$$

The co-ordinates at corner point W are therefore $D = 6\frac{2}{3}, B = 16\frac{2}{3}$. We can now solve for Z at W.

$$Z_w = 10B + 15D$$

$$Z_w = 10(16\frac{2}{3}) + 15(6\frac{2}{3})$$

$$Z_w = 166\frac{2}{3} + 100$$

$$Z_w = £266\frac{2}{3}$$

Clearly, the objective function, Z, reaches its maximum value at corner point W. This implies that the profit-maximising firm should produce a daily output of $16\frac{2}{3}$ Basic items (B) and $6\frac{2}{3}$ Deluxe items (D). If only whole units are possible in terms of production, then this will round down to 16B and 6D.

Figure 7.6 summarises the previous analysis graphically. The Z function reaches its maximum value (i.e. is furthest from the origin) at the combination of products given by corner point W.

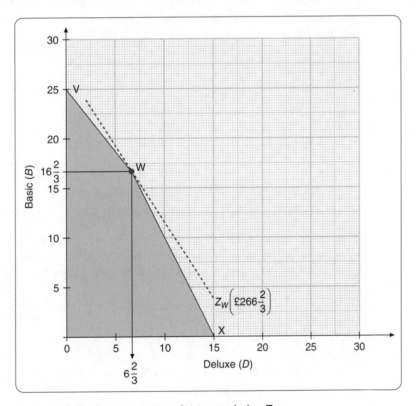

Figure 7.6 Finding a corner point to maximise *Z*

The value of the Z function in this case is £$266\frac{2}{3}$.

Using the simultaneous equation method will usually provide a more accurate solution for the co-ordinates of a corner point which cannot be observed directly from a sketch diagram.

Worked Example 7.2 uses the above approach for solving a linear programming problem. This problem again involves maximisation, but this time with *three* structural constraints.

Any solution always involves the following four stages:

- identifying the relevant variables in the problem;
- expressing the objective function;
- stating the structural and non-negative constraints;
- solving the problem.

Worked example 7.2

Tesco uses its own resources to produce lighting equipment for sale in its superstores. It uses three types of factor input, namely labour, capital and raw material, in producing two products, X and Y. Each unit of X contributes £20 to profit, each unit of Y contributes £30 to profit. To produce 1 unit of X requires 1 unit of labour, 1 unit of capital and 2 units of raw material. To produce 1 unit of Y requires 1 unit of labour, 2 units of capital and 1 unit of raw material. The firm has 50 units of labour, 80 units of capital and 80 units of raw material available.

Use a linear programming approach to find the feasible output combination of products X and Y that will maximise profit for Tesco. What is the value of total profit at this combination?

Solution

Set out as a linear programming problem.

Maximise Z = 20X + 30Y objective function.

Subject to:

$$1X + 1Y \leq 50 \ldots \text{labour constraint}$$

$$1X + 2Y \leq 80 \ldots \text{capital constraint}$$

$$2X + 1Y \leq 80 \ldots \text{raw material constraint}$$

$$X \geq 0, Y \geq 0 \ldots \text{non-negative constraints}$$

It is always useful to draw a diagram (see Figure 7.7) to represent the feasible region. Using graph paper will help you to draw the diagram more accurately even if we subsequently use algebra (simultaneous equations) to solve for the co-ordinates of some of the corner points.

As we can see, the *feasible region* that meets all the constraints is given by area 0MNPQ in Figure 7.7.

We now solve for *Z*, the objective function, at each of the *corner points* of the feasible region.

The value of Z is easiest to solve at corner points M and Q, since the co-ordinates are known for these corner points.

Worked
example
7.2
(cont'd)

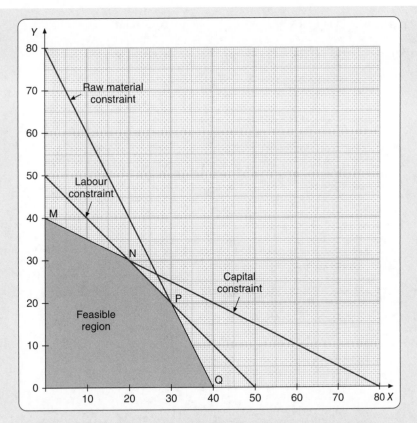

Figure 7.7 Graphing the constraints as equalities to find the feasible region

- Value of Z at M (X = 0, Y = 40)

$$Z_M = 20\,(0) + 30\,(40)$$

$$Z_M = £1,200$$

- Value of Z at Q (X = 40, Y = 0)

$$Z_Q = 20\,(40) + 30\,(0)$$

$$Z_Q = £800$$

Value of Z at N

We can find the co-ordinates at N *either* by a precise graph or by using simultaneous equations. Here we use the latter approach.

Two lines intersect at N – that is, they have the same (simultaneous) values in terms of X and Y at N. These intersecting lines are the equalities for the labour and capital constraints.

Worked example 7.2 (cont'd)

$(1) \ldots 1X + 1Y = 50$ labour constraint

$(2) \ldots \underline{1X + 2Y = 80}$ capital constraint

subtracting $Y = 30$ $(-Y = -30)$

substituting $Y = 30$ in equation (1)

$$1X + 30 = 50$$

$$\underline{X = 20}$$

$$Z_N = 20\,(20) + 30\,(30)$$

$$Z_N = \mathbf{£1{,}300}$$

Value of Z at P

Here the two lines that intersect are the equalities for the labour and raw material constraints.

$$(1) \ldots 1X + 1Y = 50 \ldots \text{labour constraint}$$

$$(2) \ldots 2X + 1Y = 80 \ldots \text{raw material constraint}$$

$(1) \times (2)$ $(3) \ldots 2X + 2Y = 100$

$(2) - (3)$ $- 1Y = -20$

$$Y = 20$$

substituting $Y = 20$ in equation (1)

$$1X + 20 = 50$$

$$X = 30$$

$$Z_p = 20\,(30) + 30\,(20)$$

$$Z_p = 600 + 600$$

$$Z_p = \mathbf{£1{,}200}$$

Clearly, the objective function, Z, is a maximum at £1,300 at corner point N, when the firm produces 20 units of product X and 30 units of product Y.

PAUSE FOR THOUGHT 7.4

Would your conclusion differ if the profitability of each unit of X were to rise from £20 per unit to £25 per unit in Worked Example 7.2?

Many of the linear programming problems are relatively simple to solve graphically and algebraically. Larger problems with many constraints, however, are time-consuming to solve but can be handled with relative ease using Excel. The example below provides a good basis to explore the procedure.

Linear programming

A large toy retailer makes and sells two types of doll, Basic and Deluxe. Both pass through three production processes which take the following times to complete.

	Process 1	Process 2	Process 3
Basic (b)	12 mins.	10 mins.	10 mins.
Deluxe (d)	16 mins.	10 mins.	20 mins.

Both processes 1 and 3 are available for 8 hours per day (480 mins.) but process 2 is available for 10 hours per day (600 mins.). The contribution to profit of each doll is £5.50 for the Basic doll and £9.50 for the Deluxe doll.

If the firm's objective is to maximise profit find out how many of each doll should be produced each day using the Excel 'Solver' tool.

Let b = Basic and d = Deluxe

Maximise

$Z = 5.5b + 9.5d$ ... the linear objective function

Subject to

Process 1	$12b + 16d \leq 480$	
Process 2	$10b + 10d \leq 600$	the linear structural constraints
Process 3	$10b + 20d \leq 480$	

and

$b \geq 0, d \geq 0$ ... the non-negativity constraints

PAUSE FOR THOUGHT 7.5

Can you represent this linear programming problem by drawing a graph such as that in Figure 7.7? Then can you solve for each corner point position and identify the output of Basic and Deluxe dolls which will maximise profit?

Solving this linear programme in the conventional way will be a useful check as you work through the spreadsheet solution below.

Spreadsheet solution

The following solution is illustrated using the 'Solver' tool in Excel.

The first stage is to prepare for the optimisation process as follows.

Step 1. Set up the maximising table.

Label three cells: **Model**; **Contribution**; **Quantity**.

Place the coefficients of the objective function into the **Contribution** column – that is, 5.5 and 9.5.

Worked
example
7.3
(cont'd)

Set any value in the **Quantities** column (they will change). Zero is the simplest option for the initial entry.

For ease of reading, label the corresponding rows with the terms from the objective function – that is, b **(basic)** and d **(deluxe)**.

Step 2. Translate the objective function into a spreadsheet formula:

From $z = 5.5b + 9.5d$

to $= (B4*C4) + (B5*C5)$

if **A3 to C5** contains the maximising table.

Step 3. Construct a table of linear structural constraints – for this you need three columns.

Label cells in the last two rows of the constraints table: **Constraints**; **Quantities**.

The next three rows calculate the constraints – that is, $12b + 16d$ and so on.

Use the cells that contain the quantities of b and d in your Excel formula – even though they still contain zero at this point. Therefore if **A3 to C5** contains the maximising table then the next row should contain three cells as follows:

Process 1 $= (12*\$C\$4) + (16*\$C\$5)$ 480

Enter the respective formulae for the remaining two processes.

Step 4. Your spreadsheet should now resemble:

	A	B	C
3	Model	Contribution	Quantities
4	b		
5	d		
6			
7			
8	Objective function	0	
9			
10		Constraints	Quantities
11	Process 1	0	480
12	Process 2	0	600
13	Process 3	0	480

Step 5. From **Data** on the menu bar select **Solver**.

Hint: If **Solver Add-in** is not listed in the **Add-Ins available** box, click **Browse** to locate the Add-in.

If you get prompted that the Solver Add-in is not currently installed on your computer, click **Yes** to install it.

After you have loaded the Solver Add-in, the **Solver** command will be available in the **Analysis** group on the **Data** tab.

Worked example 7.3 (cont'd)

Step 6. Complete the entry boxes.

Set target cell to: ... the cell that contains the objective function (**B8** in the above).

Equal to: ... as the aim is to maximise the objective function select **Max**.

By changing cells ... the values that can be changed are the quantities of *b* and *d* (i.e. the values in cells **C4** and **C5**).

Subject to the constraints ... click the Add icon and enter all the constraints including the non-negativity constraints (e.g. **B11** < = **C11**).

When you have finished entering all five constraints (three process and two non-negativity) click Solve and enter **OK**.

Finally, click on the **Options icon** and ensure that the **Assume linear model** is selected – leave the other options in their default setting.

The Solver dialogue box should now resemble Figure 7.8.

Select Solve.

Step 7. A menu box entitled **Solver Results** will appear and as we are not, at this level, carrying out any sensitivity analysis select Keep Solver Solution and press the **OK** icon.

Step 8. You should find the optimal solution to be:

Profit maximise when we produce 12 **Deluxe** and 24 **Basic dolls**. Profit will be £246.

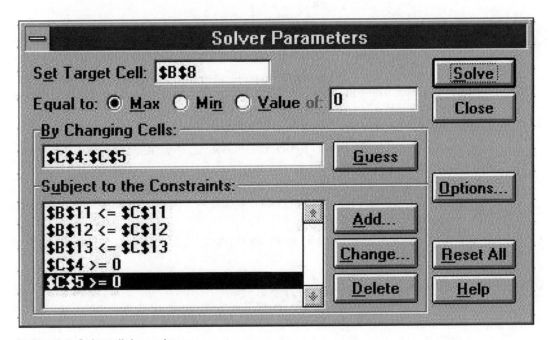

Figure 7.8 Solver dialogue box

Self-check questions 7.3

Q1. A retail store expects to sell 8,000 units of its product each year at a price of £4 a unit, a variable cost of £2 a unit and fixed costs of £15,000. New technology reduces variable costs to £1.50 a unit of sales, but raises fixed costs to £20,000. Budgeted output remains unchanged at 8,000 units per year and price unchanged at £4 a unit.

(a) Draw a break-even chart to compare the situation before and after technical change. Which break-even solution might the retail store prefer? Explain your reasoning.

(b) Consider the assumptions and limitations of your analysis.

Q2. A confectionery company makes and sells in its retail outlines, among other products, two similar brands of sweet marketed as Rockets (R) and Starships (S). Both contain a colouring agent, E132, and an anti-oxidant, E320.

Each Rocket contains 2.5 g of E132 and 5.0 g of E320, whereas each Starship contains 5.0 g of E132 and 2.5 g of E320. Each Rocket generates a profit of 5.0 pence and each Starship 2.0 pence.

For a particular production run, 80 kg of E132 and 70 kg of E320 are available. Marketing considerations restrict the number of Rockets produced to no more than 10,000 but there is no such restriction on Starships.

How many of each brand would you advise the confectionary company to make and sell in order to maximise its profits on this production run? What will be the level of profit?

Note: Answers to Self-Check Questions can be found on the instructor's website, www.pearsoned.co.uk/wall

7.4 Solving the linear programme: minimisation

The procedure for solving a minimisation problem by linear programming is essentially the same as that for a maximisation problem. The solution will involve a tangency between an objective function, Z, and one or more corner points of a feasible region.

However, a number of differences can usefully be noted.

- The minimum value for the objective function will involve a line that is feasible but *nearest to the origin* and therefore of lowest value.

- The feasible region will reflect inequalities of the *greater than or equal to* variety; in other words, the feasible region will include combinations on or to the right of the structural constraints.

A Worked Example will help illustrate these points.

Worked example 7.4

A travel company operates two types of vehicle, A and B, in providing weekend visits with overnight stays to places of interest. Vehicle A can carry 40 passengers and 30 tons of baggage; vehicle B can carry 60 passengers but only 15 tons of baggage. The travel company is contracted to carry at least 960 passengers and 360 tons of baggage per weekend visit. If vehicle A costs £1,000 to operate per journey and vehicle B costs £1,200 to operate per journey, what choice of vehicles will minimise the TC per weekend visit?

Worked
example
7.4
(cont'd)

Solution

We can set out the problem as a linear programme.

Minimise $Z = 1,000A + 1,200B$

where Z = total cost (£)

subject to:

$40A + 60B \geq 960$ ... passenger constraint

$30A + 15B \geq 360$ ... baggage constraint

$A \geq 0, B \geq 0$ ... non-negative constraints

We can graph the *objective function* as in Figure 7.9A and the *feasible region* as in Figure 7.9B.

As before, Figure 7.9A indicates that the *position* of the objective function, Z (total cost in £), depends on its value, and the *slope* of the objective function depends on the relative costs (profits in the previous example) of the two products $\left(\dfrac{C_B}{C_A} = \dfrac{1200}{1000} = \dfrac{6}{5}\right)$.

We can see that the nearer to the origin is the line representing the Z function, the lower is its value. So, for example, total cost (Z) is £6,000 when the firm uses six vehicles of type A and zero vehicles of type B, or five vehicles of type B and zero vehicles of type A, or any combination of vehicles given by points along the Z_1 line.

Of course the solution to the minimisation linear programme will involve the corner point (or points) that gives the lowest value for Z, but which is *feasible* in terms of meeting the various constraints. In this problem, the solution will be the combination of vehicle inputs that can meet the passenger and baggage constraints at lowest total cost to the travel company.

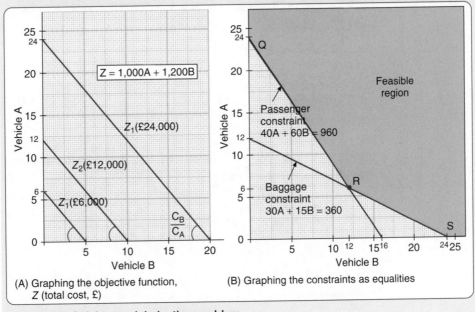

(A) Graphing the objective function,
Z (total cost, £)

(B) Graphing the constraints as equalities

Figure 7.9 Solving a minimisation problem

Figure 7.9B graphs these passenger and baggage constraints as equalities. The company must *meet or better* these constraints ($\geq$) giving the shaded area to the right of the constraint lines as the *feasible region* of combinations of vehicle inputs.

The value of the objective function, Z, will be at a minimum at one or more of the corner points – that is, at Q, R or S respectively.

Value of Z at Q (A = 24, B = 0)

$$Z_Q = 1{,}000\,(24) + 1{,}200\,(0)$$

$$Z_Q = £24{,}000$$

Value of Z at S (A = 0, B = 24)

$$Z_S = 1{,}000\,(0) + 1{,}200\,(24)$$

$$Z_S = £28{,}800$$

Value of Z at R

Here the co-ordinates are, as yet, unknown unless our graph is drawn precisely so that we can read off the co-ordinates directly from the graph. Even then, we can use simultaneous equations to solve the co-ordinates at R.

We have two lines that intersect at point R – that is, i.e. that have the same (simultaneous) values of A and B at point R.

(1) ... $40A + 60B = 960$ ... passenger constraint

(2) ... $30A + 15B = 360$ ... baggage constraint

Multiplying equation (2) by 4 gives equation (3).

(3) $120A + 60B = 1440$

(1) − (3) $-80A = -480$

$$A = \frac{-480}{-80} = 6$$

$$A = 6$$

Subtracting equation (3) from equation (1) eliminates B and gives the solution A = 6. Substituting A = 6 in equation (1)

$$40\,(6) + 60B = 960$$

$$60B = 960 - 240$$

$$60B = 720$$

$$\mathbf{B = 12}$$

So the co-ordinates of corner point R are A = 6, B = 12.

Worked example 7.4 (cont'd)

The value of Z at point R is:

$$Z_R = 1,000(6) + 1,200(12)$$

$$Z_R = £20,400$$

Clearly, the company can minimise its total cost by providing 6 vehicles of type A and 12 vehicles of type B per journey. This will cost the company £20,400, which is the lowest feasible TC given that 960 passengers and 360 tons of baggage must be carried per journey.

Self-check question 7.4

A health food restaurant produces its own special dish using two ingredients, X and Y. Each unit of ingredient X costs £2, each unit of ingredient Y costs £3.

Each unit of ingredient X provides 1 g of protein and 1 g of vitamins, whereas each unit of ingredient Y provides 1 g of protein and 2 g of vitamins. To match the promotional claim for its special dish, each serving must contain at least 10 g of protein and at least 14 g of vitamins.

What combination of these ingredients, X and Y, will minimise the firm's TCs of production while still meeting the protein and vitamin requirements?

Note: Answers to Self-Check Questions can be found on the instructor's website, www.pearsoned.co.uk/wall

---

REVIEW QUESTIONS

R7.1. A new and large retail business is established with annual fixed costs of £3 million, variable costs of £8 per unit sold and an average selling price of £20 per unit. The large retail business has annual budgeted sales of 400,000 units.

   (a) Find the BEP for annual sales and the margin of safety.

   (b) Find the new BEP and margin of safety as compared to your answer in (a) above in each of the following.

   (i) The average selling price falls to £18 per unit.

   (ii) The annual fixed costs rise to £4 million.

   (iii) The variable costs per unit sold rise to £10.

R7.2. (a) From the following information construct a linear programme to maximise profit and interpret the results:

   A retail company uses its own workshops to manufacture two products, A and B.

   Profits per unit are: *A* £4 and *B* £3.

   Total labour hours available are 110 hours.

   Labour required per unit is: A 1 hour and B 2 hours.

   Production capacity limitations are: 70 units of A, 150 units of B (i.e. output of the respective products cannot exceed these levels given restrictions on production capacity).

(b) Owing to uncertainty about aspects of the information in (a) above, you are required to carry out a simple sensitivity test of the results obtained in (a) and to state your findings in each of the following cases:

(i)   a £1 decrease in profits per unit for B;

(ii) a 10 hour increase in total labour hours available;

(iii) a 10% increase in labour hours required per unit of A.

Treat each case separately in relation to the solution you obtained in (a).

R7.3.   A farm sells its own produce in its large retail and wholesale outlets. It can produce potatoes (X) or barley (Y) with its resources. The farm makes a net profit of £70 per acre of potatoes (X) and £100 per acre of barley (Y). The farm manager draws up the following summary statement of his resources and input requirements.

Requirements per acre

Resources	X (potatoes)	Y (barley)	Amount available
Labour	12 staff days	3 staff days	1,080 staff days
Equipment	3 machine days	5 machine days	450 machine days
Land	1 acre	1 acre	100 acres

Find the number of acres the farmer should devote to each product in order to maximise total net profit. What is the net profit in this situation?

R7.4.   A specialist supplier of motorcycles to its own retail and wholesale outlets manufactures a 1500 cc and 2000 cc version. Each 1500 cc motorcycle makes a net profit of £3,700 and each 2000 cc motorcycle makes a net profit of £3,600. Manufacture of these motorcycles involves three key processes. The hours required for each process and the hours available per month are shown below.

Process	Hours required per motorcycle		Hours available per month
	1500 cc	2000 cc	
Motorcycle assembly	600	1,200	9,000
Component manufacture	300	300	3,000
Engine shop	900	0	6,300

Use a linear programming approach to find the output mix of the two types of motorcycle that will maximise total net profit. Comment on your results.

R7.5.   A farm produces home-grown beef for sale in its own retail outlets in a major city. The farm manager mixes two foodstuffs, X and Y, to produce cattle feed. The following table indicates the presence of three types of nutrient in each ton of foodstuff, X and Y.

Units of nutrient per ton of foodstuff

Nutrient	X	Y	Total requirement
Vitamin	3 units	10 units	9 units
Protein	3 units	3 units	6 units
Starch	8 units	3 units	12 units

The farm manager has received advice as to the total requirement of each type of nutrient needed to feed the cattle. This is shown in the last column of the table. The farm manager must not fall below these requirements. If each ton of foodstuff X costs £120 and each ton of foodstuff Y costs £110, what combination of X and Y will minimise the total cost of the cattle-feed while meeting his total nutrient requirements?

*R7.6. High-street shops are coming under increased competition from online purchasing of the same products. This is motivating many large retailers such as John Lewis or the Curry's group, which have been traditional high-street stores, to support shoppers who are increasingly displaying mixed-mode shopping habits – for example, browsing in the stores but price checking through mobile devices.

Many well-known high-street stores have gone into administration because they have not adapted their business model to the changing behaviour of shoppers on the high street. Those that remain are having to make choices about how best to respond to the various labour constraints, raw material constraints and capital constraints to achieve the best outcomes for their customers and their sales revenue, while recognising that the online stores do not have the same levels of fixed or even variable costs.

One company is seeking to develop its own line of baby prams so that it can offer a unique product to its customers on the high street. There will initially be two types: Compact and Rugged. The Compact will contribute £75 to profit and the Rugged will contribute £150 to profit. To produce 1 unit of the Compact pram requires 2 units of labour, 1 unit of capital and 1 unit of raw material. To produce 1 unit of the Rugged pram requires 4 units of labour, 1 unit of capital and 4 units of raw material. The company has 80 units of labour, 50 units of capital and 100 units of raw material available.

Use a linear programming approach (or use Excel Solver) to find the feasible output combination of Compact and Rugged prams that will maximise profit for the company. What is the value of the total profit at this combination?

Note: Answers to Review Questions can be found on the instructor's website, www.pearsoned.co.uk/wall

Further practice

You can find more questions (with solutions) on business modelling on the instructor's website, www.pearsoned.co.uk/wall.

Spreadsheets: video guide

You can also find a step-by-step account that takes you through the actual use of a spreadsheet when solving the type of problems you have encountered in this chapter. Go to the instructor's website, www.pearsoned.co.uk/wall.

Chapter 8

Business modelling
Non-linear relationships

Introduction

In this chapter we look at various techniques we can use to model situations involving non-linear (curved) relationships. We have already seen (Chapter 7) how we can find maximum or minimum solutions involving *linear* relationships between variables. Here we review techniques that will help us find maximum or minimum solutions involving *non-linear* relationships between variables.

We shall see that finding 'turning points' in non-linear situations, which can be either maximum or minimum values, will involve the process of *differentiation*. This can help solve problems such as the output that maximises revenue or profit, or the output that minimises cost, or the price that should be charged to maximise revenue or profit, and so on. We also review another key process that will help us find the area under a curve, namely *integration*. This can help solve problems such as finding the value of the total revenue or the total profit when revenue or profit are a maximum, or finding the value of the total costs incurred when average costs are a minimum.

The box below indicates some of the fast-moving developments in the media sector, in this case the changing readership of print versus digital news.

Digital news on the rise

A study of 11,000 internet users across six countries in 2013 by the Reuters Institute of Oxford University found that the proportion of people paying for news in digital form had more than doubled from 4% to 9% over the previous year, with the biggest rise among those aged 25–34 years. Broadcasters such as the BBC are 'trusted' by 79% of these digital news readers, broadsheet newspapers (e.g. *Times*, *Guardian*) by 60%, but blogs or social media such as Facebook and Twitter are 'trusted' by less than 10%. Interestingly 48% of commuters on public transport read news on mobile phones and 6% on tablets, compared to 34% of commuters on public transport reading news on newspapers.

Although an increasing number of sources now charge for digital news, the decline in revenue from advertising in newspapers and print media has outweighed the growth in these revenues from digital news. The advertising multinational WPP predicts that print advertising revenue will fall by 8% during 2013, and 10% during 2014 – that is, a loss of over £400 million in advertising revenue.

Of course the rise of digital alternatives in many media-related activities is challenging the business models of existing media companies which must now continually review their projected revenue and cost functions. Whereas only 1 in 20 readers of glossy magazines viewed the magazine on a digital device such as an iPad, Galaxy tablet or similar device in 2012, the Audit Bureau of Circulation reported that as many as 1 in 5 readers did so in 2013.

'Big data' is claimed to be an increasingly important resource for predicting actual consumer and producer behaviour, and therefore for developing the revenue, cost and profit functions for which we seek to find turning points, whether maximum or minimum. 'Big data' refers to the wealth of new data on consumer behaviour and characteristics now available via social media such as Facebook or Twitter, or via the vast number of connected devices such as satellites, closed circuit TV cameras, audio and video recording equipment, payment terminals, mobile phones and sensors. 'There are an estimated 5bn connected devices in the world, a total expected to rise to 20bn by 2020, all of them gathering or creating data' ('Big data: Treasure hides in everyday details', *Financial Times*, 26 June 2013). It is not only the increased availability of this data but the easier application of techniques to processing such data via 'cloudbased' analytic services, which is raising the profile of 'big data'.

Learning objectives

When you have read this chapter you should be able to:

- use the process of *differentiation* to calculate turning points, both maximum and minimum, for non-linear relationships;
- solve a variety of business-related problems using the process of differentiation, such as the price the business must set and the output it must produce if it seeks to maximise revenue or profit, or to minimise cost, or the quantity of inventory (stock) the business must hold to minimise cost and so on;
- apply differentiation to situations involving two variables *and* to situations involving more than two variables (*partial differentiation*);
- use the process of *integration* to calculate areas under a curve for non-linear relationships;
- solve a variety of business-related problems using the process of integration, such as the total revenue, total profit or total cost from producing various levels of output;
- apply non-linear analysis to the solution of business-related problems in the media sector and more generally.

Some basic mathematical techniques are reviewed in Appendix 1 (p. 314) which may help you with this chapter.

8.1   Differentiation

Differentiation refers to the process whereby we calculate the gradient to a curve at any point. Clearly for a *linear function* or equation $y = mx + c$ the gradient, m, is a constant at every point. In Figure A.5 (p. 335) the gradient of the curve $y = 3x + 2$ is clearly $+3$ at all points along that curve.

However, to find the gradient to a *non-linear function* we would need to draw a straight line touching the curve at each particular point (the *tangent* to that point) and then find the slope (*gradient*) of that tangent. Clearly in Figure A.6A and Figure A.6B (p. 335) gradients to these non-linear (quadratic) functions will be changing at each and every point (i.e. for different values of *x*). It would be extremely tedious to draw and measure the gradients to a large number of points along non-linear functions.

We can short-circuit this whole process by using the technique of *differentiation*. We can then establish a formula that will give the value of the tangent drawn to any point on the curve. This formula is often referred to as the *first derivative* of the curve. So important is this technique to our understanding of much of the analysis underpinning the solution of business-related problems that we shall consider it in some detail.

Did you know?

'Big data' (p. 253) is playing a key role in helping identify the relationships and equations that underpin consumer behaviour. This is helping organisations devise more accurate revenue, cost and profit functions to use in finding turning points. For example, Eric Siegel, in his recent book *Predictive Analytics: The Power to Predict Who Will Click, Buy, Lie or Die*, reveals how big data techniques have yielded surprising insights into consumers' habits. Pharmacy chains have found that if you buy nappies you are likely to buy beer; insurance companies have found that a low credit rating means you are more likely to have a car accident. All these newly discovered variables and their relative importance can be introduced into the key equations determining revenue, cost and profit to help identify what policies may be needed if an organisation is to maximise revenue, minimise cost or maximise profit.

8.1.1 Gradients and limits

The idea of limits is central to understanding the process of differentiation. In fact we shall see that the slope of a *tangent* just touching a curve is in fact the limit of the slope of a *chord* joining two points along that curve. In Figure 8.1 we can connect two separate points on the curve, namely *P* and *Q*, by drawing the straight line *PQ*. This chord can easily be depicted as the hypotenuse of the right-angled triangle *PQR*, and from trigonometry we know that the tangent of angle *QPR* will give us the slope of the chord.

Slope of chord $PQ = \tan. QPR$

$$= \frac{\text{side opposite}}{\text{side adjacent}}$$

$$= \frac{QR}{PR}$$

PAUSE FOR THOUGHT 8.1

Can you suggest three other examples illustrating the idea of a limit?

We can always calculate the slope of a chord since we can find the actual values for *QR* and *PR*. However, we can't actually calculate the slope of a tangent. But what we can do is

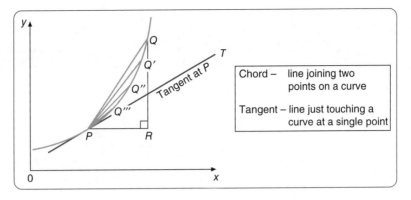

Figure 8.1 Gradients and limits

take the *limit* of the slope of a chord as a close approximation to the slope of a tangent to that point on the curve. It will be useful to use Figure 8.1 to explain this.

As Q approaches (gets nearer to) P along the curve, the slope of the chord PQ gets closer and closer to the slope of the *tangent* at P, namely PT. Of course another way of expressing the idea of Q approaching P is to say that PR (the base of the triangle) tends to zero – that is, $PR \rightarrow 0$. As long as P and Q are separate points along the curve, the slope of PQ will never actually equal the slope of PT, but it will become so close to the value of PT that for all intents and purposes it can be regarded as identical. We can use the following shorthand to express this idea.

Slope of tangent PT = limit to the slope of the chord PQ, as Q approaches P

i.e. Slope of tangent $PT = \text{limit} \left(\dfrac{QR}{PR} \right)$

$$PR \rightarrow 0$$

We now apply these ideas to curves involving the dependent variable y and the independent variable x. For purposes of illustration we shall use the simple *quadratic* relationship $y = x^2$ as in Figure 8.2. The symbol Δ refers to a *change* in any variable.

We construct a chord PQ connecting point P (with co-ordinates x^*, y^*) and point Q (with co-ordinates $x^* + \Delta x, y^* + \Delta y$).

Following our earlier reasoning we can state the following:

Slope of tangent to curve at $P = \text{limit} \left(\dfrac{QR}{PR} \right)$

$$PR \rightarrow 0$$

Slope of tangent to curve at $P = \text{limit} \left(\dfrac{\Delta y}{\Delta x} \right)$

$$\Delta x \rightarrow 0$$

Slope of tangent to curve at $P = \dfrac{dy}{dx}$

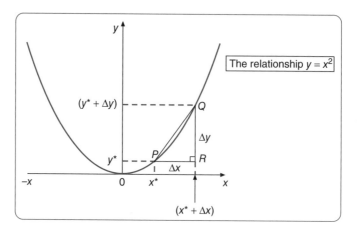

Figure 8.2 Process of differentiation

The expression $\dfrac{dy}{dx}$ is merely shorthand for the expression directly above it, and is termed the *first derivative*. Put another way, we have *differentiated* the variable y with respect to x. Of course what we have done is to find an expression for the slope of the *tangent* to any point on the curve as being the limit of a known expression for the slope of the *chord* to that curve.

From Figure 8.2 we can show that for the curve $y = x^2$, the first derivative will always be $\dfrac{dy}{dx} = 2x$ at each and every point on that curve. The workings behind this solution are indicated in Box 8.1 at the end of this chapter (p. 281).

This extremely powerful result tells us that for any given value of x we can find the slope of the tangent to the curve at that point.

Thus for $x = 1$, the slope of the tangent to the curve at $x = 1$ is $\dfrac{dy}{dx} = 2x = 2(1) = 2$;

for $x = 2$, the slope of the tangent to the curve at $x = 2$ is $\dfrac{dy}{dx} = 2x = 2(2) = 4$; and so on.

If we repeat this process for other curves then we shall see that a *pattern* emerges which forms the basis for an important formula used in differentiation.

Suppose we differentiate (find $\dfrac{dy}{dx}$ for) the curve $y = 3x^2$ using our earlier approach. As we can see from Box 8.2 at the end of this chapter (p. 282), the solution will be that $\dfrac{dy}{dx} = 6x$.

Thus for $x = 1$, the slope of the tangent to the curve $y = 3x^2$ at $x = 1$ is $\dfrac{dy}{dx} = 6x = 6(1) = 6$; for $x = 2$, the slope of the tangent to the curve at $x = 2$ is $\dfrac{dy}{dx} = 6x = 6(2) = 12$; and so on.

General formula for differentiation

In fact the pattern that will always result from such differentiation will give us the following general formula.

If $y = ax^n$

when a = any constant

x = any variable

n = any power

then $\dfrac{dy}{dx} = nax^{n-1}$

Thus if $y = 1x^2$

$$\frac{dy}{dx} = 2.1\,x^{2-1} = 2x$$

and if $y = 3x^2$

$$\frac{dy}{dx} = 2.3\,x^{2-1} = 6x$$

and so on.

This extremely powerful result will allow us to find (in the limit) the slope of the tangent drawn to any point on a particular curve.

PAUSE FOR THOUGHT 8.2

Can you suggest what we get if we differentiate the equations respectively for the following curves:

(a) total cost;

(b) total revenue;

(c) total profit?

Self-check questions 8.1

Q1. Use the 'rule' for differentiation to find the gradient $\left(\dfrac{dy}{dx}\right)$ to each of the following expressions:

(a) $y = 9x$ (b) $y = 4x^2$ (c) $y = 3x^3$ (d) $y = 5x^4$

(e) $y = \dfrac{x^3}{3}$ (i.e. $y = \dfrac{1}{3}x^3$)   (f) $y = \dfrac{x^4}{4}$ (i.e. $y = \dfrac{1}{4}x^4$)

(g) $y = \sqrt{x^2}$ (i.e. $y = x^{\frac{1}{2}}$)   (h) $y = 10$ (i.e. $y = 10x^0$)

Note: Questions (g) to (h) make use of your knowledge of powers/indices – see Appendix 1 (p. 314).

(continued)

Q2. For each of the curves or lines given by the expressions in Q1 above, find the value of the gradient at:

(a) $x = 1$;   (b) $x = 2$.

Note: Answers to Self-Check Questions can be found on the instructor's website, www.pearsoned.co.uk/wall

8.2   Turning points

Clearly the ideas of *maxima* and *minima* (i.e. turning points) are vital to many business-related problems. As we can see from Figure 8.3A the value of the first derivative (the gradient) $\dfrac{dy}{dx}$ will be zero for any turning point, whether maximum or minimum. In other words, we can differentiate the equation of the curve $y = x^3$ by finding $\dfrac{dy}{dx}$. If we plot $\dfrac{dy}{dx}$ ($= 3x^2$) against x, as in Figure 8.3B, set $\dfrac{dy}{dx} = 0$ and solve for x, then for a quadratic equation we can expect two solutions for the turning points x_1 and x_2.

Unfortunately we will not, at this stage, be able to distinguish between the maximum and minimum solutions. However, by taking second derivatives (i.e. finding the gradient to the gradient), we can distinguish between the different turning points.

Figure 8.3C shows the gradient $\left(\dfrac{dy}{dx}\right)$ of the gradient $\left(\dfrac{dy}{dx}\right)$ already displayed in Figure 8.3B. This is known as finding the *second derivative* and is expressed as $\dfrac{d^2y}{dx^2}$ of $\left(\dfrac{dy}{dx} \text{ of } \dfrac{dy}{dx}\right)$.

- Where we have the *maximum* at x_1, the value of the first derivative is zero, and the value of the second derivative (at x_1) is *negative*.

- Where we have the *minimum* at x_2, the value of the first derivative is zero, and the value of the second derivative (at x_2) is *positive*.

PAUSE FOR THOUGHT 8.3

Can you suggest why finding turning points might be important to a media company?

The following worked example illustrates this approach.

Worked example 8.1

$y = x^3 - 27x + 3$
Find the turning points for this equation.
   Distinguish between maximum and minimum turning points.

Solution

$\dfrac{dy}{dx} = 0$ at a turning point

i.e. $\dfrac{dy}{dx} = 3x^2 - 27 = 0$ (applying our general formula for differentiation to each term separately)

Worked
example
8.1
(cont'd)

$$3x^2 = 27$$

$$x^2 = 9$$

$$x = +3 \text{ or } -3 \text{ are the turning points}$$

$\dfrac{d^2y}{dx^2} = 6x$ (second derivative, applying $\dfrac{dy}{dx}$ to the previous $\dfrac{dy}{dx}$)

At $x = +3$, second derivative $= +18$

$\quad x = +3$ is a minimum

At $x = -3$, second derivative $= -18$

$\quad x = -3$ is a maximum

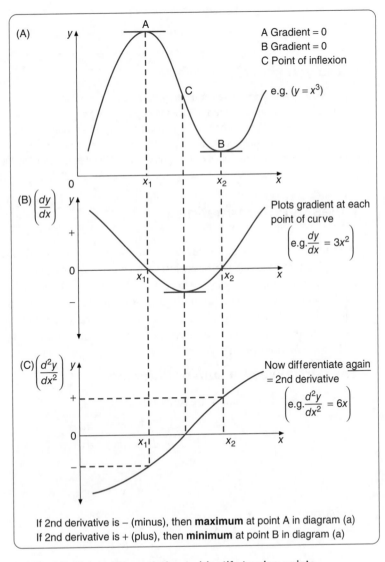

If 2nd derivative is − (minus), then **maximum** at point A in diagram (a)
If 2nd derivative is + (plus), then **minimum** at point B in diagram (a)

Figure 8.3 Using differentiation to identify turning points

259

Self-check questions 8.2

Q1. Can you suggest how this idea of finding turning points might be helpful to managers of a publishing company in achieving their objectives? Suppose that consultants to the publishers have worked out equations showing how revenue and cost vary with annual output of the books they publish?

Q2. Find the maximum and/or minimum turning points for the following curves.

(a) $y = x^2 - 10x + 16$ (b) $y = 9 - 6x + x^2$

(c) $y = 12 + 4x - x^2$ (d) $y = x^3 - 27x + 6$

(e) $y = x^3 - 3x^2$ (f) $y = \dfrac{x^3}{3} - \dfrac{7}{2}x^2 + 12x$

(*Note:* Use your 'rule' to differentiate each term separately, not forgetting the sign in front of each term).

Note: Answers to Self-Check Questions can be found on the instructor's website, www.pearsoned.co.uk/wall

Did you know?

Pearson, the world's largest educational publisher, announced a major shift in corporate strategy in 2013, having experienced a 50% fall in profits in the previous year. Pearson announced that it would 'strengthen dramatically its position in digital education', which now generated 50% of turnover and is predicted to generate 70% of turnover by 2015. This strategic change reflected major revisions to profitability functions of both digital and non-digital publishing respectively.

8.3 Rules of differentiation

We can set out our earlier 'rule' for differentiating an expression more formally. In all the examples above we were differentiating an expression involving sums (plus signs) or differences (minus signs). However, there are other types of expression to which our rule could apply, such as those involving multiplication (product) or division (quotient).

In all the following 'rules' we use the letters u and v to stand for parts of the expression we are differentiating, with each of these parts involving the variable x in some way (i.e. u and v are functions of x).

8.3.1 The derivative of a sum or difference

If $y = u + v$ (where u and v are functions of x)

$$\frac{dy}{dx} = \frac{du}{dx} + \frac{dv}{dx}$$

Worked example 8.2

$$y = 2x^4 - 4x^2$$

Solution

$$\frac{dy}{dx} = 8x^3 - 8x$$

8.3.2 The derivative of a product

If $y = uv$ (where u and v are functions of x)

$$\frac{dy}{dx} = u\frac{dv}{dx} + v\frac{du}{dx}$$

Worked example 8.3

$$y = (3x + 1)(3x^2) \qquad \left(u = 3x + 1, \frac{du}{dx} = 3\right.$$

$$\left. v = 3x^2, \frac{dv}{dx} = 6x\right)$$

Solution

$$\frac{dy}{dx} = (3x + 1)\cdot(6x) + (3x^2)\cdot(3)$$

$$\frac{dy}{dx} = 18x^2 + 6x + 9x^2$$

$$\frac{dy}{dx} = 27x^2 + 6x$$

8.3.3 The derivative of a quotient

$y = \dfrac{u}{v}$ (where u and v are functions of x)

$$\frac{dy}{dx} = \frac{u\dfrac{dv}{dx} - v\dfrac{du}{dx}}{v^2}$$

Worked example 8.4

$$y = \frac{3x - 2}{5x + 3} \qquad \left[u = 3x - 2, \frac{du}{dx} = 3\right.$$

$$\left. v = 5x + 3, \frac{dv}{dx} = 5\right]$$

Solution

$$\frac{dy}{dx} = \frac{(3x - 2)\cdot(5) - (5x + 3)\cdot(3)}{(5x + 3)^2}$$

$$\frac{dy}{dx} = \frac{15x - 10 - 15x - 9}{25x^2 + 30x + 9}$$

$$\frac{dy}{dx} = \frac{-19}{25x^2 + 30x + 9}$$

8.3.4 The derivative of a function of a function

If $y = f(u)$ where $u = f(x)$

$$\frac{dy}{dx} = \frac{dy}{du} \cdot \frac{du}{dx}$$

Worked example 8.5

$$y = (3x^2 + 2)^4 \qquad \left[y = u^4, \frac{dy}{du} = 4u^3 \right.$$

$$\left. u = 3x^2 + 2, \frac{du}{dx} = 6x \right]$$

Solution

$$\frac{dy}{dx} = 4u^3 \cdot 6x$$

$$= 24x \cdot u^3$$

$$= 24x \cdot (3x^2 + 2)^3$$

Self-check question 8.3

Differentiate each of the following expressions using an appropriate rule.

(a) $y = 7x^5 + 3x^2$

(b) $y = 4x^5 - 4x^3$

(c) $y = (2x + 3)(2x^3)$

(d) $y = (3x + 4)(3x^4)$

(e) $y = \dfrac{(2x + 3)}{2x^2}$

(f) $y = \dfrac{4x^2 - 2}{2x^2 + 4}$

(g) $y = (2x^2 + 3)^2$

(h) $y = (3x^3 + 4)^3$

Note: Answers to Self-Check Questions can be found on the instructor's website, www.pearsoned.co.uk/wall

---

8.4 Applications of differentiation

8.4.1 Revenue, cost and profit

Obviously turning points, involving maximum or minimum outcomes, are likely to have widespread applications in economics or business. These applications make use of the definitions involving revenue, cost or profit.

- Total Revenue (TR) = Price (Average Revenue) × Quantity Sold

Average Revenue (AR) = Price = $\dfrac{\text{TR}}{\text{Quantity}}$

- Total Cost (TC) = Total Fixed Cost (TFC) + Total Variable Cost (TVC)

Average total cost (ATC) = $\dfrac{\text{TC}}{\text{Quantity}}$

- Total Profit (TP) = Total Revenue − Total Cost

The example below uses Facebook as an application of differentiation.

BREAK-OUT BOX 8.1

Facebook

Automatic example generator

In the Excel sheet Chapter8_Example_1 you will find data for revenues of Facebook, over the period Q1 2011 to Q4 2012. Over this period Facebook had roughly 900 million monthly active users (10.8 billion active users a year) and received an average of $814.81 income per user, per year, mostly from advertising to those users.

Excel has the ability to generate a trend line and to show the equation of that trend line. The dotted line on the graph is a trend line that Excel has fitted to the data points.

Did you know?

Shifts in media habits by users can have major impacts on the revenue, cost and profit functions for media companies. For example, in 2013 a survey by the National Literacy Trust in the United Kingdom found that, for the first time, children and young people are spending more time reading on computers or other electronic devices than they are reading on printed books, magazines and comics. The findings showed that 8- to 16-year-olds spend 39% of their reading time each day using electronic devices, including tablets and e-readers, which is more than the time spent on any other form of reading. In fact the number in this age group reading e-books had doubled in the previous two years from 6% to 12%. However, the survey also showed that those mainly reading print media were around twice as likely to be 'above-average readers' compared to those mainly reading electronic media, and more than four times as likely to say they 'enjoy reading'.

Suppose that the owner of a glossy, high-priced monthly magazine has used consultants to estimate its annual demand (average revenue) curve and average total cost curve for the firm as follows:

$$D = AR = 21 - x$$

$$ATC = \frac{x^2}{3} - 3x + 9$$

where x = output (000) in units per month

AR = Average Revenue (£)

ATC = Average Total Cost (£)

The consultants can use *differentiation* to advise the magazine owners as to the monthly output and sales needed to maximise either total revenue or total profit.

1. *Maximum total revenue*

Total revenue = average revenue (price) × quantity (output)

$$TR = AR \times x$$
$$TR = (21 - x) \times x$$
$$TR = 21x - x^2$$

If we let $y = TR$

then $\dfrac{dy}{dx} = 0$ for a turning point

i.e. $21 - 2x = 0$

$$21 = 2x$$
$$10.5 = x$$

Second derivative $= \dfrac{d^2 y}{dx^2} = -2$

So the turning point is a maximum since the second derivative is negative.

An output of 10.5 units (i.e. 10,500 magazines per month) will maximise total revenue.

2. *Maximum total profit*

Remember, Total Profit (TP) = Total Revenue − Total Cost

Total Revenue (TR) = Average Revenue × Quantity (Output)

Total Cost (TC) = Average Total Cost × Quantity (Output)

So $TR = (21 - x).x = 21x - x^2$

$$TC = \left(\dfrac{x^2}{3} - 3x + 9 \right).x = \dfrac{x^3}{3} - 3x^2 + 9x$$

$$TP = TR - TC$$

$$TP = [21x - x^2] - \left[\dfrac{x^3}{3} - 3x^2 + 9x \right]$$

$$TP = -\dfrac{x^3}{3} + 2x^2 + 12x$$

If we let $y = TP$

then $\dfrac{dy}{dx} = 0$ for a turning point

i.e. $-x^2 + 4x + 12 = 0$

$(-x + 6)(x + 2) = 0$ (factorising)

i.e. $x = 6$ and $x = -2$ are the solutions.

Taking the second derivative

$$\dfrac{d^2y}{dx^2} = -2x + 4$$

- when $x = +6$, 2nd derivative is negative (-8)

  so $x = +6$ is a maximum

- when $x = -2$, 2nd derivative is positive ($+8$)

  so $x = -2$ is a minimum.

An output of 6 units (i.e. 6,000 magazines per month) will maximise total profit.

The (maximum) total profit earned at an output of 6 units is:

$$TP = -\frac{6^3}{3} + 2(6)^2 + 12(6)$$

i.e. $TP = -72 + 72 + 72$

$$TP = 72 \text{ (i.e. £72,000 per month)}$$

3. *Price*

We can, of course, easily find the price at which the monthly magazine must be sold. Remember, price = average revenue.

Price $= AR = 21 - x$

when $x = 10.5$ (maximum TR), price $= 21 - 10.5 = £10.5$

when $x = 6$ (maximum TP), price $= 21 - 6 = £15$

4. *Minimum cost*

The consultants to the magazine owner in our previous example have estimated that the average total cost (ATC) for producing the magazine is given by the expression

$$ATC = \frac{x^2}{3} - 3x + 9$$

where ATC = average total cost (£)

$\quad\quad x$ = output (000) in units per month.

We may now wish to find the 'technical optimum' output – that is, that level of monthly output for which ATC is a minimum. Again, we can use our rules of differentiation to solve such a problem.

Let $y = ATC$

$\frac{dy}{dx} = 0$ for a turning point

$\frac{2}{3}x - 3 = 0$

$\frac{2}{3}x = 3$

$x = 4.5$

To check that this turning point is a minimum, we find the second derivative.

$\frac{d^2y}{dx^2} = +\frac{2}{3}$

The sign of the second derivative is positive, so the turning point is a minimum.

An output of 4.5 units (i.e. 4,500 magazines per month) will minimise ATC – that is, be a technically efficient output.

Figure 8.4 presents a visual overview of these solutions involving revenue, profit, price and cost.

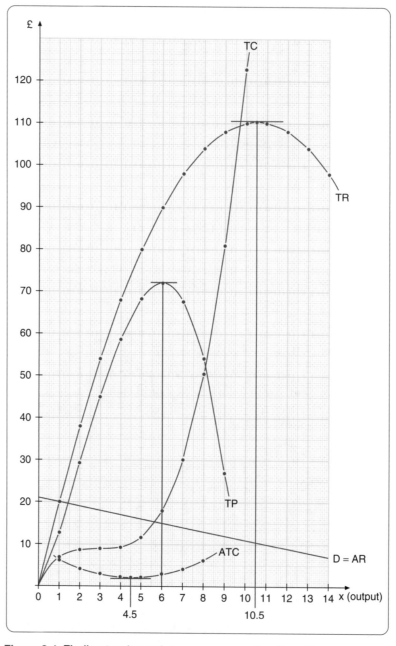

Figure 8.4 Finding turning points: revenue, cost and profit

News Corp adopts new media model

As the media sector has 'matured', rapid technological change has resulted in substantial shifts in both revenue (via impacts on demand) and cost functions. These have led to changes in the business models adopted by the media sector, as is well illustrated by recent developments in News Corp, the world's largest media group.

News Corp analysts see very different revenue and cost functions for entertainment assets such as film and television networks (e.g. 21st Century Fox and BSkyB) than they see for its 130 newspaper and other print publishing assets (e.g. Times Newspapers and *Wall Street Journal*). This is the reason why, in 2013, News Corp split its company into two separate companies reflecting these increasingly different types of media assets, the new 21st Century Fox covering entertainment and News Corp covering print publishing respectively.

Other media companies have also revised upwards their revenue functions for entertainment-related assets, such as Viacom, Disney and Time Warner, each of which has delivered more than double the S&P 500's average return of 6.1% over the past five years. In contrast these media companies have disposed of many of their newspaper and other print-related assets, which have experienced little or no growth in value over the past five years under increased digital competition from e-books, tablets and smartphones.

Self-check questions 8.4

Q1. A local newspaper publisher has been given the following information by its production and sales department.

$$\text{Average revenue (£)} = 32 - \frac{2}{3} \cdot x^2$$

$$\text{Average cost (£)} = \frac{1}{3}x^2 - x + 11$$

where x = output (000) in newspapers per day.

(a) Find an expression for
  (i) total revenue;
  (ii) total cost;
  (iii) total profit.

(b) At what output is total profit a maximum?
  How much profit is earned at this output?
  What price is charged for this output?

Q2. The total revenue and total cost curves for a book-binding company are indicated below:

$$TR = 40x - 8x^2$$
$$TC = 8 + 16x - x^2$$

where TR = total revenue (£)
  TC = total cost (£)
  x = output of books (000 units)

(a) Find the level of output at which total profit (y) is a maximum. What price will be charged for this output? How much profit will be earned?

(b) If the firm were to seek to maximise total revenue rather than profit, how would your output target differ from (a) above? What profit would be earned at this new output level?

(continued)

Q3. Suppose the total cost function for a business producing A3 size posters is as follows.

$$TC = \frac{x^3}{3} - x^2 + 11x$$

where C = total cost (£)

x = output of posters (000 units)

(a) What output would make average Total Cost a minimum?

Note: Answers to Self-Check Questions can be found on the instructor's website, www.pearsoned.co.uk/wall

8.4.2 Marginal analysis

In some of the solutions to problems involving revenue, cost and profit we needed to differentiate (find the gradient to) the total revenue, total cost and total profit curves respectively. When we did this we were in fact finding the expressions for *marginal* revenue, *marginal* cost and *marginal* profit respectively.

We can usefully illustrate this idea in terms of marginal revenue (MR). Remember that MR is the addition to total revenue (TR) from selling the last unit of output. We can therefore say that MR is, in the *limit*, the rate of change of TR with regard to output. In other words, MR is the slope of the tangent to any particular point on the TR curve. We have already noted that the slope of that tangent is *zero* (i.e. MR = 0) when TR is a maximum.

If we differentiate (find the gradient to) the total revenue, total cost and total profit curves respectively, then we will find marginal revenue, marginal cost and marginal profit.

- If Total Revenue (TR) $= y$

  then Marginal Revenue (MR) $= \dfrac{dy}{dx}$

- If Total cost (TC) $= y$

  then Marginal Cost (MC) $= \dfrac{dy}{dx}$

- If Total Profit (TP) $= y$

  then Marginal Profit (MP) $= \dfrac{dy}{dx}$

Self-check questions 8.5

Q1. Total revenue $= y = 20x - 2x^2$
   (a) Find an expression for marginal Revenue.
   (b) Plot the total revenue and marginal revenue curves on a graph ($x = 0$ to $x = 8$).

Q2. Total cost $= y = \dfrac{1}{3} \cdot x^3 - x^2 + 11x$

   (a) Find an expression for marginal cost.
   (b) Plot the total cost and marginal cost curves on a graph ($x = 0$ to $x = 6$)

Note: Answers to Self-Check Questions can be found on the instructor's website, www.pearsoned.co.uk/wall

8.4.3 Price elasticity of demand

Price elasticity of demand (PED) is a measure of the responsiveness of demand for a product to a change in its own price. It is an extremely important concept for business since its value will impact directly on the pricing strategy of the firm.

$$\text{PED} = \frac{\% \text{ change in quantity demanded of } x}{\% \text{ change in price of } x}$$

Here we use P for the original price and Q for the original quantity, and Δ for any change in that price or quantity. We can now say that:

$$\text{PED} = \frac{\dfrac{\Delta Q}{Q} \cdot 100}{\dfrac{\Delta P}{P} \cdot 100}$$

$$\text{PED} = \frac{\Delta Q}{Q} \div \frac{\Delta P}{P} \text{ (100s cancel out)}$$

$$\text{PED} = \frac{\Delta Q}{Q} \cdot \frac{P}{\Delta P} \text{ (to change divide to multiply, turn one fraction on its head)}$$

$$\text{PED} = \frac{P}{Q} \cdot \frac{\Delta Q}{\Delta P} \text{ (collect } \Delta\text{s on one side)}$$

Clearly the ratio $\Delta Q/\Delta P$ in Figure 8.5 will now vary depending on the *direction* of price change from P and on the *magnitude* of the price change from P.

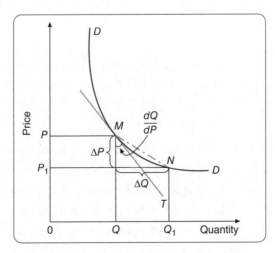

Figure 8.5 Using differentiation to calculate PED at a point on the demand curve

Point price elasticity of demand

However, at the point M there is a *unique* value for price elasticity of demand (PED). In other words, when demand is non-linear, only for infinitely small changes in price around the original price do we have a unique value of PED. We call this *point elasticity of demand* and it can be expressed as:

$$\text{Point price elasticity of demand} = \frac{P}{Q} \cdot \frac{dQ}{dP}$$

$$\left[\text{where } \frac{dQ}{dP} = \text{limit}\left(\frac{\Delta Q}{\Delta P} \right) \right]$$

$$\Delta P \to 0$$

In terms of Figure 8.5, as N approaches M (ΔP tends to zero), the slope of the chord MN (measured as angle QMN), namely $\Delta Q/\Delta P$, becomes closer and closer to the slope of the tangent MT (measured as angle QMT) at point M. In the *limit*, as N gets extremely close to M, we can regard the two slopes as identical, even though they will never quite be identical so long as N is a separate point from M on the demand curve.

In other words, at the point M, PED can be found by multiplying the ratio of initial price to initial quantity by the slope of the tangent (MT) to M. The slope of MT is expressed using derivatives (dQ/dP).

For anything other than an infinitely small change in price around the initial price, we must admit that PED will vary with both the direction and magnitude of the price change.

PAUSE FOR THOUGHT 8.4

Can you use Figure 8.5 to explain why a fall in price from P to P_1 will have a different PED over the range of the demand curve from M to N than it will have at point M?

Worked example 8.6

A book publisher used consultants to advise on its pricing policy. For its bestselling title the consultants report back that the quantity demanded (Q) of the paperback books and the price of paperback books (P) are related in the following way:

$$Q = 400 - P^2$$

where Q = quantity of paperback books in units

P = price of paperback books in £'s

(a) What is the (point) price elasticity of demand?

(b) Calculate this price elasticity at a price of £5.

(c) What do these findings suggest in regard to pricing policy for this bestselling book?

Worked example 8.6 (cont'd)

Solution

(a) $\text{PED} = \dfrac{P}{Q} \cdot \dfrac{dQ}{dP}$

where $\dfrac{dQ}{dP} = -2P$ (use our earlier 'rule' [p. 257] but Q replacing y and P replacing x)

So $\text{PED} = \dfrac{P}{Q}.(-2P)$

(b) At $P = £5$

$$Q = 400 - 5^2$$

i.e. $Q = 400 - 25 = 375$

So $\text{PED} = \dfrac{5}{375} \cdot (-10)$

So $\text{PED} = \dfrac{1}{75} \cdot (-10) = \dfrac{-10}{75}$

$\text{PED} = -0.13$

(c) The suggestion from these findings is that the publishers might consider raising the price of their bestselling paperback title to increase revenue. Strictly speaking PED is negative (-0.13 here) since the demand curve slopes downwards from left to right. However, in practice the negative sign is often ignored. Any value for PED less than 1 implies a *relatively price inelastic* demand, and suggests that a price cut will reduce total revenue, whereas a price rise will increase total revenue.

8.4.4 Inventory (stock) control

As we shall see (Box 8.3, p. 283) the use of differentiation can play an important part in deriving a formula for minimising the cost of holding *inventory* (stock).

A business in the media or any other sector of activity will need to hold inventories of its products for a variety of reasons.

- A stock of raw materials and work in progress is often needed so that the delivery of the service or product is not interrupted by shortages.

- A stock of finished products can help by acting as a buffer between customer demand and unexpected issues involving the supply chain.

However, inventory (stock) represents cash tied up in either the production process or in finished products awaiting distribution. There may therefore be a conflict between the financial department, which would like to keep inventory to a minimum in order to release as much capital for other uses, and the production and marketing departments, which would like to see adequate levels of inventory to ensure against breakdown, down-time or late delivery. The purpose of inventory (stock) control is to find the *optimum* level of inventory that reconciles these two views.

Types of inventory (stock) cost

There are three broad categories of costs involving inventories: the cost of holding stock (carrying costs), the costs of obtaining stock (ordering costs) and the costs of failing to have adequate stock (stock-out costs).

Inventory costs include the following:

- *Holding or carrying costs.* These might include insurance, storage costs (staff, equipment, handling, deterioration, obsolescence, security). These might also include opportunity costs – that is, the financial cost in terms of alternatives foregone (e.g. interest) through having capital tied up.

- *Ordering costs.* These occur when obtaining stock and might include the cost of clerical and administrative work in raising an order, any associated transport costs and inspection of stock on arrival, and so on.

- *Stock-out costs.* These are difficult to quantify but might include the following:
  - missed orders from occasional customers;
  - missed delivery dates resulting in a deterioration in customer/supplier relations;
  - penalty clauses incurred for late delivery.

Stock carrying costs can be expected to *rise* as the order size increases, for reasons already discussed. However, stock ordering costs can be expected to *fall* as the order size increases (see Figure 8.6).

If we ignore stock-out costs, which are notoriously difficult to quantify, then total (inventory) costs can be regarded as the sum of the carrying and ordering costs. These will be at a minimum for the following value of Q (output).

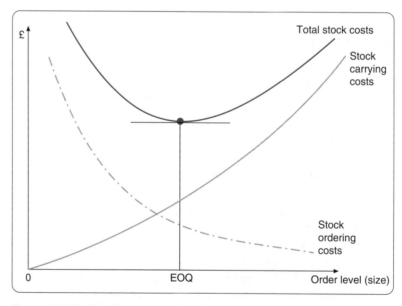

Figure 8.6 Finding the economic order quantity (EOQ)

Economic order quantity (EOQ)

$$Q = \sqrt{\frac{2.CoD}{Cc}}$$

where Q = economic order quantity

Co = ordering cost for one order

D = annual demand for stock

Cc = carrying cost for one item per annum

Note: A proof of this formula can be found in Box 8.3 (p. 283).

We call the ordering quantity that minimises the sum of inventory carrying costs and ordering the economic order quantity (EOQ).

Worked example 8.7

A training film distributor buys in 100,000 booklets per annum to accompany its videos, each of which cost the firm £10 to purchase from its supplier. The carrying cost of stocking these booklets is estimated as 15% per annum of the purchase price. The ordering costs are estimated at £200 per order. Find the economic order quantity.

Solution

$$EOQ = \sqrt{\frac{2CoD}{Cc}}$$

where Co = £10 per order

D = 100,000 units per annum

Cc = £10 × 0.15 = £1.50 per item per annum.

i.e. $EOQ = \sqrt{\frac{2.(10).(100,000)}{1.50}}$

i.e. EOQ = 1,155 units (booklets).

Of course more complex inventory control situations with variable usage rates, variable lead times and gradual (rather than instantaneous) replenishment may be encountered by firms.

Self-check question 8.6

Mondeo Ltd produces specialist e-book readers using an electronic component, EL3. Since June, Mondeo has been using a new supplier that can supply EL3 components at a much cheaper cost.

Calculate the economic order quantity if each order of EL3 components costs the firm £200, there is a carrying cost of £2 per EL3 component per annum and an annual demand for 5,000 EL3 components.

Note: Answers to Self-Check Questions can be found on the instructor's website, www.pearsoned.co.uk/wall

Of course relationships may exist between more than two variables, such as the demand for a product depending on many variables other than its own price – for example, the price of any substitutes or complements in consumption, and the income of the household. Often we want to find the rate of change between two variables (say, quantity demanded of x and its own price) while assuming that the value of each of these other variables remains constant at some particular level. We are then involved in the process of *partial differentiation*, to which we now turn.

<table>
<tr><td>8.5</td><td>**Partial differentiation**</td></tr>
</table>

Many functions have *more than one* independent variable. A function with two independent variables could be expressed:

$$y = f(x,z).$$

Similarly, a function with three independent variables could be expressed:

$$y = f(w,x,z).$$

If we differentiate the function with respect to *one* of these variables, keeping *all other variables constant*, we are using the process of partial differentiations and are finding the partial derivatives.

We can illustrate the idea of partial differentiation using Figure 8.7, which shows a situation in which the variable y depends upon two variables, x and z. Clearly we now have a three-dimensional diagram.

- When we partially differentiate y with respect to x, we use the terminology $\frac{\partial y}{\partial x}$, replacing the letter d with ∂ to indicate partial differentiation. Essentially we are seeking to find the rate of change of y with respect to x, everything else (in this case z) assumed constant.

  Suppose z is assumed to be constant at the specific value OG, then we are finding the gradient (rate of change) to segment DE of the surface at each value of x.

- Alternatively we may be seeking to partially differentiate y with respect to z, using the terminology $\frac{\partial y}{\partial z}$. In this case we are seeking to find the rate of change of y with respect

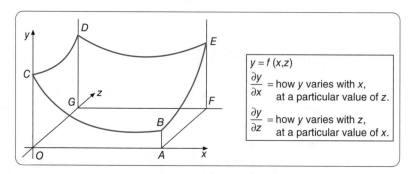

Figure 8.7 Using partial differentiation to find the gradient to a segment of a surface at a particular value of some other variable

to z, everything else (in this case x) assumed constant. Suppose x is assumed to be constant at the specific value OA, then we are finding the gradient (rate of change) to segment BE of the surface at each value of Z. On the other hand, if x is assumed to be constant at the specific value 0 (zero), then we are finding the gradient (rate of change) to segment CD of the surface at each value of z.

Strictly speaking, finding *own-price elasticities of demand* often involves the 'other things equal' assumption for variables other than the price of the product in question, and is therefore a partial elasticity. The same is true of calculations involving *cross-elasticities of demand*, where only the price of the other product is allowed to change. The *particular values* of these other variables might then affect the own-price or cross-elasticity of demand calculations, as is illustrated in the following examples.

8.5.1 Calculating partial derivatives

To differentiate a function with respect to *one* of its variables, treat the remaining variables as constants and proceed in the usual way already considered for differentiation. Here the dependent variable (y) depends on two independent variables, x and z.

Worked example 8.8

Give the partial derivatives of

$$y = x^2 + 3xz - 4z^2$$

$$\frac{\partial y}{\partial x} = 2x + 3z \text{ (treat } z \text{ as a constant when differentiating)}$$

This measures the rate of change of y with respect to x, all other variables (here z) held constant.

$$\frac{\partial y}{\partial Z} = 3x - 8z \text{ (treat } x \text{ as a constant when differentiating)}$$

This measures the rate of change of y with respect to Z, all other variables (here x) held constant.

Note that the value of each partial derivative is influenced by the particular value of the 'other variable', whether z or x.

Worked example 8.9

Find the partial derivatives of

$$y = w^3 - w^2x + x^2z - z^2$$

$$\frac{\partial y}{\partial w} = 3w^2 - 2wx \text{ (treat } x \text{ and } z \text{ as constants when differentiating)}$$

$$\frac{\partial y}{\partial x} = -w^2 + 2xz \text{ (treat } w \text{ and } z \text{ as constants when differentiating)}$$

$$\frac{\partial y}{\partial z} = x^2 - 2z \text{ (treat } w \text{ and } x \text{ as constants when differentiating)}$$

Self-check question 8.7

Find the partial derivatives of

$$y = x^3 + 3x^2z - 6z^2$$

Note: Answers to Self-Check Questions can be found on the instructor's website, www.pearsoned.co.uk/wall

8.6   Integration

This is the *opposite* process to differentiation. As Figure 8.8 illustrates, if we have gone from a particular expression or function (e.g. $y = x^2$) to the first derivative (e.g. $\dfrac{dy}{dx} = 2x$) using *differentiation*, then we go backwards from $2x$ to x^2 using *integration*.

The function $y = x^2$ in Figure 8.8 is differentiated using our earlier 'rule' (p. 257) to give the gradient $\dfrac{dy}{dx} = 2x$. But suppose we are told that the result of differentiating some function is $2x$ and are asked to find the original function! In this case we must *reverse* the differentiation process in Figure 8.8 and instead use the integration process.

Unfortunately we will encounter an immediate problem in finding an *exact* original function whose derivative is $2x$. For example, we could work back from $\dfrac{dy}{dx} = 2x$ to get *all* of the following original functions (y).

$\dfrac{dy}{dx}$	y
$2x$	$x^2 + 1$
$2x$	$x^2 + 2$
$2x$	$x^2 + 3$
.	.
.	.
.	.
$2x$	$x^2 + C$

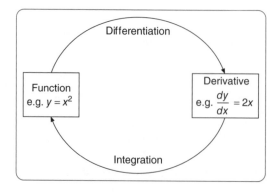

Figure 8.8 Integration as the opposite of differentiation

So if we know the derivative $\dfrac{dy}{dx}$ of a function is $2x$, we must write that the original function (y) is x^2+C where C is any constant.

The standard symbol for the integration process is $\displaystyle\int$, which looks rather like an extended letter 's'. Whenever we are integrating we must also remember that we are integrating with respect to some variable; here the variable is x, so we must write dx at the end of the function to be integrated.

We can now write our integration as:

$$\int 2x\,dx = x^2 + C$$

Examples

$$\int 2x\,dx = x^2 + C$$

$$\int 4x\,dx = 2x^2 + C$$

$$\int 6x\,dx = 3x^2 + C$$

$$\int 8x\,dx = 4x^2 + C$$

Can you see a pattern emerging from these examples?

$\dfrac{dy}{dx}$	y
$2x^1$	$\dfrac{2x^2}{2} + C$
$4x^1$	$\dfrac{4x^2}{2} + C$
$6x^1$	$\dfrac{6x^2}{2} + C$
$8x^1$	$\dfrac{8x^2}{2} + C$

We can express this pattern as a general formula.

General formula for integration

If $y = ax^n$

$$\int y\, dx = \frac{ax^{n+1}}{n + 1} + C$$

for all values of n except $n = -1$.

Of course you could *check* this general formula by reversing the process – that is, differentiating.

If $y = \frac{ax^{n+1}}{n + 1} + C$

then using our general formula for differentiating (p. 257)

$$\frac{dy}{dx} = \frac{(n + 1)ax^n}{n + 1} = ax^n$$

In other words, our process works both ways, except for the uncertainty as to C. We call C the constant of integration.

Worked example 8.10

$$\int 3x^7 dx = \frac{3x^{7+1}}{7 + 1} + C = \frac{3x^8}{8} + C$$

Worked example 8.11

$$\int 4x^8 dx = \frac{4x^{8+1}}{8 + 1} + C = \frac{4x^9}{9} + C$$

8.6.1 Integrating functions with more than one term

When the function has several terms, we apply our general formula to each term separately. However, we only apply the constant of integration, C, at the end of the process.

Worked example 8.12

$$y = 8x^3 + 6x^2 - 5x + 8$$

$$\begin{pmatrix} a = 8 \\ n = 3 \end{pmatrix} \begin{pmatrix} a = 6 \\ n = 2 \end{pmatrix} \begin{pmatrix} a = 5 \\ n = 1 \end{pmatrix} \begin{pmatrix} a = 8 \\ n = 0 \end{pmatrix}$$

Note: 8 is the same as $8x^0$ (see Appendix 1, p. 323).

Solution

We can write this integration of each term separately, as:

$$\int 8x^3 dx + \int 6x^2 dx - \int 5x\, dx + \int 8\, dx + C$$

Worked
example
8.12
(cont'd)

$$\int y \, dx = \frac{8x^{3+1}}{3+1} + \frac{6x^{2+1}}{2+1} - \frac{5x^{1+1}}{1+1} + \frac{8x^{0+1}}{0+1} + C$$

$$\int y \, dx = \frac{8x^4}{4} + \frac{6x^3}{3} - \frac{5x^2}{2} + 8x + C$$

$$\int y \, dx = 2x^4 + 2x^3 - 2{\cdot}5x^2 + 8x + C$$

8.6.2 Finding the value of C

To find the value of C, the constant of integration, we need more specific information. In the example below we are given the co-ordinates to the curve at which the derivative $\left(\dfrac{dy}{dx}\right)$ has been calculated. We can then integrate the derivative and find C in the original function.

Worked
example
8.13

Find the equation of the curve whose gradient at the point $(1,1)$ is given by $1 - 3x^2$.

Solution

Since $\dfrac{dy}{dx} = 1 - 3x^2$ then $y = \displaystyle\int (1 - 3x^2) dx$

$$\int 1 \, dx - \int 3x^2 dx + C$$

$$= \frac{x^{0+1}}{0+1} - \frac{3x^{2+1}}{2+1} + C$$

$$= x - \frac{3x^3}{3} + C$$

$$y = x - x^3 + C$$

When $x = 1$, $y = 1$ so $1 = 1 - 1 + C$
giving $C = 1$
The equation of the curve then is $y = x - x^3 + 1$.

8.6.3 Definite integrals

So far we have only considered *indefinite integrals*, whereby the process of integration has resulted in a general function, with or without a specific value for C, the constant of integration.

However, we are often interested in a *specific range* of a function. In this case we use the definite integral which evaluates the function at two specific points and allows us to find the difference between the value of the function at these points.

$$\int 4x\,dx = 2x^2 + C \text{ Indefinite Integral}$$

$$\int_1^3 4x\,dx = \left|2x^2\right|_1^3 \text{ Definite Integral}$$

$$= 2(3)^2 - 2(1)^2$$
$$= 18 - 2$$
$$= 16$$

Notice that for the definite integral we place the specific values of the function around the integration sign. These specific values are often called the limits of integration. Here we are interested in finding the *difference* between the value of $\int 4x\,dx$ at $x = 3$ and at $x = 1$.

Because we are subtracting, the constant of integration, C, cancels out and can be ignored.

The indefinite integral, without the C, is then found and enclosed by vertical lines, with the limits of integration (the 3 and the 1) placed after the second vertical line. By convention we subtract the value of the integral at the bottom limit from the value of the integral at the top limit.

Using the definite integral helps us to eliminate C, and therefore avoid having to find it. A further benefit is that using the definite integral focuses on *summing* the function over particular values of the variable. This is required when we wish to calculate the *area beneath a curve* over a particular range of that curve. This is important in a variety of business applications, such as summing marginal revenue, marginal cost or marginal profit (all first derivatives) to find total revenue, total cost or total profit respectively.

Area under a curve

The area between a curve $y = f(x)$, the x axis and the lines $x = a, x = b$ (see Figure 8.9) is defined by $\int_a^b f(x)\,dx$.

The Worked Example that follows illustrates the use of integration in such situations.

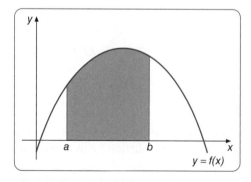

Figure 8.9 The definite interval and the area beneath a curve

Worked example 8.14

Find the area included between the curve $y = 2x + x^2 + x^3$, the x axis and the lines $x = 1$ and $x = 2$.

Solution

$$\text{Area} = \int_1^2 (2x + x^2 + x^3)\,dx$$

$$\text{Area} = \left[\frac{2x^2}{2} + \frac{x^3}{3} + \frac{x^4}{4}\right]_1^2 = \left[x^2 + \frac{x^3}{3} + \frac{x^4}{4}\right]_1^2$$

$$\text{Area} = \left(4 + \frac{8}{3} + \frac{16}{4}\right) - \left(1 + \frac{1}{3} + \frac{1}{4}\right)$$

$$\text{Area} = 9\frac{1}{12}\ \text{units}^2$$

Self-check questions 8.8

Q1. Solve the following indefinite integrations:

(a) $\int 6x\,dx$ (b) $\int 3x^5\,dx$ (c) $\int 4x^6\,dx$

(d) $\int (4x^3 + 5x^2 - 3x + 4)\,dx$ (e) $\int (2x^4 - 4x^3 + 7x)\,dx$

Q2. Find the equation of the curve whose gradient at the point (1,1) is given by $2 - 4x^2$.

Q3. Find the area included between the curve $y = 3x + 2x^2 + x^3$, the x axis and the lines $x = 1$ and $x = 2$.

Note: Answers to Self-Check Questions can be found on the instructor's website, www.pearsoned.co.uk/wall

BOX 8.1

Proof of formula for differentiation (1)

The relationship $y = x^2$ (see Figure 8.2, p. 256)

$$y^* + \Delta y = (x^* + \Delta x)^2$$

or

$$y^* + \Delta y = x^{*2} + 2x^*\Delta x + (\Delta x)^2 \text{ (see note below)}$$

but $\qquad\qquad y^* = x^{*2}$

Subtracting $\qquad \Delta y = 2x^*\Delta x + (\Delta x)^2$

and dividing throughout by Δx

gives
$$\frac{\Delta y}{\Delta x} = 2x* + \Delta x$$

and
$$\text{limit}\frac{\Delta y}{\Delta x} = 2x^*$$
$$\Delta x \to 0$$

i.e.
$$\frac{dy}{dx} = 2x*$$

Note

$$(x^* + \Delta x)(x^* + \Delta x)$$

$$x^{*2} + x^* \Delta x + x^* \Delta x + \Delta x \Delta x$$

$$x^{*2} + 2x^* \Delta x + (\Delta x)^2$$

BOX 8.2

Proof of formula for differentiation (2)

The relationship $y = 3x^2$

$$y^* + \Delta y = 3(x^* + \Delta x)^2$$

or

$$y^* + \Delta y = 3x^{*2} + 6x^* \Delta x + 3(\Delta x)^2$$

but $\qquad y^* = 3x^{*2}$

Subtracting $\qquad \Delta y = 6x^* \Delta x + 3(\Delta x)^2$

and dividing throughout by Δx

gives
$$\frac{\Delta y}{\Delta x} = 6x* + 3\Delta x$$

and $\qquad \text{limit}\dfrac{\Delta y}{\Delta x} = 6x^*$

$$\Delta x \to 0$$

i.e.
$$\frac{dy}{dx} = 6x^*$$

BOX 8.3

Derivation of basic EOQ formula

Let D = annual demand

Q = order quantity

Co = cost of ordering for one order

Cc = carrying cost for one item per annum

$$\text{Average stock} = \frac{Q}{2}$$

$$\text{Total annual stock holding cost} = \frac{QCc}{2}$$

$$\text{Number of orders per annum} = \frac{D}{Q}$$

$$\text{Annual ordering costs} = \frac{DCo}{Q}$$

$$\text{Total (inventory) cost} = \frac{QCc}{2} + \frac{D}{Q}Co$$

The order quantity that makes the total (inventory) cost (TC) a minimum is obtained by differentiating with respect to Q and equating the derivative to zero.

$$\frac{dTC}{dQ} = \frac{Cc}{2} - \frac{DCo}{Q^2}$$

and when $\dfrac{dTC}{dQ} = 0$ costs are at a minimum

$$\text{i.e. } 0 = \frac{Cc}{2} - \frac{DCo}{Q^2}$$

and to find Q

$$\frac{DCo}{Q^2} = \frac{Cc}{2}$$

$$2DCo = Q^2Cc$$

$$\frac{2DCo}{Cc} = Q^2$$

$$Q \text{ (i.e. the EOQ)} = \sqrt{\frac{2.CoD}{Cc}}$$

REVIEW QUESTIONS

R8.1. The printing department of a major newspaper has estimated that L workers on a production line will produce Q units per day where $Q = 80L^2 - 0.1L^4$. Find the number of workers required to maximise output per day.

R8.2. The manager of book publisher has estimated that the relationship between its sales (X) and its profits (Y) can be approximated by:

$$Y = 0.6X - 0.002X^2$$

where Y = profits (£000)

   X = sales (000 units)

Find the level of sales that would maximise profits.

R8.3. Suppose a total cost function for printing books is given by $TC = 0.01Q^2 + 5Q + 100$, where TC is total cost (£) and Q is output (books). Find the output level that minimises average total cost (ATC).

R8.4. Investment in new printing machines increases output and hence revenue while at the same time increasing costs. Suppose each printing machine costs £1,800 and revenue from sales occurs as follows: $R = 5000X - 20X^2$ where X is the number of printing machines.
   (a) Find the number of printing machines that maximises revenue.
   (b) Find the number of printing machines that maximises profits (revenue – cost of machines).
   (c) What is the break-even number of printing machines?

R8.5. The daily demand equation for the app of a digital news provider is given by $P = -5Q + 1,500$. The daily total cost equation of the digital news provider is given by $TC = 50Q + 10,000$. All values are in £ and quantities in units. Determine:
   (a) the quantity of apps that maximises revenue;
   (b) the quantity and price of apps that maximise profits;
   (c) the maximum profit of the digital news provider.

R8.6. Suppose the government wishes to support newsprint providers and discourage the purchase of the apps produced by the digital news provider in the previous example. It imposes a tax of £60 per app produced, so that the new total cost relationship is $TC = 50Q + 10,000 + 60Q = 110Q + 10,000$.
   (a) How does this affect profit-maximising output and price?
   (b) What is the new maximum profit?
   (c) What proportion of the tax is passed on to the consumer?

R8.7. The total revenue an advertising company obtains from selling x sports adverts and y food adverts is given by the function

$$TR = -2x^2 + 6x - 3y^2 + 6y + 10xy + 50$$

Find
   (a) the MR from selling one additional sports advert, when $x = 4$ and $y = 3$;
   (b) the MR from selling one extra food advert when $x = 4$ and $y = 3$.

R8.8. The demand for newspapers depends on its own price (P), the income of consumers (Y) and the price of digital news (P_B). The demand equation is given by
   $Q = -2P^2 + 4P_BY$
   if $P = 5, P_B = 4$ and $Y = 50$.
Find
   (a) the own-price elasticity of demand
   (b) the income elasticity of demand;
   (c) the cross-elasticity of demand (CED). Are the products substitutes or complements?

R8.9. The MR function for a film production company is as follows.

$$MR = \frac{dTR}{dQ} = 100 - 40Q - 6Q^2$$

Find the demand equation.

R8.10. In the manufacture of an app, fixed costs are £500 per week. Suppose the marginal cost function for producing the app is given by $MC = 2.4Q^2 - 0.8Q + 10$, where Q is daily output. Find the total cost of producing 100 apps a day.

R8.11. The management of an investment fund are considering investing in one of two possible media firms in two years' time when resources become available. Analysts have estimated that the equations for net profits over the next eight years for the respective media firms are as follows:

Y = net profits (£000,000) and X = the year in question from 1 to 8

Media firm A: $Y = 30 + 10X - X^2$

Media firm B: $Y = \frac{80}{X^2} + 8x - 10$

Calculate the total net profits that each media firm is expected to make from the end of the second year to the end of the eighth year (i.e. evaluate from years 2 to 8).

R8.12. The marginal cost function of a CD manufacturing company is:

$$MC = \frac{dTC}{dQ} = 0.8Q + 9$$

Production is currently set at Q = 50 units per minute.

How much more would it cost to increase output to 80 units per minute?

R8.13. A publishing firm estimates its total profit curve to have the formula

$$TP(y) = x^3 + 2x^2 + 3x$$

where x = output (000) units.

Use the process of integration to find the total profit earned if the firm increases output from x = 2 to x = 3.

R8.14. A video company produces and distributes its own videos, and has annual sales of 90,000 videos. Each video it produces requires a component to be ordered that costs £2 and each component it stores has an estimated carrying cost of 10% per annum of the purchase price. Find the economic order quantity (EOQ).

Note: Answers to Review Questions can be found on the instructor's website, www.pearsoned.co.uk/wall

Further practice

You can find more questions (with solutions) on business modelling on the instructor's website, www.pearsoned.co.uk/wall

Spreadsheets: video guide

You can also find a step-by-step account that takes you through the actual use of a spreadsheet when solving the type of problems you have encountered in this chapter. Go to the instructor's website, www.pearsoned.co.uk/wall

Chapter 9

Project management

Introduction

Prosol is a well-established project management consultancy that offers services ranging from project design to actual project implementation. Projects are typically self-contained and involve a set of related activities. They usually have clearly defined objectives, a set completion date, are often unique one-off events, and are different from routine activities. They have resources allocated specifically to them, often in the form of a project budget and normally involve a team of people. All projects are significant sets of activities that are important to the organisation and mistakes can cause financial, organisational and even political problems, especially when the public sector is involved. In this chapter we review the project planning and monitoring techniques that can be used in all projects, from the most simple to the most complex. Specialist project management software packages are available but many of the basic techniques can be learned and performed using less sophisticated approaches.

Prosol will need to be aware of the following as it prepares to manage any complex project.

- Many of the issues in project management revolve around managing a team of people who must be able to communicate effectively with each other. Some people involved in a project may come from outside the organisation and so managing their input may be particularly difficult.
- Communication with key stakeholders will be a significant part of the project itself. The project 'customer' may keep changing their requirements.
- There will always be expected and unexpected problems that may throw the project off course. Constant monitoring and re-planning is therefore required.
- The fact that the 'benefit' of the project is not normally realised until the project is complete means that there is constant pressure and scrutiny from the 'customer' and other stakeholders during the project.

Prosol can be confident that its consultancy expertise will be in continuing demand. In a study in 2013 by the Project Management Institute it identified a serious shortage in project management expertise, with an estimated 1.57 million additional project management roles being required globally every year until 2020. It also identified 80% of organisations as already struggling to find qualified project managers to fill positions.

9.1 Defining projects

The project management triangle (Figure 9.1), also sometimes referred to as the 'iron triangle', defines the main constraints for any project. The overall cost or budget set for the project is one constraint, the time allowed for the project is a second constraint and the scope of the project is a third constraint. The scope refers to the overall objectives set for the project, including the detailed specification, performance and quality.

Managing projects therefore requires the simultaneous balancing of time, cost and the scope of the project, since none of these three factors can be changed without affecting one or both of the others. For example, if the scope of the project is increased then the project will cost more and may take more time. Good project management will seek to anticipate issues and attempt to avoid the common pitfalls identified in Table 9.1.

Developing a very clear specification, setting out the objectives of the project, is a critical starting point. It should be written down and agreed by all interested parties before the project is planned in detail.

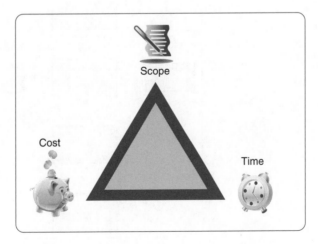

Figure 9.1 The project management triangle

Table 9.1 Issues faced by project managers

Time	Cost	Scope
The durations of individual activities within the project are not estimated accurately.	Project designers underestimate the costs of resources – sometimes significantly.	Project managers fail to recognise that the activities are not achieving the objectives of the project.
Specific time-saving technologies do not fulfil expectations.	Unrealistic or out-of-date assumptions have been made about the cost and availability of materials or other resources.	The project customers keep changing their requirements.

Did you know?

Crossrail, one of the largest construction projects ever undertaken in Europe, will deliver a major new metro rail service for London. Construction began in 2009 and is expected to be completed in 2018. Its objective is to increase London's rail-based transport network capacity by 10% and dramatically cut journey times across the city. The Crossrail project will create thousands of jobs and the overall economic benefits are estimated to be at least £42 billion (see www.crossrail.co.uk). However, the magnitude of the project management challenge is indicated by the fact that over the course of the project it is estimated that Crossrail and its supply chain will support the equivalent of 55,000 full time jobs.

The key stages of any project, then, proceed as illustrated in Figure 9.2.

Prosol has been engaged in helping to define and project manage a wide range of projects. Some examples are:

● *Construction*: building and infrastructure projects;

● *IT*: implementation of new computer systems;

● *Manufacturing*: design and installation of a new production line;

● *Commercial*: establishing retail facilities in a new market;

● *Event management*: planning a major industry showcase event.

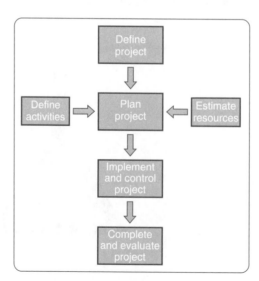

Figure 9.2 Project stages

Some projects can have fairly defined top-level objectives but be more open ended with regard to when milestones can be achieved, such as scientific and medical research. Project management techniques are difficult to apply in these cases.

Having a shared understanding of the project's objectives is an essential starting point for any project. But even before this can happen the first task is to identify the project stakeholders: those individuals or groups who will affect the project or be affected by it. Talking to these various stakeholders in a structured way will start the process of defining the project scope, the available budget and the expectations of project duration. The project objectives must then be written down and checked by the stakeholders and amended as necessary to gain agreement and 'buy-in' to the project. In larger, especially public sector, projects this may require a formal stakeholder consultation process.

Keeping focused on the agreed objectives of the project is one of the keys to successful project delivery. Sometimes, however, situations change and project objectives are no longer applicable. A formal process for reviewing and amending objectives should be built into the overall project process to ensure that the top-level project objectives remain relevant in changing circumstances, while avoiding stakeholder pressure for frequent review and amendment which will inevitably delay and add cost to projects.

NHS project on critical list

By Nicholas Timmins

Back in 2002, the idea of a full patient record, available anywhere in an emergency, was the principal political selling point for what was billed as "the biggest civilian computer project in the world": ... Roll-out was meant to start in 2005 and be completed by 2010 ... The decision to scrap the central database is a symbolic moment for a £12bn programme that has struggled to deliver from day one. It is currently running at least four years late – and there looks to be no chance in the foreseeable future of its delivering quite what was promised.

So what went wrong? Too much ambition, too much speed, too much centralisation, too little local ownership and not enough choice have been just some of the problems.

 Timmins, N. (2009) NHS project on critical list. *Financial Times*. 20 August.
© The Financial Times Limited. All Rights Reserved.

PAUSE FOR THOUGHT 9.1

Who were the stakeholders in this case and how might you have included them in the project definition?

Project definition is therefore a critical phase in the overall project management process. Clear and agreed project definition is likely to increase the chances of a successful outcome considerably. Approaches that can be used to help define projects clearly can include:

- ensuring that enough time and appropriate specialist expertise are applied to the project definition phase;
- close liaison with customers and other affected stakeholders;
- if possible, piloting or modelling of projects;
- drawing on prior experience in a structured way.

Table 9.2 Factors used by organisations to determine project 'success'

Factor	Percentage of organisations identifying as key factor in project 'success'
Satisfaction of stakeholders	20
On-time delivery	19
On budget	18
Delivery of benefits	17
Quality	15
Acceptable return on investment (ROI)	9
Other	2

A project definition should include:

- a clear and concise description of the project;
- key milestones and measures;
- the budget;
- team members (individuals, groups or organisations) with their key accountabilities;
- monitoring, review and change authorisation procedures.

Table 9.2 provides some useful insights into what factors organisations use to measure 'success' in project performance. Of course defining and planning the project will depend in large part on what outcomes will be required to deem the project a 'success' by the key stakeholders.

Satisfaction of stakeholders, on-time, on-budget and benefits delivered account for 74% of the key factors or objectives identified by organisations as constituting project 'success'.

PAUSE FOR THOUGHT 9.2

How might *Prosol* seek to operationalise some of these key factors in any given project?

Self-check questions 9.1

Q1. If a project falls behind schedule which *two* of the following actions could realistically be taken to bring it back on schedule?

(a) Reduce the time allocated to future activities.

(b) Increase the project budget by paying for additional resources to make up the time lost.

(c) Reduce one or more of the objectives of the project.

Q2. Explain how your answer to Q1 above might be relevant to *Prosol*.

Note: Answers to Self-Check Questions can be found on the instructor's website, www.pearsoned.co.uk/wall

9.2   Planning a project

All projects, whether large or small, require careful planning if they are to be completed on time and on budget. When building low-cost, long-life mines BHP Billiton, the world's largest mining operator for natural resources such as copper and iron ore, learned a harsh lesson in project planning. In 2012 it discovered that the special 4 metre tyre needed for its huge diggers and trucks would now need to be ordered as much as three years in advance, as the Japanese tsunami of March 2011 had destroyed key production plants for these specialised tyres and global demand now exceeded global supply. Because of failing to secure long-term supply of such tyres from more than one supplier, BHP Billiton and other companies have had to extend the time horizons for project completion, thereby raising costs and losing orders.

Even very large and complex projects need to start with a listing of the main activities that need to take place, beginning at the top level and then progressively adding more detailed activities under each section.

Did you know?

The London 2012 Olympic Games facilities were planned under the following main headings relating to specific time slots (www.london2012.com):

- up to the Beijing 2008 Games: 'Demolish, Dig, Design';
- to 27 July 2009: 'The Big Build: Foundations';
- to 27 July 2010: 'The Big Build: Structures';
- to 27 July 2011: 'The Big Build: Completion'.

Having set top-level activities, the next stage is to drill down and split each of these into a set of more detailed activities. The following extract from the Olympic Delivery Authority illustrates the 'second-level' activities or milestones that the first phase of the project, 'Demolish, Dig, Design', was divided into. Imagine how many more levels of detailed activity planning would have been necessary for any one of the milestones mentioned.

Did you know?

In April 2007 the Olympic Delivery Authority (ODA) set out 10 major milestones that it planned to achieve by the Closing Ceremony of the Beijing 2008 Games. These milestones were used to provide the foundations for the delivery of the venues and infrastructure of the London 2012 Olympic and Paralympic Games and the legacy beyond. The delivery of these milestones for the London Olympic Games on time and within budget was underpinned by five priority themes: 'design and accessibility; equality and inclusion; health and safety; legacy; and sustainability'.

Milestone 01 The majority of the Olympic Park will be cleared and cleaned.

Milestone 02 With the tunnels and cabling complete, the power for the Olympic Park will be set to switch underground.

Milestone 03 The main temporary roads and bridges will have been built, giving access to a safe and secure construction site for the 'big build'.

(continued)

Milestone 04 The installation of new water and energy systems that will serve the Olympic Park during and after the London 2012 Games will have started.

Milestone 05 The regeneration of the waterways will have started, improving the environment and access for the 'big build'.

Milestone 06 The transport enhancements that will open up east London and support the London 2012 Games will have started, with many complete.

Milestone 07 Construction will have started on the bridge that will take people over the Aquatics Centre to the Olympic Stadium. Building work on the Stadium will be about to begin

Milestone 08 Construction on the Olympic Village will have started.

Milestone 09 Contracts will have been let and designs agreed for the 'big four' venues in the Olympic Park – and at venues outside London, work on site will have started.

Milestone 10 The development of the Legacy Masterplan Framework (LMF) for the Olympic Park will be well advanced.

(See: www.london2012.com)

Worked example 9.1

Prosol is undertaking a project that involves the project management of a factory extension for the manufacture of a new product. Table 9.3 lists the 10 top-level activities that it identified as needing to take place.

Achieving each of these top-level activities may in turn require a list of still more detailed activities that will need to be undertaken. For example, for Activity C, 'Recruit production engineer/manager', *Prosol* identified a further eight activities (see Table 9.4).

Table 9.3 Top-level activities

A	Purchase construction materials
B	Choose and purchase new production equipment
C	Recruit production engineer/manager
D	Prepare site
E	Construction
F	Install utilities
G	Internal finishing (lay floor, paint, etc.)
H	Install production equipment
I	Recruit production staff
J	Train staff

Table 9.4 Second-level activities

A	Draft and place advertisement
B	Read applications and shortlist for interview
C	Contact all applicants with result of first sift
D	Set assessment criteria and brief interviewers
E	Conduct interviews
F	Choose successful candidate
G	Contact all interviewees with results
H	Brief successful candidate

9.2.1 Dependencies

At first sight we now have a simple sequence of activities at various levels of detail. However, projects are not always conducted by following one activity after another. If, in the 2012 Olympic Park example, each of the venues had not been started until another was finished, it would have taken a very long time and the deadline would have been missed. In the vast majority of projects many of the activities can be carried out in parallel rather than sequentially. Determining the activities that cannot be started before another has been finished and those that can be carried out in parallel is fundamental to effective project management.

If, for example, Activity B cannot take place until Activity A has been completed then we say that Activity B is 'dependent' on Activity A.

Think about each of the activities individually.

Identify which prior activity or activities must be completed before the next activity can begin.

Some activities may not be dependent on any prior activity being completed.

Table 9.5 outlines the 'dependencies' identified by *Prosol* for each of the 10 top-level activities required for the factory extension.

9.2.2 Estimating

Estimating is an important skill when planning and managing projects. Estimates of time, resources and cost are basic inputs to the planning process. Inaccurate estimates can lead to very significant delays and cost penalties in projects and, as activities in a project are interdependent, poor estimating can have significant knock-on effects in other areas of the project.

So how are good estimates made?

Estimates can be improved by:

- ensuring you have good information from the project customer about exactly what is required;
- taking into account previous experience based on what actually happened;
- not being too optimistic, or too pessimistic;
- reviewing estimates regularly throughout the project.

Estimating can be difficult in situations that involve new technology or new processes.

Table 9.5 Dependencies

	Activity	Dependencies
A	Purchase construction materials	None
B	Choose and purchase new production equipment	None
C	Recruit production engineer/manager	None
D	Prepare site	None
E	Construction	A, D
F	Install utilities	E
G	Internal finishing (lay floor, paint, etc.)	F
H	Install production equipment	B, G
I	Recruit production staff	C
J	Train staff	I, H

Did you know?

EDF, the French nuclear utility, has warned that the cost of its flagship next-generation atomic reactor in northern France has soared to EUR8.5bn, raising fresh concerns about its plan to build a similar plant in the UK.

The latest cost overrun means the price of the EPR reactor, being built at Flamanville in Normandy, is more than double the original EUR3.3bn forecast. Evidence of the rising cost comes as questions have been raised about whether nuclear power is becoming unaffordable after the atomic disaster at Fukushima in Japan last year. Hervé Machenaud, the company's engineering director, said: "There is no other means of energy production with as low a cost." Before the Fukushima disaster, the utility said building a new reactor in the UK would cost about pound(s) 4.5bn.

EDF is the world's largest generator of nuclear power by electricity produced but its project to build a new, more advanced 1.65GW reactor in France, the country's first in 15 years, has been beset by delays. The reactor was meant to enter service this year, but is now likely to start operating in 2016.

Another EPR project in Finland, built by French manufacturer Areva, has been hit by similar delays and cost overruns. Mr Machenaud blamed the Flamanville overruns on the fact that the reactor is the first of its kind. He said the additional safety costs after Fukushima had taken a significant toll but added there had also been design changes and the unexpected replacement of important components.

Boxell, J. (2012) EDF overruns at reactor may hit UK plans. *Financial Times*. 3 December.
© The Financial Times Limited. All Rights Reserved.

Self-check questions 9.2

Q1. Imagine you own a building firm and you have quoted a customer £100,000 to build a large extension on their home. You estimate that the job will cost you £80,000 so that you will make an estimated profit of £20,000. However, if you have underestimated your costs by 10% how will this affect your profit? How much will your profit be reduced by in pounds and in per cent?

Q2. Complete this table showing the dependent activities for each of the steps:

	Activity	Dependencies
A	Draft and place advertisement	
B	Read applications and shortlist for interview	
C	Contact all applicants with result of first sift	
D	Set assessment criteria and brief interviewers	
E	Conduct interviews	
F	Choose successful candidate	
G	Contact all interviewees with results	
H	Brief successful candidate	

Note: Answers to Self-Check Questions can be found on the instructor's website, www.pearsoned.co.uk/wall

> ### Did you know?
>
> Research by the Project Management Institute (PMI) in 2013 suggested that only 62% of projects met their original business goal in 2012, falling from 72% in 2008. *Prosol* might be interested to note that organisations using formalised project management practices and training reported a 70% 'success rate' while those with no such formalised practices only reported a 47% 'success rate'.

9.3 Network diagrams

Network diagrams are visual representations of a project process. They help to show clearly the project activities and the interrelationships between activities. We have already noted the many interrelated activities involved in completing major projects such as the Olympic Park for London 2012. Some 240 UK businesses were awarded contracts for various activities that were required to complete the venues and over 5,250 people worked on these activities. To manage such interrelationships effectively, those responsible for overall delivery needed to have a 'road map' which specified how the various activities were interrelated.

9.3.1 Basic rules

It is important to learn how to draw a network diagram for a project using the appropriate notation (see Table 9.6).

9.3.2 Drawing network diagrams

The Worked Example 9.2 helps identify the basic network.

Table 9.6 Rules for drawing a network diagram

A diamond shape is used to start and finish the network diagram.
A circle or 'node' represents an event that marks the start and end of each activity.
Each event must have at least one preceding activity.
Each event must have at least one subsequent activity.
Any two events can be joined by only one activity.

Worked example 9.2

Prosol is planning a project for a client to build a new retail unit. Table 9.7 lists the main top-level activities identified by *Prosol*.

Table 9.7 Project activities and dependencies

Activity	Description	Dependencies
A	Lay foundations	None
B	Build walls	A
C	Lay drainage	A
D	Install utilities (electricity, water)	A

➡

Worked
example
9.2
(cont'd)

Activity	Description	Dependencies
E	Fit window frames	B
F	Fit door frames	B
G	Fit windows	E
H	Fit doors	F
I	Plastering inside walls	G, H
J	Lay floor	C
K	Internal wiring and pipework	D
L	Shop fitting	I, J, K

Figure 9.3 presents a draft network diagram that *Prosol* consultants have developed to represent this sequence of activities. Notice that building walls is to be done in parallel with laying drains and installing utilities and that the structure is complete and secure before the plastering of the inside walls of the retail unit.

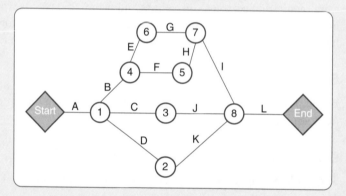

Figure 9.3 Sequence of activities as a network diagram

Note: The length of the line joining two 'nodes' (circles) does not represent the time taken for the activity. Sometimes, in network diagrams, arrows are used instead of lines to represent activities.

9.3.3 Dummy activities

Consider the following simple project sequence, as shown in Table 9.8, for increasing capacity for a client of *Prosol*, a website design company.

Notice that Activity D is dependent on more than one preceding activity being completed. However, the rules of network notation state that any two events can be joined by only one activity. Dummy activities are used to overcome this and preserve the logic of the network. Dummy activities have no time and no resource requirement and are represented as a dotted line.

Table 9.9 identifies the rules associated with dummy activities in a network diagram.

The network diagram for the website design company project would therefore be as shown in Figure 9.4.

Table 9.8 Project activities for capacity expansion

Activity	Description	Dependencies
A	Purchase and install new servers	None
B	Prepare operating software	A
C	Recruit new website designers	A
D	Load software onto servers and develop test websites	B, C

Table 9.9 Rules for dummy activities

Dummy activities are drawn with a dotted line.

Dummy activities take zero time.

Dummy activities require zero resources.

Dummy activities are required if more than one preceding activity must be completed.

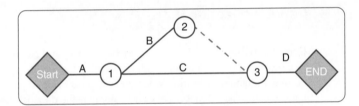

Figure 9.4 Adding a dummy activity

Worked example 9.3

Before moving on to look at how we add more information to network models we will review the development of a network diagram using the factory extension project that *Prosol* is managing for its client. Table 9.10 gives the list of activities.

Table 9.10 Factory extension project

	Activity	Dependencies
A	Purchase construction materials	None
B	Choose and purchase new production equipment	None
C	Recruit production engineer/manager	None
D	Prepare site	None
E	Construction	A, D
F	Install utilities	E
G	Internal finishing (lay floor, paint, etc.)	F
H	Install production equipment	B, G
I	Recruit production staff	C
J	Train staff	I, H

Worked
example
9.3
(cont'd)

The network diagram for this project is shown in Figure 9.5. Notice how it complies with the rules for network diagram notation and uses dummy activities.

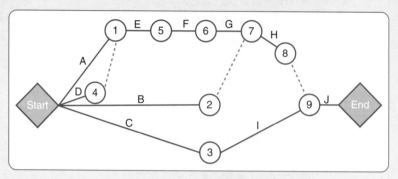

Figure 9.5 Network diagram for factory extension project

Self-check question 9.3

Consider the situation of waking up in the morning and getting ready for college or work. What is your normal morning routine? Identify the various activities that make up your normal morning routine from when you wake up to when you leave for work or college. Label the activities alphabetically and determine the dependencies between each activity. For example, getting dressed is dependent on having a shower first, as you can't shower with your clothes on! Try to be as specific as possible. Use a table like this one.

Activity	Description	Dependencies
A		
B		
C		
etc.		

Use this information to draw a network diagram just using pencil and paper. Your diagram should show all the dependencies and any activities that can take place simultaneously.

Note: Answers to Self-Check Questions can be found on the instructor's website, www.pearsoned.co.uk/wall

9.4 Critical path analysis

'Time is money' and this saying is particularly true for projects. Every day that a project overruns it incurs the cost of using resources for longer than was budgeted and often also results in additional penalty costs as specified in the contract.

We have seen how network diagrams are used to provide a visual image to help manage the overall project. The network can now be developed further by:

- incorporating the estimated duration of each activity;
- calculating the earliest finish times for each activity;

- calculating the latest finish times for each activity;
- identifying the *critical path* through the network.

Being able to determine the *critical path* through the network will allow us to identify the minimum time needed to complete the entire project.

At this point it is worth thinking about why the shortest time for a project to be completed is the time of the (critical) path with the longest duration!

The shortest time to complete the project will always be given by the *critical path*, but the critical path is always the longest of all paths through the network. This may seem a contradiction but remember you start with all the individual durations of all the activities, then you work out dependencies and then draw the network to determine the various paths through the network. But also remember that ALL activities in the entire network have to be completed. The purpose of the network diagram is to see where time can be saved by *doing tasks in parallel*. The critical path (the longest path) has no float time on it, therefore it determines the shortest possible time in which you can complete ALL the activities in the network (not just on that path). This is given by analysing the network diagram as the project duration cannot be set in advance.

Here is the *Business Dictionary* definition of critical path:

> Longest sequence of activities in a project plan which must be completed on time for the project to complete on due date. An activity on the critical path cannot be started until its predecessor activity is complete; if it is delayed for a day, the entire project will be delayed for a day unless the activity following the delayed activity is completed a day earlier.

By adding time information to a network diagram we can find out which activities are critical to keeping the overall project to schedule.

9.4.1 Identifying the critical path

The longest route through the network is called the *critical path*. The activities on this path are the *critical activities*. The critical activities are the ones that must be completed on time if the overall project is to be completed on time. So a delay in one of the activities on the critical path will delay the whole project unless time can be reduced on other critical activities. However, as we have already discussed, the duration of a project must be balanced against both the cost and the scope. Therefore, if activity durations have been estimated accurately the only way to reduce the time taken will be either to increase the cost of the project by allocating more resources to activities, or to reduce the expectation of the outcome from a particular activity, which may not be possible.

Worked example 9.4

In the factory extension project that *Prosol* consultants are working on they liaise with the client and suppliers to estimate, as accurately as possible, the duration of each of the activities and add this information to the activities table (see Table 9.11).

Table 9.11 Activity durations for factory extension project

	Activity	Dependencies	Duration (weeks)
A	Purchase construction materials	None	8
B	Choose and purchase new production equipment	None	12
C	Recruit production engineer/manager	None	12

Worked
example
9.4
(cont'd)

	Activity	Dependencies	Duration (weeks)
D	Prepare site	None	2
E	Construction	A, D	6
F	Install utilities	E	2
G	Internal finishing (lay floor, paint, etc.)	F	1
H	Install production equipment	B, G	2
I	Recruit production staff	C	4
J	Train staff	I, H	1

The simplest way to identify the *critical path* is to consider each of the paths through the network and identify which is longest (see Figure 9.6).

The paths through the network and their durations are listed in Table 9.12.

The critical path is the longest path, which has a total duration of 20 weeks. The activities on this path A-E-F-G-H-J are *critical activities* and *Prosol* must work to ensure that these activities are completed on time in order not to delay the project beyond 20 weeks in total.

It is possible to have more than one critical path through a network. They will be paths with equal durations which are longer than the other paths through the network. All activities on any critical path will become critical activities.

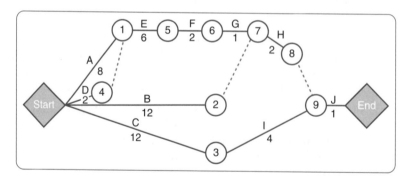

Figure 9.6 Activity durations

Table 9.12 Identifying the critical path

Path	Durations in the path (weeks)	Total duration (weeks)
A-E-F-G-H-Dummy-J	8 + 6 + 2 + 1 + 2 + 0 + 1	20
D-Dummy-E-F-G-H-Dummy-J	2 + 0 + 6 + 2 + 1 + 2 + 0 + 1	14
B-Dummy-H-Dummy-J	12 + 0 + 2 + 0 + 1	15
C-I-J	12 + 4 + 1	17

9.4.2 Identifying float times for non-critical activities

The duration information can be used to give more detailed data that will help with management of the project. Activities that are not on the *critical path* are non-critical activities and, within limits, they can start late and/or take longer than the time estimated in the original project plan. The additional time that any non-critical activity can take without affecting the total project duration is called the *float time*. In order to calculate the *float time* we need first to calculate the earliest finish time (EFT) and latest finish time (LFT) for each activity in the network. This information can be added to the network diagram, as shown in Figure 9.7.

The EFT for an activity is the earliest time at which the event that marks the end of that activity could possibly be reached, knowing which preceding activities have to be completed first.

The LFT for an activity is the latest time the activity can be completed without changing the total time for the overall project. For many activities the LFT will be the same as the EFT but for activities where there is more than one path to reach them the EFT and the LFT may be different.

The *float time* for any activity is the difference between the LFT and the EFT. It represents the amount of time the activity can be delayed by or the additional time that can be taken for that activity without affecting the overall project duration.

Extending the duration of a non-critical activity up to or beyond its planned duration plus its float time will change the critical path through a network. Different activities will then become critical activities.

PAUSE FOR THOUGHT 9.3

If an activity has zero float time, what does this indicate?

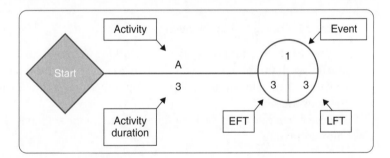

Figure 9.7 Notation

Worked example 9.5

Prosol first calculates the EFT for each event in the network for the factory expansion project. Working through the network from left to right the EFT is calculated by adding the duration of each activity on to the total duration along each path at each step, remembering that dummy activities have zero duration. Where two paths feed into one event, the EFT from the longest pathway is used. The total minimum duration for this project is 20 weeks and this is added to the end of the network. Figure 9.8 shows the EFT information added to the network.

Worked
example
9.5
(cont'd)

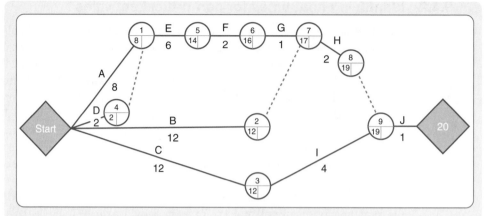

Figure 9.8 Adding EFT information

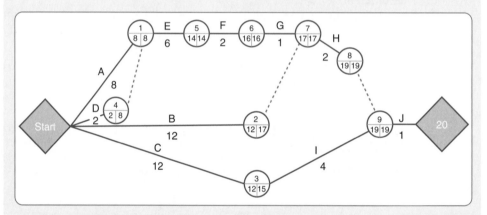

Figure 9.9 Adding LFT information

The LFT information is calculated by working from right to left through the network. Starting with the total project duration of 20 weeks the duration of each activity is subtracted sequentially along each path. Figure 9.9 shows the LFT information added to the network.

Prosol then calculates the float times for each of the activities. Table 9.13 summarises this information.

Table 9.13 Float time calculations

	Activity	Dependencies	Duration (weeks)	EFT	LFT	Float
A	Purchase construction materials	None	8	8	8	0
B	Choose and purchase new production equipment	None	12	12	17	5
C	Recruit production engineer/manager	None	12	12	15	3

Worked example 9.5 (*cont'd*)

	Activity	Dependencies	Duration (weeks)	EFT	LFT	Float
D	Prepare site	None	2	2	8	6
E	Construction	A, D	6	14	14	0
F	Install utilities	E	2	16	16	0
G	Internal finishing (lay floor, paint, etc.)	F	1	17	17	0
H	Install production equipment	B, G	2	19	19	0
I	Recruit production staff	C	4	16	19	3
J	Train staff	I, H	1	19	19	0

Prosol checks the critical path by looking for *float times* that have a value of zero. This confirms that A-E-F-G-H-J is the *critical path* for this project. *Prosol* must ensure that all activities in the project are monitored regularly because, for example, if one of the non-critical activities such as the recruitment and appointment of a production engineer/manager takes longer than expected it may alter the *critical path*.

> Even though you have already identified the critical activities (the activities on the critical path) you should also calculate the float time for these activities using the EFT and LFT. Activities on the critical path will all have zero float time. This is a double check that you have identified the critical path correctly.

The network diagram can be used throughout the project as a monitoring tool to check actual progress against planned progress as the project develops. The information contained in the diagram will enable the project manager to determine the project duration, to prioritise between activities, knowing which are critical and non-critical, and therefore to assess the impacts that any changes in individual activity duration will make to the project as a whole.

Self-check question 9.4

A group of drama students are planning to make a video to enter into a competition. Construct a network diagram for the project using the information in the table below. Find the critical path and calculate the float times for all activities.

	Activity	Dependencies	Duration (days)
A	Write storyboard	None	4
B	Research locations	A	2
C	Choose cast and crew	A	4
D	Obtain camera and lighting equipment	None	16

(continued)

	Activity	Dependencies	Duration (days)
E	Write script	B	12
F	Obtain costumes and props	C	12
G	Learn script and rehearse	E	8
H	Shoot video	G, F, D	2
I	Edit and upload	H	4

Note: Answers to Self-Check Questions can be found on the instructor's website, www.pearsoned.co.uk/wall

Did you know?

Prosol might look to the emerging-market economies for future business opportunities. A 2013 report by the International Monetary Fund (IMF) suggested that by 2025, 440 emerging-market cities, such as Shanghai, Mexico City and New Delhi, will deliver around 50% of global GDP growth, providing extensive project management opportunities.

9.5 Gantt charts

In practice, software tools are used extensively for project management. Although the techniques applied to network diagrams are the basis for project management software the output is displayed in a way that can be more easily reproduced on screen and in print in the form of Gantt charts. Using Gantt charts also enables further resource information to be added to assist the project manager, in particular, in planning and allocating people to a project.

A Gantt chart is an adaptation of a horizontal bar chart. It is therefore much easier to use in a computerised environment. It also has the advantage of showing activity durations and *float times* more clearly but the interrelationships between activities are not quite as clear as on a network diagram.

The other advantage of using a Gantt chart is that information to help the project manager plan the number of people needed at each stage of the project can be easily added. The project manager can see from the chart when additional staff need to be brought into the project.

Worked example 9.6

Prosol constructs a Gantt chart with outline resource information for the factory extension project, as shown in Figure 9.10. They are able to see from the chart that, because of the available float time on Activity D, they could delay clearing the site until just before construction and this would mean that the same team of people could be used continuously to clear the site and then commence construction. There is little risk in this option, as the time taken to clear the site is straightforward to estimate with little chance of overrun or unexpected delays. In contrast, they also recommend to their client that, although there is three weeks float time on Activity C (recruit production manager), this activity should start at the commencement of the project due to the inherent uncertainty around selection and recruitment.

Worked
example
9.6
(cont'd)

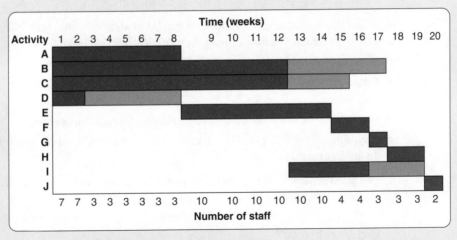

Figure 9.10 Gantt chart with resource information

Refer back to the network diagram of your morning routine that you constructed earlier on this topic, and reproduce this as a Gantt chart. You can either do this by hand on squared paper or use a spreadsheet. Try to think of all the activities you need to complete. If you live with other people and split activities you can take account of that by adding resource information as covered in the previous study session. For example, does someone else make coffee while you are in the shower?

PAUSE FOR THOUGHT 9.4

What are the advantages and disadvantages of using a Gantt chart rather than a network diagram in presenting information?

9.5.1 Project management software

In practice, project management software packages are used for more complex projects. One popular software application is Microsoft Project ®. For simpler projects Gantt charts can be produced using a spreadsheet such as Excel.

The information that you would input into a specialised project management software application would include:

- the description of the activity;
- the duration for each activity;
- the dependencies for each activity;
- resource requirements and availability.

Did you know?

In a 2013 survey 77% of organisations in the United Kingdom made use of project management software, with 45% using Microsoft Project software.

The advantages of using project management software are as follows.

- In the initial planning stage projects can be modelled to show the effects of changes to different elements before a final project plan is decided upon.
- Data from earlier projects can be accessed to improve estimating.
- Actual progress can be shown against planned progress to allow constant project monitoring.
- Re-planning can be done quickly and easily as circumstances change.
- High-quality project planning documents can be produced for both print and online dissemination.

The main drawback is that if the project is frequently revised and updated it can have a detrimental effect on the focus of the project as a whole.

Did you know?

Prosol might be well advised to carefully review the previous history in project management of the organisations for which it secures contracts. The Project Management Institute (PMI) reported in 2013 that for every $1 billion spent on a project in organisations with a history of completing less than 60% of previous projects on time, target and budget, as much as $280 million is 'at risk'. However, for the same expenditure on a project in organisations completing over 80% of previous projects on time, target and budget, only $20 million is 'at risk'.

Self-check question 9.5

Construct a Gantt chart for the student video project described in Self-Check Question 9.4.

Note: Answers to Self-Check Questions can be found on the instructor's website, www.pearsoned.co.uk/wall

9.6 Taking account of uncertainty: PERT

Project evaluation and review technique (PERT) is a method of adding further information on activity durations to critical path analysis. Activity durations are often uncertain and difficult to predict with accuracy. PERT accounts for this uncertainty by using simple statistical methods.

When considering any specific activity we can make a judgement on the following three different bases:

- OD: the optimistic estimate;
- MD: the most likely estimate;
- PD: the pessimistic estimate.

Each one applies different assumptions as to what may happen.

With our three separate time estimates, OD, MD and PD, we can use a simple formula to derive an overall *expected duration* which we can use in our network analysis:

$$\text{Expected Duration} = \frac{OD + 4MD + PD}{6}$$

So for an activity that has the following:

OD = 9 days

MD = 10 days

PD = 13 days

the expected duration would be:

$$ED = \frac{9 + (4 \times 10) + 13}{6} = 10.33 \text{ days}$$

9.6.1 Variance and standard deviation

We can also work out the variance and standard deviation for each activity, using the measures of variability that were considered in Chapter 2. This information will enable us to determine the probability of an activity finishing at a certain time. More importantly, adding the variances along the critical path and determining the standard deviation will enable the project manager to give a statistically based probability of the whole project finishing within a certain time. The project manager may be asked what the probability would be of the project finishing, for example, 'two weeks early' or 'no more than 4 weeks late' and they would be able to provide that answer using these techniques. To do this we need to calculate the variance and standard deviation of all of the activities in the network that are considered uncertain. Variance and standard deviation are calculated as follows:

$$Variance = \frac{(PD - OD)^2}{36}$$

$$SD = \sqrt{variance}$$

So following from the above example:

$$Variance = \frac{(13 - 9)^2}{36}$$

$$Variance = 0.44$$

$$SD = 0.66$$

It is meaningless to look at one activity alone and, in practice, the estimated duration, variance and standard deviation would be calculated by summing all the activities on the critical path. Probability tables can then be used to answer a question on whether the project is likely to be 'x days early' or 'more than y days late'. By doing this we are assuming the principles of *normal distribution*. For this to be valid there needs to be a large number of activities on the critical path and their durations are assumed to be completely independent of each other.

> **Worked example 9.7**
>
> *Prosol* has considered the activities on the critical path of the factory extension project and believes there may be uncertainty around three particular activities: A, E and H. It may be that one or more of the materials needed for construction are on a much longer than expected lead time, if the weather is particularly bad construction may be delayed and the production equipment, which involves new technology, may take longer than expected to install. *Prosol* calculates the expected durations of these three activities, ➡

taking into account pessimistic and optimistic estimates in addition to the most likely duration. It also calculates the standard deviation. The results are given in Table 9.14.

Prosol then uses these new expected duration times to re-evaluate the overall project duration and finds that the total project time increases by just over 1 week from 20 to 21 weeks, as shown in Table 9.15. The total variance is 2.27 giving a standard deviation of

$$SD = \sqrt{2.27} = 1.5 \text{ weeks}$$

If we assume this follows the rules of normal distribution the project has a mean duration of 21 weeks and a standard deviation of 1.5 weeks. *Prosol* has been asked by the client to state the probability of the project overrunning by 2 weeks or more. It uses the Z score and probability tables to do this.

$$Z = \frac{X - 21}{SD} = \frac{23 - 21}{1.5} = 1.33$$

The probability (from tables) is 0.0918 or around 9%. So *Prosol* can tell its client that there is more than a 90% probability that the project will be complete within 23 weeks.

Table 9.14 Activity expected duration and variance calculations

	Activity	OD	MD	PD	Expected duration (weeks)	Variance
A	Purchase construction materials	6	8	14	8.66	1.77
E	Construction	5	6	8	6.16	0.25
H	Install production equipment	1	2	4	2.33	0.25

Table 9.15 Project duration and variance

	Activity	Duration (weeks)	Variance
A	Purchase construction materials	8.66	1.77
E	Construction	6.16	0.25
F	Install utilities	2	0
G	Internal finishing (lay floor, paint etc)	1	0
H	Install production equipment	2.33	0.25
J	Train staff	1	0
	Total	21.15	2.27

PERT techniques can be used to calculate expected durations for all activities in a project network by considering the optimistic and pessimistic durations in addition to the 'most likely' estimates. It may change the critical path of the project if there is considerable uncertainty around some activities.

Self-check question 9.6

Calculate the estimated durations and variance for the following uncertain activities on the critical path of the student video project. How many more days than the original estimate of 32 days is the project likely to need if this uncertainty is taken account of? What is the total variance for the project? What is the probability that the project will be complete within 35 days?

	Activity	OD	MD	PD	Expected duration (days)	Variance
E	Write script	10	12	15		
G	Learn script and rehearse	6	8	15		

Note: Answers to Self-Check Questions can be found on the instructor's website, www.pearsoned.co.uk/wall

9.7   Project costs and crashing

It is sometimes possible to reduce overall project time by allocating additional people to work on the project. This will inevitably come at an additional cost. The process of reducing project times is called 'crashing' and the cost of the shortened activity is the 'crash cost'. If the crash time and cost can be found then the project manager can decide whether the additional benefit of a shorter project is worth the extra cost.

The ability to shorten project times can lead to big savings. Saving time is the key way of keeping costs down when building a skyscraper. The new skyscraper in London, The Shard, at 306 metres (1,003 ft), completed in April 2012, is Western Europe's tallest habitable building, with 95 floors above ground and 44 elevators. Construction began in March 2009 and innovative techniques were used to speed up the build, one of which was to construct the basement floors in parallel with the first of the above-ground storeys, something that had never been attempted before. At every stage issues involving 'crashing' and 'crash costs' would have been relevant to managing this construction.

If an activity has an estimated duration of, say, five days it may be possible to reduce it to, say, three days by allocating extra people and other resources at an additional cost. The shorter time is referred to as the *crash time* and the new cost is the *crash cost*.

For each activity in a project, crash time and crash cost can potentially be determined. For example, if an activity is estimated to take five days at a cost of, say, £1,000 but could be reduced to three days by allocating extra people, at a cost of £1,500, then the crash cost per day is calculated using the following formula:

$$Crash\ cost\ per\ day = \frac{Additional\ cost\ (£)}{Time\ saved\ (days)}$$

$$Crash\ cost\ per\ day = \frac{1,500 - 1,000}{5 - 3} = \frac{500}{2} = £250$$

Considering one activity alone is of little value to the project manager, who will need to weigh up how best to spend any additional budget available by crashing the activity or activities that provide the greatest benefit at the lowest cost.

9.7.1 Prioritising

Let us imagine that we have calculated the crash time and cost for activities on the critical path that are able to be *crashed*. There is little point considering reducing the duration of *non-critical activities* since these will have no effect on the overall duration of the project and the additional money would be wasted.

We can now use this information to prioritise and determine which activities would be most cost-effective to crash. The first step is to calculate the crash cost per day for each of the activities. This means that we can then compare on the same basis. We would then choose to crash activities that have the lowest crash cost per day to use our budget most effectively.

Worked example 9.8

Prosol has been able to calculate the costs of the factory extension project and has estimated where activities on the critical path could be shortened in duration by utilising additional resources, primarily additional staff or adding overtime shifts, at extra cost. This information is shown in Table 9.16. *Prosol* can advise its client that to utilise additional purchasing resource at the very start of the project would cost very little, £500 or £50 per day saved, and could shorten the project by up to 10 days. In addition, its client could take the decision for the construction team to work through the weekends on overtime and this could potentially save 10 days on the project at an additional cost of £1,800 or £180 per day.

These decisions cannot be made in isolation. Crashing activities on the critical path could make other paths through the network critical. In this case the other paths through the network take 14, 15 and 17 weeks and so if the critical path is shortened by 3 weeks (15 days) or more, then other activities will become critical and money spent on shortening the activities on the original *critical path* any further would be wasted money.

The extra costs of the project that may be used by crashing can be weighed against the additional benefits received of finishing the project early. In this case the production of the new product that will be made in the factory extension could start early and this is estimated to generate an additional profit for the company in the first year of £2,000 per week. The factory extension could be completed 15 days early at an estimated additional cost of:

$$£50 \times 10 \text{ days} + £180 \times 5 \text{ days} = £1,400$$

This would give *Prosol*'s client a net benefit. This is an example of how good project management can save time and money and give a competitive advantage.

Table 9.16 Prioritising using crash costs

	Activity	Normal			Crash		
		Duration (weeks)	Duration (days)	Cost (£)	Duration (days)	Cost (£)	Crash cost (per day)
A	Purchase construction materials	8	40	500	30	1000	50
E	Construction	6	30	15,000	20	16,800	180
F	Install utilities	2	10	3000	8	3,840	420

Worked example 9.8 (cont'd)

		Normal			Crash		
	Activity	Duration (weeks)	Duration (days)	Cost (£)	Duration (days)	Cost (£)	Crash cost (per day)
G	Internal finishing (lay floor, paint, etc.)	1	5	1000	4	1400	400
H	Install production equipment	2	10	4000	8	4000	–
J	Train staff	1	5	2000	4	2500	500

Self-check questions 9.7

Q1. In the previous Worked Example, which two activities would you consider first to crash? In other words, which would you spend extra money on first to reduce the time, and hence reduce the overall time of the project? Explain your answer.

Q2. (a) If an activity is scheduled to take five days but could be completed in three days by bringing in extra staff, what is the crash time of this activity?

(b) If the same activity is scheduled to take five days at a cost of £1,000 but could be completed in three days at a cost of £1,500, as staff will be needed to work overtime at higher rates, what is the crash cost of this activity?

(c) What is the crash cost per day of crashing this same activity?

Note: Answers to Self-Check Questions can be found on the instructor's website, www.pearsoned.co.uk/wall

REVIEW QUESTIONS

R9.1. Read the article below and answer the questions that follow.

Why do we need to pay billions of pounds for big projects?

By John Kay

The London Olympics of 1908 cost £20,000. The budget for the austerity games of 1948 was £750,000. The estimate for the cost of the Olympics in 2012 was £11bn.

This escalation in price is extraordinary, but today big schemes seem to imply very big budgets. The earliest underground railway lines in London – and the world – cost half a million pounds a mile to build. Roughly, you can assume that average prices in Britain multiplied by 10 between the Victorian era and 1960, and by another factor of 10 in the 50 years following. The cost of the Victoria line, built in the 1960s, had risen in line with general inflation and came in at about £7m per mile.

This, however, now seems an astonishing bargain. A decade later, the Jubilee line cost £36m per mile to build and its extension in the 1990s 10 times as much. The tunnels for Crossrail, the newest underground railway connection in London, are budgeted at almost £1bn per mile. The explosion of the cost of mega projects appears to be a phenomenon of the past 50 years. The Forth Bridge, an engineering marvel that connects Edinburgh with Fife, was completed in 1890 at a cost of £3.2m. The parallel road bridge erected in the 1960s cost £19.5m – broadly in line with general inflation. The budget for a third crossing is currently £1.6bn.

The Victorians were cavalier in their view of human life and the rights of – most – people who lived near these huge schemes, in a way we could not now accept. Perhaps 100 people died building the first Forth Bridge and many more were injured. The big change in social attitudes occurred long ago, however; for the second bridge, casualties were reduced by more than 90 per cent. In the Victorian era, the men behind great projects had a strong sense of public mission but there were always many snouts in the trough.

The Brooklyn Bridge, completed in 1883 at a cost of only $15.5m, linked the Tammany Hall fiefdom of Boss William Tweed with the Brooklyn stronghold of Boss Hugh McLaughlin. That bridge was built by a private company, as were the Metropolitan line (the first London Underground railway) and the Forth Bridge. Similar projects go ahead today only if underwritten from the public purse.

The history of big projects, from the Victorian era to our own, is that contractors and financiers prosper at the expense of the stockholders or taxpayers who put up the cash. A plethora of consultants is attached to every modern project, and although the purpose is to ensure more cost effective management, it would appear that this hope is not fulfilled. Only a few global companies are now perceived as capable of running mega projects, and they are hired by often inept public sector purchasers. These clients change their minds frequently and are prone to insist on idiosyncratic specifications. Perhaps the principal culprit is technological overkill. The argument that we need the best and latest is powerful in political decision making, even among people who would never behave that way in their everyday lives.

We see the same phenomenon in medicine and military hardware. Real, but marginal, improvements may add greatly to the cost. The British aircraft carrier, HMS Ark Royal, torpedoed and sunk by the Germans in 1941, cost £3m to build a decade earlier. A later Ark Royal, launched in 1981 and decommissioned in 2011, cost £250m; new British carriers today are budgeted at £3.5bn and rising. The ships have become massively more sophisticated – yet an aircraft carrier is, fundamentally, a very large floating platform. The decommissioned Ark Royal is currently awaiting its fate, after spending a year on the government website edisposals.com. It may still serve a purpose in future, although probably on dry land – perhaps as a nightclub, a school in China or a casino in Hong Kong.

Perhaps technological advance has reduced rather than increased productivity, by offering enhancements that do not represent value for money. The result is that big projects cannot be afforded or, if they are afforded, squeeze out smaller advances that would add more to human welfare. To start with, we need to take a much tougher line with the proponents of Edinburgh's £1bn tram, the Royal Navy's £5bn ship, the £11bn Olympics, and the planned £30bn high-speed train.

 Kay, J. (2012) Why do we need to pay billions of pounds for big projects?. *Financial Times*. 21 August. © The Financial Times Limited. All Rights Reserved.

(a) What patterns and trends identified in the article might be seen by *Prosol* as opening new business opportunities?

(b) What patterns and trends identified in the article might be seen by *Prosol* as resulting in new business threats?

Note: Answers to Review Questions can be found on the instructor's website, www.pearsoned.co.uk/wall

R9.2. Figure 9.11 shows the network diagram drawn by *Prosol* with a completion time of 24 days and activities B, D, E, F, H critical. Table 9.17 shows the crash calculations. The first activity to crash is D and we can reduce the project time by two days. E is the next activity to crash. F is the next activity to crash but can only reduce its time by one day before A and C also become critical. Overall project time is now down to 20 days.

(a) What choices are available to reduce the project?
(b) Which is the most cost effective choice?

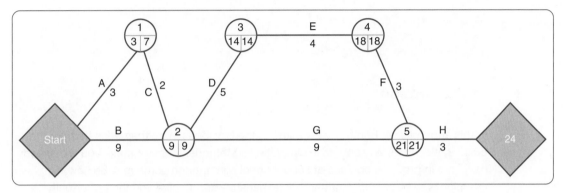

Figure 9.11 Network diagram drawn by *Prosol*

Table 9.17 Crash information

Activity	Time available (days)	Crash Cost per day £
A	2	500
B	3	600
C	1	400
D	2	300
E	1	350
F	2	450
G	5	350
H	1	1,000

R9.3. A client of *Prosol* has commissioned it to draw the network diagram for the following project. *Prosol* has also been asked to determine the earliest and latest finish times for each event, find the critical path and the shortest completion time, together with the floats.

Activity	Dependencies	Expected time (days)
A	None	10
B	None	6
C	A	4
D	A	10
E	A	6
F	C	4
G	D	8
H	B, E	12
I	H, C	4
J	F, G, I	12

Appendix 1

Review of basic mathematics

Introduction

In this appendix we briefly review some of the key ideas in mathematics that are the building blocks for any course in Quantitative Methods. Many of these you will already have met in previous courses at school or college, though some may be new. The intention is to be *selective* rather than exhaustive and to give you the opportunity to revise and practise some important numerical skills. By following through the various Worked Examples and trying the Self-Check and Review Questions (with answers) it is hoped that you will gain confidence in handling numbers and data, which is so important for your success in Quantitative Methods.

Learning objectives

By the end of this appendix you should be able to:

- deal with arithmetic problems involving whole numbers, fractions and decimals;
- 'round off' to a given number of decimal places or significant figures;
- perform calculations involving percentages and ratios;
- handle expressions involving powers or roots of a variable;
- be familiar with the simple rules of algebra;
- draw graphs and solve problems involving linear and non-linear equations;
- solve pairs of simultaneous equations.

A.1 Whole numbers, fractions and decimals

A.1.1 Whole numbers

Numbers such as 3, 5, 9 are referred to as whole numbers or *integers*.

Such numbers can be positive ($+3$) or negative (-3).

Some simple rules apply to situations involving negative numbers.

Negative number arithmetic

- To *add two negative numbers*, add the 'numbers' and make the answer negative.

  Example:

  $$-4 + -3 \quad \text{or} \quad -4 - 3 = -7$$

- To *add a negative and a positive number*, take the smaller number away from the bigger number and give your result the sign of the 'bigger number'.

  Examples:

  $$-11 + 4 = -(11 - 4) = -7$$

  $$5 + -7 \quad \text{or} \quad 5 - 7 = -(7 - 5) = -2$$

- To *subtract a negative number*, you read the two minuses $(- -)$ as a $+$

  Example:

  $$5 - -3 = 5 + 3 = 8$$

These various rules involving negative numbers can usefully be illustrated by the *number line*. Look at the number lines in Figure A.1. All numbers to the right of 0 are the *positive* numbers, and all those to the left of 0 are the *negative* numbers.

- When we *add a negative number*, it is the same as *subtracting a positive number*: we always move towards the left on the number line. Check the following examples in Figure A.1.

  (a) $3 + -2 = 1$ or $3 - 2 = 1$

  (b) $-1 + -3 = -4$ or $-1 - 3 = -4$

  (c) $-2 + -3 = -5$ or $-2 - 3 = -5$

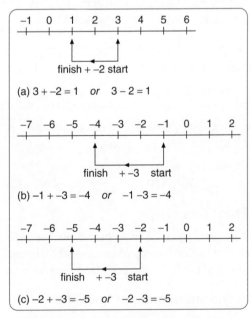

Figure A.1 Adding a negative number (same as subtracting a positive number)

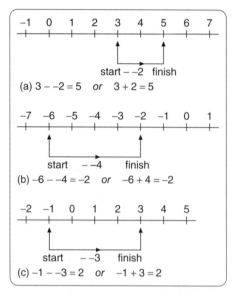

Figure A.2 Subcontracting a negative
number (same as adding a positive number)

- When we *subtract a negative number*, it is the same as *adding a positive number*: we always move towards the right on the number line. Check the following example in Figure A.2.

  (a) $3 - -2 = 5$ or $3 + 2 = 5$

  (b) $-6 - -4 = -2$ or $-6 + 4 = -2$

  (c) $-1 - -3 = 2$ or $-1 + 3 = 2$

The rules for *multiplying and dividing with negative numbers* are very easy after you have learnt the rules for addition and subtraction:

If the signs are the same, the answer is a positive.

If the signs are different, the answer is a negative.

Examples:

$$2 \times 5 = 10 \qquad -3 \times -4 = 12 \qquad -18 \div -3 = 6$$
$$-2 \times 5 = -10 \qquad 3 \times -4 = -12 \qquad 18 \div -3 = -6$$

A.1.2 Fractions

A fraction is usually part of something. It can be defined as the ratio of two numbers, one (the *numerator*) placed on top of another (the *denominator*).

Work through the following rules involving fractions.

Addition and subtraction of fractions

To add or subtract two fractions, change them to *equivalent fractions* (see below) with the same bottom number. Then we can add or subtract.

Worked example A.1	$$\frac{1}{3} + \frac{2}{5} = \frac{5}{15} + \frac{6}{15} = \frac{11}{15}$$ We use 15 since it is the smallest multiple of both 3 and 5.

Worked example A.2	$$\frac{7}{8} - \frac{5}{6} = \frac{21}{24} - \frac{20}{24} = \frac{1}{24}$$ We use 24 since it is the smallest multiple of both 8 and 6.

Multiplication of fractions

To multiply two fractions you simply need to multiply the top numbers and the bottom numbers of the fractions.

Worked example A.3	$$\frac{3}{5} \times \frac{3}{4} = \frac{9}{20}$$

Division of fractions

To divide two fractions, you turn the second fraction upside-down and then multiply the two fractions together.

Worked example A.4	$$\frac{2}{3} \div \frac{4}{5} = \frac{2}{3} \times \frac{5}{4} = \frac{10}{12} = \frac{5}{6}$$

Cancelling fractions

Worked Example A.4 illustrates the fraction $\frac{10}{12}$ being cancelled down to $\frac{5}{6}$ by dividing both top and bottom by the same number, in this case a 2.

Equivalent fractions

These are fractions that have the same value. For example, 1/4, 3/12, 6/24 are all equivalent to each other, and so are called equivalent fractions.

A.1.3 Decimals

Decimals are simply found by dividing the top (numerator) of the fraction by the bottom (denominator) of the fraction.

Worked example A.5	Change $\frac{5}{8}$ to a decimal number. Divide 5 by 8 to give 0.625

When a number is written in decimal form, the digits on the right-hand side of the decimal point are called the *decimal places*.

Worked example A.6	83.7 is written to one decimal place (1 d.p.). 0.439 is written to three decimal places (3 d.p.).

A.2 Rounding off

In many tasks you will need to 'round off' your answer to a suitable number of *decimal places* (d.p.) or *significant figures* (s.f.)

A.2.1 Decimal places

- Decide on the number of decimal places you wish to round off to – say, to two decimal places.
- Look at the number in the next (here, third) decimal place.
- If it is less than 5, then the two decimal places remain the same.
- If it is 5 or more than 5, then think of the first two decimal place numbers as together forming a number between 1 and 99, and then add 1 to this. This new number now represents your two decimal places.

Worked example A.7	• 9.5427 will round off to 9.54 (the 2 of the third decimal place is less than 5, so we keep 54). • 11.1873 will round off to 11.19 (the 7 of the third decimal places is more than 5, so we need to add 1 to 18, making 19). • 23.6154 will round off to 23.62 (the 5 of the third decimal place causes us to add 1 to 61, making 62).

A.2.2 Significant figures

Counting the number of actual *digits* (numbers) will often tell us the number of significant figures involved.

Worked example A.8	8 has 1 significant figure. 9.3 has 2 significant figures. 47.7 has 3 significant figures. 0.1845 has 4 significant figures.

However, when 0s are in the number, we must know when to count them as significant figures and when not to.

- When the 0s come at the end of the number or at the beginning of the number, then we do *not* count them as significant figures.

Worked example A.9

60	has	1	significant figure.

60   has 1 significant figure.

500   has 1 significant figure.

57,000   has 2 significant figures.

0.68   has 2 significant figures.

0.009   has 1 significant figure.

0.00013 has 2 significant figures.

- When the 0s come between digits, we *do* count them as significant figures.

Worked example A.10

105   has 3 significant figures.

2070 has 3 significant figures.

5002 has 4 significant figures.

The rules for rounding off for significant figures are similar to those for decimal places.

- Decide on the number of significant figures you wish to round off to. Look at the next digit which then 'has to go'.
- If this is less than 5, then leave the digits on the left (if there are any) alone.
- If the digit is 5 or more than 5, then add 1 to the digit on the left.
- Then put 0s in to keep the place value of the original number.

Worked example A.11

832 to 1 s.f. is 800 since the 3 is less than 5.

8.7621 to 2 s.f. is 8.8 since the 6 is more than 5.

Look at the following table to see how these rules work for the numbers chosen:

Number	Correct to 1 s.f.	Correct to 2 s.f.	Correct to 3 s.f.
34.87	30	35	34.9
159.2	200	160	159
10.942	10.000	11.000	10.900
0.07158	0.07	0.072	0.0716

A.3 Percentages and ratios

A.3.1 Percentages

A percentage means 'out of a hundred'. So:

- 1% means 1 out of a 100 or 1/100 or 0.01
- 3% means 3 out of a 100 or 3/100 or 0.03

Changes of form

Fractions to percentages

To change any *fraction* into a percentage, all you need to do is to multiply the fraction by 100. What this is doing is finding the fraction of 100.

For example:

$$\frac{5}{8} \text{ would become } \frac{5}{8} \times 100 = 62.5\%.$$

You should know the common fractions expressed as a percentage.

$$\frac{1}{2} = 50\% \quad \frac{1}{4} = 25\% \quad \frac{3}{4} = 75\% \quad \frac{1}{10} = 10\% \quad \frac{1}{5} = 20\% \quad \frac{1}{3} = 33\tfrac{1}{3}\%$$

Percentages to fractions

To change a *percentage* into a fraction, simply express the percentage as a fraction over 100 and then cancel down. For example,

$$45\% = \frac{45}{100} = \frac{9}{20} \text{ (cancelled by 5s)}$$

$$31\% = 100 \text{ (will not cancel)}$$

Decimals to percentages

To change any *decimal* into a percentage, simply multiply by 100. For example,

$$0.35 \text{ becomes } 0.35 \times 100 = 35\% \text{ as a percentage.}$$

$$1.26 \text{ becomes } 1.26 \times 100 = 126\% \text{ as a percentage.}$$

Percentages to decimals

To change a *percentage* to a decimal, simply divide the percentage by 100. This is done by moving the decimal point two places to the left. For example,

$$35\% \text{ becomes } 0.35 \text{ as a decimal.}$$

$$6\% \text{ becomes } 0.06 \text{ as a decimal.}$$

Percentage of

To calculate the *percentage of* something you first change the percentage to a decimal and then multiply.

Worked example A.12	Find 8% of £135. Calculate $0.08 \times 135 = £10.80$. So 8% of £135 is £10.80.

Percentage increase

Change the percentage to a decimal, add 1, then multiply by the figure that needs increasing.

Worked example A.13

Increase £6 by 5%.
Change 5% to a decimal, add 1, then multiply by £6.
$$1.05 \times £6 = £6.30$$

Percentage decrease

Change the percentage to a decimal and take it away from 1, then multiply it by the original figure.

Worked example A.14

Decrease £8 by 4%. Change 4% to a decimal and take it away from 1.
$$1 - 0.04 = 0.96$$

Multiply this by the original.
$$0.96 \times £8 = £7.68$$

'As a percentage'

We express one quantity *as a percentage* of another by setting up the two numbers as a fraction of each other and converting that fraction to a percentage by simply multiplying by 100.

Worked example A.15

Express £7 as a percentage of £25.
Set up the fraction $\frac{7}{25}$ and multiply by 100. This becomes $(7 \div 25) \times 100 = 28\%$.

Reverse percentage

There are times when we know a certain percentage and we wish to get back to the original amount.

Worked example A.16

The 31 pupils who were absent represented only 4% of the pupils in the school. How many pupils should have been at school?
Since 4% represents 31 pupils, then 1% will represent $31 \div 4$ pupils $= 7.75$, so 100% will be represented by $(7.75 \times 100) = 775$ pupils.

A.3.2 Ratios

To divide any amount in a given ratio, you simply multiply the amount by the fraction of the ratio.

Worked example A.17

Divide £60 between John and Kevin in the ratio of 2:3.
From the ratio we see that John receives $\frac{2}{5}$ and Kevin receives $\frac{3}{5}$. Hence

$$John \text{ receives } £60 \times \frac{2}{5} = £24 \text{ and}$$

$$Kevin \text{ receives } £60 \times \frac{3}{5} = £36.$$

Sometimes you may know only part of the information.

Worked example A.18

Two business partners, Sue and Trish, divide their profits in the ratio 3:5. If Sue receives £1,800, how much does Trish receive?

Sue receives £1,800 which is $\frac{3}{8}$ of the whole profit. So $\frac{1}{8}$ = £1,800 ÷ 3 = £600. So Trish's share which is $\frac{5}{8}$ will be £600 × 5 = £3,000.

Self-check questions A.1

Q1. Solve:
- (a) −4 + −2
- (b) −4 − −2
- (c) −4 × −2
- (d) −4 ÷ −2
- (e) −16 × −6
- (f) −81 ÷ −9

Q2. Correct each of the following to the number of decimal places or significant figures indicated.
- (a) 2.643 (2 d.p.)
- (b) 1.338 (2 d.p.)
- (c) 17.64 (1 d.p.)
- (d) 7.5474 (2 s.f.)
- (e) 17.6 (1 s.f.)
- (f) 0.00587 (1 s.f.)

Q3. Express each of the following as a percentage (to no more than 1 d.p.).
- (a) £5 out of £24
- (b) 4 kg out of 32 kg;
- (c) 2.5 m out of 10 m
- (d) 40 cm out of 3 m

Q4.
- (a) Divide £3.25 in the ratio of 2:3.
- (b) Three footballers score 21, 15 and 9 goals respectively. Their club pays out £9,000 in bonus money to these players. They share the bonus in the same ratio as the goals they score. Calculate the share of the bonus for each player.

A.4 Powers and roots

In the expressions x^4 and x^2, the letter x is called the *base* and the numbers 4 and 2 are called the *powers* (or *indices* or *exponents*).

$$x^4 = x \times x \times x \times x$$

$$x^2 = x \times x$$

A.4.1 Rules for powers

Whenever powers have the *same base*, then a number of rules can be applied. You should make sure that you are familiar with these simple rules.

- Multiplying powers (Indices)

$$4^3 \times 4^2 = (4 \times 4 \times 4) \times (4 \times 4) = 4 \times 4 \times 4 \times 4 \times 4 = 4^5$$

> To multiply, just add the powers:
> $$\text{i.e. } x^a \times x^b = x^{a+b}$$

- Dividing powers (Indices)

$$3^5 \div 3^2 = \frac{3 \times 3 \times 3 \times 3 \times 3}{3 \times 3} = 3 \times 3 \times 3 = 3^3$$

> To divide, just subtract the powers:
> $$\text{i.e. } x^a \div x^b = x^{a-b}$$

- The power zero

e.g. $2^3 \div 2^3 = 2^{3-3} = 2^0$

but $2^3 \div 2^3 = \dfrac{8}{8} = 1$

so $2^0 = 1$

> $$x^0 = 1$$

- Negative powers

e.g. $3^1 \div 3^3 = 3^{1-3} = 3^{-2}$

but $3^1 \div 3^3 = \dfrac{3}{27} = \dfrac{1}{9} = \dfrac{1}{3^2}$

so $3^{-2} = \dfrac{1}{3^2}$

> $$x^{-a} = \frac{1}{x^a}$$

- Fractional powers

Fractional powers will be used to indicate *roots* (see below)

$$x^{\frac{m}{n}} = {}^n\!\sqrt{x^m} = ({}^n\!\sqrt{x})^m$$

$$x^{\frac{1}{n}} = {}^n\!\sqrt{x}$$

A.4.2 Roots

A root is the mathematical word for a solution of a *quadratic* equation.

Root of a number

The root of a number is generally taken to be the *square root*. So, root 9 will be 3 or -3.

The *n*th root

The *n*th root of a number, A, is that number which, when multiplied by itself N times, gives A. Examples:

- The square root of 25: $\sqrt{25} = 5$ or -5, because $5 \times 5 = 25$ and $-5 \times -5 = 25$.
- The cube (3rd) root of 64: $^3\!\sqrt{64} = 4$, because $4 \times 4 \times 4 = 64$.
- The 4th root of 81, $^4\!\sqrt{81} = 3$ or -3, because $3 \times 3 \times 3 \times 3 = 81$ and $-3 \times -3 \times -3 \times -3 = 81$.

You can use your calculator to find any root of any number by using the $x^{1/y}$ key, where y is the *n*th root you want. You will most likely need to use the shift or inv or 2ndf key also. For example, if you want to find the 5th root of 7776, key in 7776 $x^{1/y}$ 5: this will give the result 6.

Self-check questions A.2

Solve the following using your knowledge of the rules for dealing with powers.

Q1. (a) $t^3 \times t^4$
(b) $m^2 \times m$
(c) $3x^2 \times 2x^5$
(d) $5p \times 3p^4$
(e) $7m^3 \times 4m$
(f) $3w \times 4w^2$

Q2. (a) $x^7 \div x^3$
(b) $p^6 \div p^4$
(c) $8d^3 \div 2d$
(d) $6m^4 \div 3m^3$
(e) $12c^3 \div 6c^3$
(f) $9m^4 \div 6m^3$

(continued)

Q3. (a) $3^8 \div 3^5$

    (b) $2^9 \div 2^7$

    (c) $10^3 \div 10^2$

    (d) $10^7 \div 10^3$

    (e) $7^7 \div 7^6$

    (f) $19^8 \div 19^7$

Q4. Write the following in fraction form:

    (a) 7^{-2}

    (b) 8^{-3}

    (c) x^{-4}

    (d) m^{-1}

    (e) $4g^{-2}$

    (f) $5m^{-2}$

    (g) $(2t)^{-3}$

    (h) $\dfrac{1}{2}t^{-4}$

Q5. (a) $6m \div 3m^2$

    (b) $8t^2 \div 6t^5$

    (c) $9x^3 \div 6x^4$

    (d) $cd^3 \div d^5$

    (e) $a^2b \div ab$

    (f) $3ab \div b^2$

    (g) $9q^2 \div 5q^3$

    (h) $12m^2 \div 6mp$

    (i) $3x \div 4x$

    (j) $15x^2 \div 3x^2$

    (k) $4t^2 \div 3t^{-1}$

    (l) $5t^{-1} \div 2t^{-1}$

Q6. Write each of the following as a power.

    (a) $\sqrt{3}$

    (b) $\sqrt{42}$

    (c) $\dfrac{1}{\sqrt{7}}$

    (d) $\dfrac{1}{\sqrt{5^2}}$

    (e) $\sqrt[3]{3^2}$

    (f) $\sqrt[4]{5^3}$

A.5 Simple algebra

Algebra is the use of letters for numbers and is often known as the language of mathematics. A number of processes are often involved.

A.5.1 Substitution

One of the most important features of algebra is the use of expressions and formulae and the substitution of real numbers into them.

The value of an expression such as $3x + 2$ will change with the different values of x *substituted* into it.

Worked example A.19

Suppose the formula is given by $A = \dfrac{h(a + b)}{2}$

Then if $a = 4, b = 7$ and $h = 8$

$$A = \frac{8(4 + 7)}{2} = 44$$

A.5.2 Transposition

It is often necessary to be able to change a formulae round to help you find a particular piece of information.

This changing round of formulae is called *transposition* of formulae and what we are doing is changing the subject of a formula. The *subject* of a formula is the single letter, or word, usually on the left-hand side all by itself.

For example:

t is the subject of the formula $t = \dfrac{d}{v}$

Here are some rules for changing the subjects of formulae:

Rule 1

You can move any letter, or word, from one side of the equation to the other as long as it is operating on *all* the rest of that side.

For example, in the formula $v = u + 6t$, the u can be moved since it is adding to the rest of that side, but the t cannot be moved yet as it is only multiplying the 6.

This simple list of formulae should help you see when we can move terms:

- $v = u + 6t$ we could move either the u or the $6t$
- $A = lb$ we could move either the l or the b
- wage $=$ hours $\times$ hourly rate   we could move either hours or hourly rate
- $t = \dfrac{d}{v}$ we could move either the d or the v
- $x = \dfrac{y + 1}{7}$ we could move either the 7 or the $(y + 1)$
- $w = n\,(y - 10)$ we could move either the n or the $(y - 10)$

> ### Rule 2
>
> When a letter, or word, has been moved from one side to the other, it does the *opposite thing* to the other side.

For example, if something was added, then when it moved it would be subtracted, or if something was multiplied then when it moved it would divide.

Worked example A.20

The following examples will help to illustrate these points:

- $v = u + 6t$ can be changed to $v - u = 6t$

  or $\quad v - 6t = u$

- $A = lb$ can be changed to $\dfrac{A}{l} = b$

  or $\quad \dfrac{A}{b} = l$

- $t = \dfrac{d}{v}$ can be changed to $tv = d$

  or $\quad \dfrac{t}{d} = \dfrac{1}{v}$

- $y = 6x - 10$ can be changed to $y + 10 = 6x$

  or $\quad y - 6x = -10$

All your transposition or manipulation involving algebra can be summarised in the following principle.

> If it is doing what it is doing to everything else on that side of the equation, then it can be moved to the other side and perform the opposite job.

A.5.3 Simplification

This is what we do in algebra to make expressions look as simple as possible. Only *like* terms can be added or subtracted, as follows:

$3x + 4x = 7x$ $\qquad$ $6x - 2x = 4x$ $\qquad$ $3x^2 + 4x^2 = 7x^2$

$5y + y = 6y$ $\qquad$ $4t - t = 3t$ $\qquad$ $3y^3 + 2y^3 = 5y^3$

Simplification can also involve either the *expansion* of brackets or the opposite process, namely *factorisation*, whereby a more complex expression is reduced to a simpler one involving brackets.

A.5.4 Expansion

'Expand' in mathematics means to multiply out the brackets.

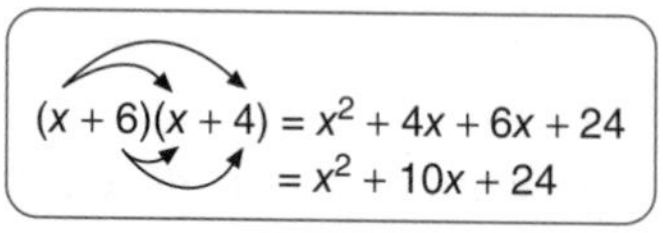

$$(x + 6)(x + 4) = x^2 + 4x + 6x + 24$$
$$= x^2 + 10x + 24$$

Figure A.3 Expanding brackets

For example:

Expand $3(2x - 5)$

means multiply the 3 by everything inside the bracket to give $6x - 15$.

If you are asked to expand $(x + 6)(x + 4)$ you need to multiply everything inside the first bracket by everything inside the second bracket:

$$(x + 6)(x + 4) = x(x + 4) + 6(x + 4)$$
$$= x^2 + 4x + 6x + 24$$
$$= x^2 + 10x + 24$$

This can be illustrated with a diagram (see Figure A.3).

A.5.5 Factorisation

This means to separate an expression into the parts that will multiply together to give that expression. The two (or more) parts are usually connected by brackets.

For example:

$$4x + 8y \text{ would factorise and simplify to } 4(x + 2y)$$

$$3y - 3x \text{ would factorise and simplify to } 3(y - x)$$

As we note below, these examples of factorisation involve *linear* expressions. However, we are often faced with examples involving *quadratic* (highest power is a square) expressions.

A.5.6 Quadratic factorisation

For example:

Factorise and simplify the quadratic expression

$$6x^2 + 5x - 6$$

This process is the opposite to that shown in Figure A.3 above for a quadratic expansion. We know that quadratic factorisation will involve *two* brackets. The quadratic expression can be thought to be of the general type:

$$ax^2 + bx + c$$

1. When the last sign in the quadratic $ax^2 + bx + c$ is *positive*, then both signs in the brackets are the *same as the first sign* in the quadratic. For example:

$$x^2 + 5x + 4 = (+)(+)$$

and

$$x^2 - 5x + 4 = (-)(-)$$

2. When the last sign in the quadratic $ax^2 + bx - c$ is *negative*, then the signs in the brackets are *different*. For example:

$$x^2 + 5x - 5 = (+)(-)$$

or

$$= (-)(+)$$

Once you have sorted out the *signs*, then you need to look at the *numbers*. Follow through these two examples to see how to do this.

Worked example A.21

Factorise $6x^2 + 7x + 2$.

Solution

By looking at the signs we see that the brackets both contain a '+', so:

$$6x^2 + 7x + 2 = (+)(+).$$

We see that the end numbers in each bracket must multiply to give 2, and the only way to do this is to have 2×1.

Hence $6x^2 + 7x + 2 = (+2)(+1)$.

Now we see that the first numbers in each bracket must multiply to give 6, and we could have 3×2 or 2×3 or 6×1 or 1×6, but the combination we need must multiply with the 2 and the 1, so that their sum is 7. We ask ourselves which of

$$\{3 \times 1\} \{2 \times 1\} \{6 \times 1\} \text{ or } \{1 \times 1\}$$
$$\{2 \times 2\} \{3 \times 2\} \{1 \times 2\} \{6 \times 2\}$$

give a combined total of 7, and we that the only one which does is

$$\{3 \times 1\}$$
$$\{2 \times 2\}$$

so the factorisation is $(3x + 2)(2x + 1)$.

Worked example A.22

Factorise $2x^2 + 5x - 3$.

Solution

We factorise by looking at the signs and noticing that both signs will be different, hence $(+)(-)$. The -3 indicates we need a 3 and a 1 at the end of each bracket to give $(+3)(-1)$ or $(+1)(-3)$. Now, a product of 2 for the first numbers in each bracket, that is, 2 and 1, must combine with the 3 and 1 in such a way as to give a difference of $+5$. This will give us $(x + 3)(2x - 1)$.

A.6 Solving equations

To *solve* an equation is to find the value or values that satisfy that equation.

For example:

Solve $4x + 3 = 23$.

This is a *linear* equation (highest power is 1) and has a unique solution, namely $4x = 23 - 3$, giving $x = 5$. Only when $x = 5$ is this equation satisfied. Linear equations have only one solution.

When we are solving *quadratic* equations, we may find up to two solutions, that is, two values of the variable that satisfy that equation. In solving quadratic equations it is usual to use either *factorisation* or the *formula method*

A.6.1 Factorising quadratic equations

Take the general form of the quadratic equation:

$$ax^2 + bx + c = 0$$

If we can *factorise* this equation, that is, reduce it to two brackets multiplied together, then we can set *either* bracket $= 0$ and find a solution.

Worked example A.23

Solve $x^2 + 2x - 15 = 0$.

Solution

This factorises into $(x - 3)(x + 5) = 0$

The only way that this expression can ever equal 0 is if one of the brackets is worth 0. Hence either

$$(x - 3) = 0 \quad \text{or} \quad (x + 5) = 0$$

$$\text{hence } x = 3 \quad \text{or} \quad x = -5$$

The solutions then are $x = 3$ and $x = -5$.

Whether or not an equation will factorise, the next method will always give you the solution to a quadratic equation (where a solution exists!).

Formula for solving quadratic equations

A formula has been derived that can be used to solve any quadratic equation (or used to tell you that there is no solution). For a quadratic equation of the general form $ax^2 + bx + c = 0$:

$$x = \frac{-b \pm \sqrt{(b^2 - 4ac)}}{2a}$$

The use of the $\pm$ reflects the fact that a square root has a positive and a negative solution.

Worked example A.24

Solve the equation $3x^2 - 8x + 2 = 0$, correct to 2 d.p.

Solution

Use $x = \dfrac{-b \pm \sqrt{(b^2 - 4ac)}}{2a}$

where

$a = 3$
$b = -8$
$c = 2$

Worked example A.24 (cont'd)

$$= \frac{8 \pm \sqrt{\{64 - 4(3)(2)\}}}{6}$$

$$= \frac{8 \pm \sqrt{40}}{6} = \frac{8 + \sqrt{40}}{6} \text{ and } \frac{8 - \sqrt{40}}{6}$$

$$= 2.39 \text{ or } 0.28$$

A.7 Simultaneous equations

In business and economic situations we may, for example, need to find the price at which supply equals demand. We call this the *equilibrium price*, as it balances both supply and demand. Put another way, it is the price that solves both the demand and supply equations *at the same time* (i.e. simultaneously).

It is therefore important that you know how to go about solving simultaneous equations. The idea in the example below is to *eliminate* either the x or the y variable, whether by addition or subtraction, so that we are left with one equation with one unknown variable. Having solved this equation we can then use the result to solve for the other unknown variable. Work through these examples yourself.

Worked example A.25

Solve the simultaneous equations:

$$6x + y = 15$$

$$4x + y = 11$$

Solution

Since both equations have a y term the same we can *subtract* one equation from the other to give

$$2x = 4$$

which solves to give

$$x = 2$$

We now substitute $x = 2$ into one of the first equations (usually the one with the smallest numbers involved). So substitute $x = 2$ into $4x + y = 11$ to give $8 + y = 11$ which gives

$$y = 11 - 8$$

$$y = 3$$

We test our solution in the other initial equation.

Substitute $x = 2$ and $y = 3$ into $6x + y$ to give $12 + 3 = 15$, which is correct. So we can confidently say that our solution is $x = 2$ and $y = 3$.

Worked example A.26

Solve the simultaneous equations:

$$4x - 2y = 12$$
$$2x + 2y = 18$$

Solution

Since both equations have a $2y$ term but one with a $+$ and one with a $-$ then we can *add* one equation to the other to give

$$6x = 30$$
$$x = 5$$

Substitute $x = 5$ into, say, the lower equation to get

$$2 \times 5 + 2y = 18$$
$$10 + 2y = 18$$
$$2y = 18 - 10 = 8$$
$$y = 4$$

The solution of $x = 5$ and $y = 4$ can be checked in the top equation to give

$$(4 \times 5) - (2 \times 4) = 20 - 8 = 12$$

which is correct. So our solution is $x = 5$ and $y = 4$.

Worked example A.27

Solve the simultaneous equations:

$$4x + 2y = 32$$
$$3x - y = 19$$

Here we do not have any equal terms so we have to start creating them because that is the only way we can solve simultaneous equations. We can see that by multiplying *all* of the second equation by 2 we get

$$(3x - y = 19) \times 2 \Rightarrow 6x - 2y = 38$$

Our pair of equations is now

$$4x + 2y = 32$$
$$6x - 2y = 38$$

and we can solve these as we did in Worked Example A.26 by *adding* them together.

$$10x = 70, \text{ gives } x = 7 \text{ and } y = 2.$$

Worked example A.28

Solve the simultaneous equations:

$$5x + 4y = 22$$
$$2x + 3y = 6$$

Solution

Notice that we cannot simply multiply one equation by anything to give us equal terms. So we have to multiply *both* equations.

The choice is now up to us: we can either make the xs the same or the ys the same. Sometimes there is an obvious choice; sometimes it does not matter. In this example it does not matter which you do since there is no great advantage in choosing either.

Let us choose the xs to be made equal. We will have to multiply the first equation through by 2 and the second equation through by 5. This gives

$$(5x + 4y = 22) \times 2 \Rightarrow 10x + 8y = 44$$

and

$$(2x + 3y = 16) \times 5 \Rightarrow 10x + 15y = 80$$

We now solve these by *subtracting* them from each other, giving $-7y = -36$, $y = 5\frac{1}{7}$ and $x = \frac{2}{7}$.

A.8 Inequalities

Inequalities behave similarly to normal equations. The difference is that they have an inequality sign instead of an equals sign.

A.8.1 Linear inequalities

For linear inequalities we use the same rules to solve inequalities as we do linear equations.

Solve $\dfrac{5x + 7}{3} < 12$

Solution

$$5x + 7 < 14 \times 3$$
$$5x + 7 < 42$$
$$5x < 42 - 7$$
$$5x < 35$$
$$x < 35 \div 5$$
$$x < 7$$

Solve the inequality $1 < 5x + 3 \le 17$.

Solution

We need to treat each side separately as

$$1 < 5x + 3 \qquad 5x + 3 \le 17$$
$$1 - 3 < 5x \qquad 5x \le 17 - 3$$
$$-2 < 5x \qquad 5x \le 14$$
$$\frac{2}{5} < x \qquad x \le \frac{14}{5}$$
$$-0.4 < x \qquad x \le 2.8$$

Hence $-0.4 < x \le 2.8$.

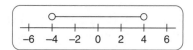

Figure A.4 Inequalities

A.8.2 Inequalities involving x^2

Consider $x^2 < 16$. Now, the solution to $x^2 = 16$ is $x = +4$ and $x = -4$. When we look at the $x = 4$ part we can see that, yes, $x < -4$ just does not work. In fact the solution to do with $x = -4$ needs the inequality sign changing round to give us the solution $x > -4$ which can be turned to give $-4 < x$.

Put all this onto a number line and you see the solution (Figure A.4).

The solution is $-4 < x < 4$.

Worked example A.31	Solve the inequality $x^2 > 25$. *Solution* The solution to $x^2 > 25$ will be $x > 5$ and $x < -5$. Notice the difference between the types $x^2 < a^2$ and the types $x^2 > a^2$

A.9 Graphs and functions

A *function* is a rule describing the relationship between variables. Using the notation $y = f(x)$, we are indicating, in a type of shorthand, that the variable y *depends upon* (is a function of) some other variable, x. We could then say that y is the *dependent variable* and x the *independent variable*, though our study of economics will alert us to the fact that relationships between variables are rarely in a single direction only.

The function or rule describing the relationship between variables may be specified more precisely. Thus $y = f(x) = 3x + 2$ will tell us that y takes the value 2 when $x = 0$ and rises by 3 units for every unit rise in x. This is an example of a *linear function*, of the general form $y = mx + c$, where c is the vertical intercept and m is the slope or gradient.

A.9.1 Linear function

Where the highest power of the independent variable is 1, as in $y = 3x^1 + 2$, then we have a linear function or relationship. A *graph* or picture of this linear relationship between the variables is shown in Figure A.5.

A.9.2 Quadratic function

Where the highest power of the independent variable is 2, as in the case of $y = ax^2 + bx + c$, then we have a quadratic function or relationship. A graph of such a quadratic relationship between the variables is shown in Figure A.6. The shape of this graph is called a *parabola*, and will be $\cup$ shaped where a is positive and $\cap$ shaped where a is negative. The vertical intercept will again be determined by the value of c.

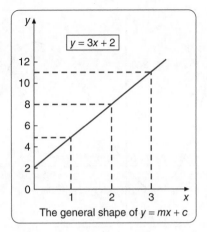

Figure A.5 Linear function

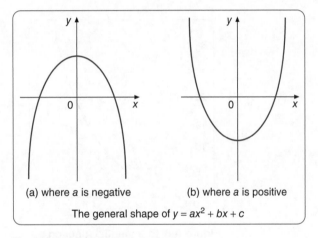

Figure A.6 Quadratic function

A.9.3 Cubic function

Where the highest power of the independent variable is 3, as in the case of $y = ax^3 + bx^2 + cx + d$, then we have a cubic function or relationship. A graph of such a cubic relationship between the variables is shown in Figure A.7.

You should, of course, be familiar with other functional relationships.

- *Exponential:* of the form $y = a^x$, where a is any constant >1 and x is any variable. Figure A.8 graphs the exponential relationship $y = 2^x$ over the values $x = 1$ to $x = 5$.

- *Reciprocal (hyperbolic):* of the form $y = \dfrac{a}{x}$, where a is any constant and x any variable. Figure A.9 graphs the reciprocal (hyperbolic) relationship of $y = \dfrac{6}{x}$ over the values $x = 1$ to $x = 6$.

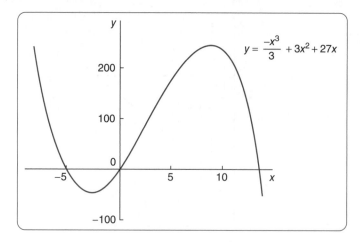

Figure A.7 Cubic function

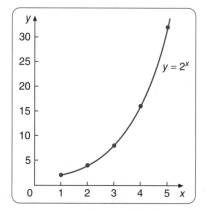

Figure A.8 Exponential function

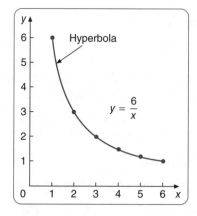

Figure A.9 Reciprocal (hyperbolic function)

A.9.4 Gradients to graphs

Linear functions

The general form of the linear function is:

$$y = mx + c$$

where m is the gradient and c the vertical intercept.

The slope or gradient of the line joining two points measures how 'steep' the line is and is defined as the fraction:

$$\frac{\text{difference between the } y \text{ co-ordinates of the points}}{\text{difference between the } x \text{ co-ordinates of the points}}$$

Gradient between (x_1, y_1), (x_2, y_2)

$$\text{Gradient} = \frac{(y_2 - y_1)}{(x_2 - x_2)}$$

$$\text{Gradient} = \frac{\text{vertical distance}}{\text{horizontal distance}}$$

In Figure A.10

$$\text{Gradient} = \frac{7 - 3}{3 - 1} = \frac{4}{2} = +2$$

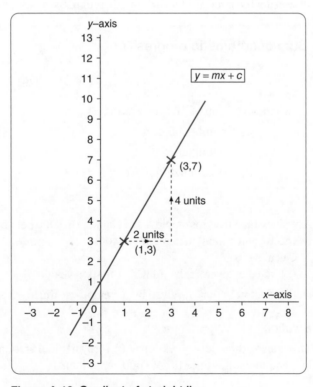

Figure A.10 Gradient of straight line

Non-linear functions

Here we use *calculus* (see Chapter 8) to find the gradient to a point on a curve. The process by which we *differentiate* the function will give us the required gradient.

A.10 Progressions

Two types of progression are frequently used in quantitative solutions, namely arithmetic and geometric progressions.

A.10.1 Arithmetic progressions (AP)

This is a sequence of terms in which an initial term, a, changes by a constant absolute amount, called the 'common difference' (d).

An *arithmetic progression* involving n terms takes the following form:

$$a, a + d, a + 2d, a + 3d, a + 4d \ldots a + (n - 1)d$$

Examples:

$$5, 7, 9, 11, 13 \ldots \ (a = 5, d = +2)$$

$$43, 39, 35, 31, 27 \ldots \ (a = 43, d = +4)$$

Note that the third term is $a + 2d$, the fourth terms is $a + 3d$, and so on, so that the nth term is $a + (n - 1) d$, where n can be any number.

If we sum the n terms of an arithmetic progression (AP), then we can use the formula

---

Sum of arithmetic progression

$$S_n = \frac{n}{2}[2a + (n - 1)d]$$

where S_n = sum of AP over n terms

n = number of terms

a = initial term

d = common difference

Worked example A.32

A businessman pays his employee a salary of £10,000 per annum; at the end of each year he receives an annual increment of £400.

Calculate:

(a) the employee's salary during the sixth year;

(b) the total salary received by the employee during the six years.

Solution

This is an arithmetic progression (AP) with an initial amount (a) of £10,000 which rises by a common difference (d) of £400 per annum.

Worked example A.32 (cont'd)

(a)   When $n = 6$, the sixth term of an AP will be

$$a + (n - 1)d$$
$$= £10{,}000 + (6 - 1)\,£400$$
$$= £12{,}000$$

The employee receives £12,000 in the sixth year.

(b) $S_n = \dfrac{n}{2}[2a + (n - 1)d]$

$$S_6 = \frac{6}{2}[2(£10{,}000) + (6 - 1)£400]$$

$$S_6 = 3[£20{,}000 + £2{,}000]$$

$$S_6 = £66{,}000$$

The employee receives £66,000 salary during the first six years of employment.

The box below gives a proof of the formula for summing an arithmetic progression.

Proof of AP formula

$$S_n = a + [a + d] + [a + 2d] + \ \ldots \ [a + (n - 2)d] + [a + (n - 1)d]$$

$$S_n \text{ (backward)} = [a + (n - 1)d] + [a + (n - 2d)] + \ldots \ [a + 2d] + [a + d \ ] + a$$

adding term by term

$$2S_n = [2a + (n - 1)d] + [2a + (n - 1)d] + [2a + (n - 1)d]$$

$$+ [2a + (n - 1)d] + [2a + (n - 1)d]$$

$$2S_n = n[2a + (n - 1)d]$$

$$S_n = \frac{n}{2}[2a + (n - 1)d]$$

A.10.2 Geometric progressions (GP)

A geometric progression occurs where an initial amount (a) changes by a 'common ratio' (r) in successive terms.

A geometric progression involving n terms takes the following form:

$$a, ar, ar^2, ar^3 \ldots \ ar^{n-1}$$

Examples:

$3, 6, 12, 24, 48 \ldots (a = 3, r = 2)$

$200, 100, 50, 25, 12.5 \ldots \left(a = 200, r = \dfrac{1}{2} \right)$

Note that the third term is ar^2, the fourth term is ar^3, and so on, so that the nth term is ar^{n-1}, where n can be any number.

If we sum the n terms of a geometric progression (GP), then we can use the formula

Sum of geometric progression

$$S_n = \frac{a(1 - r^n)}{(1 - r)}$$

where S_n = sum of GP over n terms

n = number of terms

a = initial term

r = common ratio (as a fraction or a decimal)

Worked example A.33

An employee makes an annual investment of £1,000 in shares this year. He instructs his broker to increase this annual investment by 5% each year.

(a)   How much does he invest in the sixth year?

(b)   How much does he invest altogether over the first six years?

Solution

This is a GP, with a = £1,000 and r = 1.05

(a)   When $n = 6$, the sixth term of a GP will be:

$ar^{n-1} = ar^{6-1} = ar^5$

$£1,000 \, (1.05)^5 = £1,276.28$

He invests £1,276.28 in the sixth year.

(b) $S_n = \dfrac{a(1 - r^n)}{(1 - r)}$

$S_6 = \dfrac{1000[1 - (1.05)^6]}{(1 - 1.05)} = \dfrac{1000[1 - 1.3401]}{-0.05}$

$S_6 = \dfrac{1000[-0.3401]}{-0.05} = \dfrac{-340.1}{-0.05}$

$S_6 = £6,802$

He invests £6,802 over the six years.

The box below gives a proof of the formula for summing a geometric progression.

Proof of GP formula

$$S_n = a + ar + ar^2 + \ldots + ar^{n-2} + ar^{n-1}$$

$$\therefore rS_n = ar + ar^2, \ldots ar^{n-2} + ar^{n-1} + ar^n$$

$$S_n - rS_n = a + ar^n$$

i.e. $S_n(1 - r) = a + ar^n$

$$S_n = \frac{a(1 - r^n)}{(1 - r)}$$

Self-check questions A.3

Q1. Make y the subject of the following formulae.
  (a) $x = 2(y - 1)$
  (b) $x = y(b + 7)$
  (c) $t = 5y + \dfrac{p}{7}$

Q2. Expand the following and simplify.
  (a) $(2x - 3)(4x + 1)$
  (b) $(3x + 5)(x - 3)$
  (c) $p(2m + t) - t(3m - p)$

Q3. Factorise the following.
  (a) $3t + 7t^2$
  (b) $2m^3 - 6m^2$
  (c) $6mp^2 + 9m^2pt$
  (d) $x^2 - 7x + 12$
  (e) $x^2 - 25$
  (f) $2x^2 - x - 15$

Q4. Solve the following equations.
  (a) $2x - 3 = 11$
  (b) $3 - 5x = 8$
  (c) $4(2x - 3) = 7$

Q5. Solve the following quadratic equations, to 2 d.p. where necessary.
  (a) $x^2 + 7x + 12 = 0$
  (b) $5x^2 + 6x - 2 = 0$
  (c) $x^2 + 4x - 117 = 0$

(continued)

Q6. Solve the following pairs of simultaneous equations.
  (a) $5x + y = 0$
       $3x - 2y = 13$
  (b) $7x + 3y = 18$
       $x + y = 4$

Q7. Solve the following inequalities.
  (a) $5x > 32$
  (b) $4t < 5t - 8$
  (c) $x^2 < 36$
  (d) $-2 \leq 5x + 3 < 4$

Q8. Complete this table of values for $y = x^2 + x - 6$.

x	-4	-3	-2	-1	0	1	2	3
x^2		9			0		4	
$+x$	-4	-3				1	2	3
-6	-6	-6	-6		-6		-6	
y	6		-4	-6				

  (a) Use the table to draw the graph of $y = x^2 + x - 6$ as x takes values from -4 to 3.
  (b) Use your graph to solve $y = x^2 + x - 6 = 0$.

Q9. Find the gradient of the straight line that connects the points $(-2, -3)$ and $(4, 9)$
Q10. Use an appropriate *formula* to sum the following progressions to eight terms.
  (a) 42, 46, 50, 54...
  (b) 200,195, 190, 185...
  (c) 4, 6, 9, 13.5...
  (d) 1000, 500, 250, 125...

REVIEW QUESTIONS

RA.1. In a survey of British pop wealth in *Business Age* magazine, David Bowie came top with £550 million, Paul McCartney came second with £520 million and Gary Barlow fiftieth with £9.5 million. The youngest person in the top 50 was Baby Spice with £14.5 million.
  (a) What percentage is Gary Barlow's wealth of Baby Spice's wealth?
  (b) By what percentage would Paul McCartney's wealth have to increase before it equalled that of David Bowie?

RA.2. On Monday 27 October 1997 the Dow Jones share index in New York fell by 7% to 7,161.15 (the biggest one day fall since Black Monday in 1987). What was the index at the start of the day?

RA.3. A company produces a product for which the variable cost per unit is £5 and the fixed costs are £20,000. If the selling price is £15 per unit
  (a) how many units (Q) does the company need to sell in order to make £8,000 profit;
  (b) at what level of output would the firm break even (i.e. total revenue = total costs)?
  (c) New environmental legislation increases the company's fixed costs by 20%. By what percentage does this increase the break-even output?

(d) Plot the firm's fixed costs, total costs (before and after the increase) and total revenue on a graph. Mark the break-even outputs of (b) and (c) on the graph.
Make use of the following relationships:

$$\text{Total cost} = \text{fixed costs} + \text{variable costs}$$
$$\text{Total revenue} = \text{price per unit} \times \text{number of units sold}$$
$$\text{Profit} = \text{total revenue} - \text{total cost}$$

RA.4. It is estimated that if a price of £15 per unit is charged for a product 5 units per period will be sold. If the price is lowered to £13, sales will be 6 units per period. The supply curve for the product is given by $P = 3Q + 5$.

(a) Assuming that the demand relationship is linear, find the demand equation.

(b) Find the equilibrium price and quantity (i.e. the price where quantity demanded = quantity supplied).

RA.5. A firm's total revenue and total cost equations are given by:

$$\text{Total costs} = Q^2 + 23$$
$$\text{Total revenue} = -2Q^2 + 26Q$$

(a) Find the output levels total at which the firm just breaks even.

(b) Plot the graph of total costs, total revenue and profits and show that the profit maximising output is mid-way between the break-even outputs.

Appendix 2

Probabilities for the normal distribution

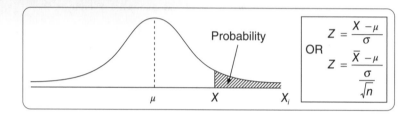

Z Score	0.00	0.01	0.02	0.03	0.04	0.05	0.06	0.07	0.08	0.09
0.0	0.5000	0.4960	0.4920	0.4880	0.4840	0.4801	0.4761	0.4721	0.4681	0.4641
0.1	0.4602	0.4562	0.4522	0.4483	0.4443	0.4404	0.4364	0.4325	0.4286	0.4247
0.2	0.4207	0.4168	0.4129	0.4090	0.4052	0.4013	0.3974	0.3936	0.3897	0.3859
0.3	0.3821	0.3783	0.3745	0.3707	0.3669	0.3632	0.3594	0.3557	0.3520	0.3483
0.4	0.3446	0.3409	0.3372	0.3336	0.3300	0.3264	0.3228	0.3192	0.3156	0.3121
0.5	0.3085	0.3050	0.3015	0.2981	0.2946	0.2912	0.2877	0.2843	0.2810	0.2776
0.6	0.2743	0.2709	0.2676	0.2643	0.2611	0.2578	0.2546	0.2514	0.2483	0.2451
0.7	0.2420	0.2389	0.2358	0.2327	0.2296	0.2266	0.2236	0.2206	0.2177	0.2148
0.8	0.2119	0.2090	0.2061	0.2033	0.2005	0.1977	0.1949	0.1922	0.1894	0.1867
0.9	0.1841	0.1814	0.1788	0.1762	0.1736	0.1711	0.1685	0.1660	0.1635	0.1611
1.0	0.1587	0.1562	0.1539	0.1515	0.1492	0.1469	0.1446	0.1423	0.1401	0.1379
1.1	0.1357	0.1335	0.1314	0.1292	0.1271	0.1251	0.1230	0.1210	0.1190	0.1170
1.2	0.1151	0.1131	0.1112	0.1093	0.1075	0.1056	0.1038	0.1020	0.1003	0.0985
1.3	0.0968	0.0951	0.0934	0.0918	0.0901	0.0885	0.0869	0.0853	0.0838	0.0823
1.4	0.0808	0.0793	0.0778	0.0764	0.0749	0.0735	0.0721	0.0708	0.0694	0.0681
1.5	0.0668	0.0655	0.0643	0.0630	0.0618	0.0606	0.0594	0.0582	0.0571	0.0559
1.6	0.0548	0.0537	0.0562	0.0516	0.0505	0.0495	0.0485	0.0475	0.0465	0.0455
1.7	0.0446	0.0436	0.0427	0.0418	0.0409	0.0401	0.0392	0.0384	0.0375	0.0367
1.8	0.0359	0.0351	0.0344	0.0336	0.0329	0.0322	0.0314	0.0307	0.0301	0.0294
1.9	0.0287	0.0281	0.0274	0.0268	0.0262	0.0256	0.0250	0.0244	0.0239	0.0233

2.0	0.0228	0.0222	0.0217	0.0212	0.0207	0.0202	0.0197	0.0192	0.0188	0.0183
2.1	0.0179	0.0174	0.0170	0.0166	0.0162	0.0158	0.0154	0.0150	0.0146	0.0143
2.2	0.0139	0.0136	0.0132	0.0129	0.0125	0.0122	0.0119	0.0116	0.0113	0.0110
2.3	0.0107	0.0104	0.0102	0.0099	0.0096	0.0094	0.0091	0.0089	0.0087	0.0084
2.4	0.0082	0.0080	0.0078	0.0075	0.0073	0.0072	0.0069	0.0068	0.0066	0.0064
2.5	0.0062	0.0060	0.0059	0.0057	0.0055	0.0054	0.0052	0.0051	0.0049	0.0048
2.6	0.0047	0.0045	0.0044	0.0043	0.0041	0.0040	0.0039	0.0038	0.0037	0.0036
2.7	0.0035	0.0034	0.0033	0.0032	0.0031	0.0030	0.0029	0.0028	0.0027	0.0026
2.8	0.0026	0.0025	0.0024	0.0023	0.0023	0.0022	0.0021	0.0021	0.0020	0.0019
2.9	0.0019	0.0018	0.0018	0.0017	0.0016	0.0016	0.0015	0.0015	0.0014	0.0014
3.0	0.0013	0.0013	0.0013	0.0012	0.0012	0.0011	0.0011	0.0011	0.0010	0.0010

Cumulative binomial probabilities

		p = 0.01	0.05	0.10	0.20	0.30	0.40	0.45	0.50
n = 5	r = 0	1.0000	1.0000	1.0000	1.0000	1.0000	1.0000	1.0000	1.0000
	1	0.0490	0.2262	0.4095	0.6723	0.8319	0.9222	0.9497	0.9688
	2	0.0010	0.0226	0.0815	0.2627	0.4718	0.6630	0.7438	0.8125
	3		0.0012	0.0086	0.0579	0.1631	0.3174	0.4069	0.5000
	4			0.0005	0.0067	0.0308	0.0870	0.1312	0.1875
	5				0.0003	0.0024	0.0102	0.0185	0.0313
n = 10	r = 0	1.0000	1.0000	1.0000	1.0000	1.0000	1.0000	1.0000	1.0000
	1	0.0956	0.4013	0.6513	0.8926	0.9718	0.9940	0.9975	0.9990
	2	0.0043	0.0861	0.2639	0.6242	0.8507	0.9536	0.9767	0.9893
	3	0.0001	0.0115	0.0702	0.3222	0.6172	0.8327	0.9004	0.9453
	4		0.0010	0.0128	0.1209	0.3504	0.6177	0.7430	0.8281
	5		0.0001	0.0016	0.0328	0.1503	0.3669	0.4956	0.6230
	6			0.0001	0.0064	0.0473	0.1662	0.2616	0.3770
	7				0.0009	0.0106	0.0548	0.1020	0.1719
	8				0.0001	0.0016	0.0123	0.0274	0.0547
	9					0.0001	0.0017	0.0045	0.0107
	10						0.0001	0.0003	0.0010

where

p is the probability of a characteristic (e.g. a defective item),

n is the sample size and

r is the number with that characteristic.

Note: All probabilities are for 'r or more successes'. Only selected values for n and r are shown in this table.

Cumulative Poisson probabilities

	$\mu = 1.0$	2.0	3.0	4.0	5.0	6.0	7.0
$r = 0$	1.0000	1.0000	1.0000	1.0000	1.0000	1.0000	1.0000
1	0.6321	0.8647	0.9502	0.9817	0.9933	0.9975	0.9991
2	0.2642	0.5940	0.8009	0.9084	0.9596	0.9826	0.9927
3	0.0803	0.3233	0.5768	0.7619	0.8753	0.9380	0.9704
4	0.0190	0.1429	0.3528	0.5665	0.7350	0.8488	0.9182
5	0.0037	0.0527	0.1847	0.3712	0.5595	0.7149	0.8270
6	0.0006	0.0166	0.0839	0.2149	0.3840	0.5543	0.6993
7	0.0001	0.0011	0.0335	0.1107	0.2378	0.3937	0.5503
8		0.0002	0.0119	0.0511	0.1334	0.2560	0.4013
9			0.0038	0.0214	0.0681	0.1528	0.2709
10			0.0011	0.0081	0.0318	0.0839	0.1695
11			0.0003	0.0028	0.0137	0.0426	0.0985
12			0.0001	0.0009	0.0055	0.0201	0.0534
13				0.0003	0.0020	0.0088	0.0270
14				0.0001	0.0007	0.0036	0.0128
15					0.0002	0.0014	0.0057
16					0.0001	0.0005	0.0024
17						0.0002	0.0010
18						0.0001	0.0004
19							0.0001

where
$\mu(= np)$ is the average number of times a characteristic occurs and r is the number of occurrences.
Note: All probabilities are for 'r or more successes'.

Appendix 5

Student *t* critical values

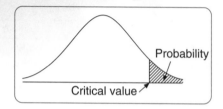

Probability

Critical value

Probability	0.10	0.05	0.025	0.01	0.005
v = 1	3.078	6.314	12.706	31.821	63.657
2	1.886	2.920	4.303	6.965	9.925
3	1.638	2.353	3.182	4.541	5.841
4	1.533	2.132	2.776	3.747	4.604
5	1.476	2.015	2.571	3.365	4.032
6	1.440	1.943	2.447	3.143	3.707
7	1.415	1.895	2.365	2.998	3.499
8	1.397	1.860	2.306	2.896	3.355
9	1.383	1.833	2.262	2.821	3.250
10	1.372	1.812	2.228	2.764	3.169
11	1.363	1.796	2.201	2.718	3.106
12	1.356	1.782	2.179	2.681	3.055
13	1.350	1.771	2.160	2.650	3.012
14	1.345	1.761	2.145	2.624	2.977
15	1.341	1.753	2.131	2.602	2.947
16	1.337	1.746	2.120	2.583	2.921
17	1.333	1.740	2.110	2.567	2.898
18	1.330	1.734	2.101	2.552	2.878
19	1.328	1.729	2.093	2.539	2.861
20	1.325	1.725	2.086	2.528	2.845
21	1.323	1.721	2.080	2.518	2.831
22	1.321	1.717	2.074	2.508	2.819
23	1.319	1.714	2.069	2.500	2.807
24	1.318	1.711	2.064	2.492	2.797
25	1.316	1.708	2.060	2.485	2.787

26	1.315	1.706	2.056	2.479	2.779
27	1.314	1.703	2.052	2.473	2.771
28	1.313	1.701	2.048	2.467	2.763
29	1.311	1.699	2.045	2.462	2.756
30	1.310	1.697	2.042	2.457	2.750
40	1.303	1.684	2.021	2.423	2.704
60	1.296	1.671	2.000	2.390	2.660
120	1.289	1.658	1.980	2.358	2.617
∞	1.282	1.645	1.960	2.326	2.576

where v is the number of degrees of freedom.

Appendix 6

χ^2 critical values

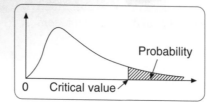

Probability ν	0.250	0.100	0.050	0.025	0.010	0.005	0.001
1	1.32	2.71	3.84	5.02	6.63	7.88	10.8
2	2.77	4.61	5.99	7.38	9.21	10.6	13.8
3	4.11	6.25	7.81	9.35	11.3	12.8	16.3
4	5.39	7.78	9.49	11.1	13.3	14.9	18.5
5	6.63	9.24	11.1	12.8	15.1	16.7	20.5
6	7.84	10.6	12.6	14.4	16.8	18.5	22.5
7	9.04	12.0	14.1	16.0	18.5	20.3	24.3
8	10.2	13.4	15.5	17.5	20.3	22.0	26.1
9	11.4	14.7	16.9	19.0	21.7	23.6	27.9
10	12.5	16.0	18.3	20.5	23.2	25.2	29.6
11	13.7	17.3	19.7	21.9	24.7	26.8	31.3
12	14.8	18.5	21.0	23.3	26.2	28.3	32.9
13	16.0	19.8	22.4	24.7	27.7	29.8	34.5
14	17.1	21.1	23.7	26.1	29.1	31.3	36.1
15	18.2	22.3	25.0	27.5	30.6	32.8	37.7
16	19.4	23.5	26.3	28.8	32.0	34.3	39.3
17	20.5	24.8	27.6	30.2	33.4	35.7	40.8
18	21.6	26.0	28.9	31.5	34.8	37.2	42.3
19	22.7	27.2	30.1	32.9	36.2	38.6	43.8
20	23.8	28.4	31.4	34.2	37.6	40.0	45.3
21	24.9	29.6	32.7	35.5	38.9	41.4	46.8
22	26.0	30.8	33.9	36.8	40.3	42.8	48.3
23	27.1	32.0	35.2	38.1	41.6	44.2	49.7
24	28.2	33.2	36.4	39.4	43.0	45.6	51.2

25	29.3	34.4	37.7	40.6	44.3	46.9	52.6
26	30.4	35.6	38.9	41.9	45.6	48.3	54.1
27	31.5	36.7	40.1	43.2	47.0	49.6	55.5
28	32.6	37.9	41.3	44.5	48.3	51.0	56.9
29	33.7	39.1	42.6	45.7	49.6	52.3	58.3
30	34.8	40.3	43.8	47.0	50.9	53.7	59.7
40	45.6	51.8	55.8	59.3	63.7	66.8	73.4
50	56.3	63.2	67.5	71.4	76.2	79.5	86.7
60	67.0	74.4	79.1	83.3	88.4	92.0	99.6
70	77.6	85.5	90.5	95.0	100	104	112
80	88.1	96.6	102	107	112	116	125
90	98.6	108	113	118	124	128	137
100	109	118	124	130	136	140	149

where v is the number of degrees of freedom.

Appendix 7

Table of random numbers

83635	18471	01664	97316	13751	22904	46465	55782	13047	64812
66791	25482	48893	34611	07709	24016	81064	00876	11197	35664
46879	05246	13006	17669	16587	25597	24106	67913	05438	97013
98520	97410	96305	57421	23489	67492	31647	85500	69477	55523
68227	06488	52064	30027	66988	20333	47881	20944	67822	01668
20034	17909	14246	28346	10972	38106	20079	99555	24768	25009
03504	71668	64982	34679	97643	18164	28640	27913	64820	57913
59731	12389	60071	04587	32881	66749	12400	64478	94613	00457
00456	67910	17219	89404	62840	37898	74613	01346	78994	00657
98015	67623	15678	01541	34613	26546	51255	25245	53345	42031
19994	64313	43100	32065	40324	60354	60106	14659	01346	43213
79844	57645	00247	61683	09830	98401	87410	01964	30687	46280
19601	68163	54387	46338	46324	57621	05151	23544	57987	98037
69771	02344	00168	98884	23467	90120	34970	35668	76137	90173
14865	05576	58425	97031	26459	73156	87109	01348	76218	40245
83116	77102	00886	01134	46905	58766	41003	28979	84341	28752
46103	25571	93826	40319	73150	46283	79134	67229	87766	35441
90087	51685	24641	35794	58525	81000	17991	77851	00356	48440
16624	00975	11300	24687	12665	78941	12265	02399	54613	87291
03154	67913	83739	19726	48505	64213	58467	91349	72344	31164

Index

absolute deviation 53
absolute magnitude in time series
    120–1
acceptance regions
  one-tailed tests 200
  two-tailed tests 197–9
average rate of return (ARR) 81–2
addition
  of fractions 316–17
  of negative numbers 315
additive model in time series 119–21
  absolute magnitude in 120–1
age distribution, changes in 182–3
algebra 325–9
  quadratic factorisation in 328–9
  simplification in 327
  substitution in 326
  transposition in 326–7
    rules 326–7
alternative hypothesis 196
AND rule 142–4, 145
arithmetic mean 39–41
  for grouped data 41
  for ungrouped data 40
arithmetic progressions 338–9
  proof of 339
  sum of 338
ARM® 36

backward induction 150–4
bar charts 10–14
  and company performance 14
base 322
BHP Billiton 291
bias in sampling 178
'Big data' 253
binomial distribution 165–70
  cumulative tables for 166–7
  discrete data in 168
  normal approximation to 167–70
    continuity correction 168–70
binomial probabilities, cumulative 346
Blanchflower, D. 107–8
break-even analysis 222–31
  break-even point (BEP) 225–30
  revenue, cost and profit 222–5

break-even point (BEP) 225–30
  budgeted output 226
  contribution per unit 226
  margin of safety 226–30
budgeted output in BEP 226

calculus 338
capital constraint line 235
carbon emissions 73
carrying costs in inventory control 272
cars
  electric 177
    charging points 184–5
  making 190
cash flow 78–9
  nominal terms 80–1
Central Limit Theorem 187–90
central location 36
  for company comparisons 50–1
  measures of 39–46
  notation 37–9
  ungrouped data 42–3
certain events 138
chance nodes 150
Chi-squared (χ^2) test 210–16
  critical values 211–13, 350–1
  data in table or matrix form 213–15
  degrees of freedom 211, 213–14
  as non-parametric test 210
  observed and expected values 210, 211
  statistic for 210–11
class boundaries 7
class frequency 8, 20
class intervals 7
class width (size) 7
coefficient of determination R^2 110–11, 114–15
  finding: coding formula 112
coefficient of variation (C of V) 60–1
  risk assessment and 60–2
component bar charts 11–13
components of time series 118–19
compound factors in financial decision making 71
compound interest 71–3
  compound factors 71
  end values 72–3
  formula for 72

conditional probability (dependent events) 144–54
  decision trees in 146–8
confidence intervals
  under normal distribution 158–9
  for population mean 193–5
    finding 195
    95% interval 194
    99% interval 194
  for sample mean 190–3
    95% interval 190–1
    99% interval 192
  in sampling 190–6
confidence limits in hypothesis testing 197
continuous data 6
  in normal distribution 168
contribution per unit in BEP 226
convenience sampling 184
corner point solutions in linear programming 237–46
correlation 108–16
  coefficient of determination R^2 110–11, 114–15
    finding: coding formula 112
  forecasting 127–9
  Pearson's coefficient of correlation *(R)* 111–15
    finding: coding formula 112
  Spearman's coefficient of rank correlation
    116–18
  and spreadsheets 114
  time series 118–26
cost
  in break-even analysis 222–5
    and linearity 224
    types 223–4
  differentiation in 262–7
crash costs in project management 309
crash time in project management 309
crashing in project management 310
Critical Path Analysis 298–305
  critical path 299–300
    definition 299
    earliest finish time 301–3
    float times, identifying 301–3
    identifying 299–300
    latest finish time 301–3
  progress, checking 303
critical values
  in hypothesis testing 197, 198, 201–2
    level of significance for 201–2
  in Student *t* distribution 208, 211–13
    level of significance for 211–12
cross-price elasticity of demand 275
Crossrail 288
cross-sectional data 118
cubic functions 335, 336

cumulative binomial probabilities 346
cumulative cash flow 80
cumulative frequency curves 25–7
  and percentiles 27–8
cumulative Poisson probabilities 347
customer retention 180
cyclical component of time series 119

data
collection of 5–7
  presenting
    in bar charts and pie charts 10–18
    in frequency tables 7–10
    in histograms 18–24
    using frequency polygons and curves 24–8
    using Lorenz curve 28–30
  types 5–6
decimals 317–18
  changing to percentages 320
  rounding 318
decision trees
  boxes 149
  circles 150
  in conditional probability 146–8
  and expected value 149–50
  pay-offs 150
definite integrals 279–81
degrees of freedom in Chi-squared (χ^2) test 211,
  213–14
dependent events 144–54
  backward induction 150–4
  expected value 148–9
dependent variable in functions 334
derivatives 256
  of a function of a function 262
  in partial differentiation 275
  of product 261
  of quotient 261
  of sum or difference 260–1
difference, derivative of 260–1
differentiation 253–76
  applications 262–74
  general formula of 257
  gradients 253–7
  inventory control 271–3
  limits 253–7
  marginal analysis 268
  partial differentiation 274–6
  price elasticity of demand 269–71
  process of 256
  proof of formula for 281–2
  rules of 260–2
  turning points 258–60

digital news 252
discount factor 75–6
    formula for 75
discount rate and NPV 87
discounted cash flow tables 84–7
discounting 75–6
discounting process 82
discounting techniques in financial decision making
        82–91
    discounted cash flow 84–7
    internal rate of return (IRR) 87–90
    net present value (NPV) 82–4
discrete data 6
    in binomial distribution 168
dispersion 36
    for company comparisons 59–60
    measures of 52–60
    notation 37–9
    for ungrouped data 58–9
division
    of fractions 317
    of powers 323
dummy activities in network diagrams 296–8

earliest finish time in critical path 301–3
economic order quantity (EOQ) 273
    formula for, derivation of 283
EDF 294
end values in compound interest 72–3
equations
    simultaneous 331–3
    solving 329–31
equilibrium price 331
equivalent fractions 317
expansion of brackets in algebra 327–8
expected profit and backward induction 150–1
expected values 148–9
    and decision trees 149–50
    and game theory 155–7
    in χ^2 test 210, 211
experimental probability 137
exponential functions 335, 336
exponents 322

Facebook 263
factorisation 327, 328
    of quadratic equations 330
feasible region in linear programming 235–6
financial decision making 66–8
    cash flow 78–9
    compound factors 71
    discounting 75–6
    and investment 68–70

non-discounting techniques 79–82
    present value 76–7
Financial Times 13, 97, 253, 294
Financial Times Share Service 60
fixed cost in break-even analysis 223
float times
    in Gantt charts 304
    for non-critical activities 301–3
        earliest finish time 301–3
        latest finish time 301–3
food vouchers 230
forecasting
    in correlation 127–9
    in regression analysis 105
fractional powers 324
fractions 316–17
    cancelling 317
    changing to percentages 320
frequencies 6–7
frequency curves 25–7
frequency density 20
frequency polygons
    presenting data in 24–5
frequency tables
    constructing 8–9
    presenting data in 7–10
Fukushima disaster 294
function of a function, derivative of
        262
functions 334–8
    differentiation of 338
future earnings 5–6

game theory 155–7
    and expected value 155–6
    stable equilibrium in 156
Gantt charts 304–6
Gauss, Robert 104
geometic progressions 339–41
    proof of 341
    sum of 340–1
Gini coefficient 29
gradients in differentiation 253–7
graduates, lifetime income 9
graphs 334–8
    gradients to 337–8
Griffiths, A. 29
grouped data
    arithmetic mean for 41
    mean deviation for 54
    median for 43–4
        formula for 44
    variance for 56–7

hazards 137
heterogeneous sampling 180, 181
Higher Education Statistics Agency 7
histograms
    presenting data in 18–24
    properties 19
holding costs in inventory control 272
Human Development Report (UN) 17
hyperbolic functions 335, 336
hypothesis testing 196–216
    Chi-squared (χ^2) test 210–16
    confidence limits 197
    critical values 197, 198
    errors in 196
    one-tailed tests 199–201
      acceptance and rejection regions 200
    seven-step plan for 201–6
    two-tailed tests 197–9
      acceptance and rejection regions 198–9

impossible events 138
indefinite integrals 279–80
independent events (AND rule) 142–4, 145
independent variable in functions 334
indices 322
inequalities 333–4
    involving χ^2 334
insurance 136
integers 314
integration 276–81
    area under a curve 280–1
    definite integrals 279–81
    functions of more than one term 278–9
    general formula for 278
    as opposite of differentiation 276
    value of C, finding 279
Intel 36
interest rates and project appraisal 70–3
internal rate of return (IRR) 87–90
    as decision criteria 89–90
International Energy Agency (IEA) 69, 78, 84
International Monetary Fund (IMF) 304
interquartile range 52
inventory control, differentiation in 271–3
    cost types 272–3
investment
    appraisal
      discounting techniques 82–91
      non-discounting techniques 79–82
     and financial decision making 68–70
     and time value of money 69
investment process 68
irregular component of time series 119

labour constraint line 234–5
latest finish time in critical path 301–3
least squares line in regression analysis
    coding formula 102
    finding 101–4
    and spreadsheets 104–5
left-hand tail under normal distribution 160
Legrendre, A.-M. 104
level of significance in hypothesis testing 196
    for critical values 197, 201–2
      in Chi-squared (χ^2) test 211–12
limits in differentiation 253–7
line graphs 16–17
linear equations 330
    in regression analysis 100
linear functions 334, 335
    graph of 337
linear inequalities 333–4
linear programming 231–7
    maximisation 237–46
    minimisation 246–9
    objective function, deriving 232–3
      position of 233
    structural constraints, deriving 234–6
linear relationships 221
    break-even analysis 222–31
    linear programming 231–7
      maximisation 237–46
      minimisation 246–9
live concerts and festivals 135–6
London 2012 Olympics 291
Lorenz curve 28–30
lower class boundaries (LCB) 44
lower quartile 27

margin of safety in BEP 226–30
marginal analysis, differentiation in 268
maxima in differentiation 258–60
maximisation in linear programming
    237–46
    corner point solutions 237–46
mean deviation 53
    for grouped data 54
    for ungrouped data 53
median 27, 42–4
    for grouped data 43–4
      formula for 44
    for ungrouped data 42–3
mergers & acquisitions 97, 109, 125
Microsoft Project® software 305
minima in differentiation 258–60
minimisation in linear programming
    246–9

mobile phones
  and food supply 55
  online shopping, growth of 50
  rare earth metals in 46
  text messages, growth 40
mode 44
monetary costs 69
monetary returns 69
moving average in time series 121–2
  finding trend 124
multiple bar charts 13
multiple regression 99, 105–8
multiplication
  of fractions 317
  of powers 323
multiplicative model in time series 119–21
  percentages in 120–1
mutually exclusive events (OR rule) 138–41

National Health Service (NHS) 289
National Literacy Trust 263
National Student Survey (NSS) 18–19
negative number arithmetic 315–16
negative powers 323
negatively skewed distributions 47
net present value (NPV) 82–4
  as decision criteria 89–90
  and discount rate 87
  formula for 84
net revenues 80
network diagrams in project management 295–8
  basic rules 295
  critical path analysis 298–305
  drawing 295–6
  dummy activities 296–8
News Corp 267
non-discounting techniques in financial decision
      making 79–82
  average rate of return (ARR) 81–2
  payback period 79–81
non-linear functions, graph of 338
non-linear relationships 252–3
non-mutually exclusive events (OR rule) 141–2
non-negative constraints 236
non-probability sampling 182
non-random sampling 180
normal approximation
  to binomial distribution 167–70
    continuity correction 168–70
  to Poisson distribution 171–2
normal distribution 158–65
  areas and probability under 158
  confidence intervals under 158–9

continuous data in 168
in PERT 307
sample means in 185–90
standard distribution 159–63
using 163
variable value when probability is known 164–5
normal distributions 46–52
  probabilities 344–5
nth root 324
null hypothesis 196
  in Chi-squared (χ^2) test 210, 211
number line 315

observed values in χ^2 test 210, 211
Ocado 221–2
oil prices, rises in 84
Olympic Delivery Authority 291–2
one-tailed hypothesis testing 199–201
  acceptance and rejection regions 200
  critical values 201–2
OR rule 138–41
  mutually exclusive events 138–41
  non-mutually exclusive events 141–2
ordering costs in inventory (stock) control 272
Oswald, A. 107–8
own-price elasticity of demand 275

partial differentiation 274–6
  derivatives, calculating 275
payback period 79–81
Pearson (Publishers) 260
Pearson's coefficient of correlation *(R)* 111–15
  finding: coding formula 112
Pearson's coefficient of skewness (SK) 47–8
percentage increase and decrease 321
percentage of 320
percentages 319–21
  changes of form 320–1
  changing to decimals 320
  changing to fractions 320
  interest rates as 70
  as a percentage 321
  reverse 321
  in time series 120–1
percentiles 27–8
pie charts 14–16
point price elasticity of demand, differentiation on
      270
Poisson distribution 170–3
  normal approximation to 171–2
Poisson probabilities, cumulative 347
population mean, confidence intervals for 193–5
population standard deviation 194

Portas Review 233
positively skewed distributions 47
Poundland 223–4
power zero 323
powers 322–4
    rules for 323–4
pre-MBA programme 4
present value 76–7
    formula for 77
price elasticity of demand (PED), differentiation on
        269–71
primary data 5
prioritising in project management 310–11
probability 137–41
    dependent events 144–54
        expected value 148–9
    distribution, choosing 172
    independent events (AND rule) 142–4, 145
    mutually exclusive events (OR rule) 138–41
    non-mutually exclusive events (OR rule) 141–2
    and uncertainty 149
    Venn diagrams 141–2
        area of overlap 141
probability sampling 182
probability tables for PERT 307
product, derivative of 261
profits 80
    in break-even analysis 222–5
    differentiation in 262–7
progressions 338–41
project appraisal and interest rates 70–3
Project Evaluation and Review Technique (PERT)
        306–9
    expected duration, estimating 306–7
    probability tables for 307
    variance and standard deviation 307–8
project management
    crashing 309–10
    critical path in see Critical Path Analysis
    dependencies 293
    estimating 293–4
    Gantt charts 304–6
    key stages 288
    managers, issues faced by 288
    network diagrams for see network diagrams
    non-critical activities 310
    objectives 289
    planning 291–5
    prioritising 310–11
    project costs 309–11
    project definition 289–90
    projects, defining 287–90
    software 305–6

    advantages of 306
    success factors 290
    success rate 295, 306
Project Management Institute (PMI) 286, 295, 306
pure chance 149
purposive sampling 183
    extreme case 183
    typical case 183

quadratic equations 330
    formula for solving 330–1
quadratic factorisation 328–9
quadratic functions 334–5
quota sampling 182–3
    features 183
quotient, derivative of 261

random number table 352
    in sampling 178
random sampling 178–80
    features 178–9
    stages 178
range 52
rare earth metals 46
ratios 321–2
reading on computers 263
reciprocal (hyperbolic) functions 335, 336
regression analysis 98–108
    forecasting 105
    least squares line
        coding formula 102
        finding 101–4
        and spreadsheets 104–5
    multiple regression 99, 105–8
    simple linear regression 99–101
rejection regions
    one-tailed tests 200
    two-tailed tests 197–9
relative dispersion 60
revenue
    in break-even analysis 222–5
        and linearity 224–5
    differentiation in 262–7
right-hand tail under normal distribution 160
risk 137
roots 324–5
rounding off 318–19

sample means, distribution of 185–90
    standard deviation of 186
    standard error 185–6
    in Student t distribution 206–7
sample standard deviation 194

sampling
    and Central Limit Theorem 187–90
        in skewed populations 188
    confidence intervals 190–6
        for population mean 193–5
        for sample mean 190–3
    small samples 206
    types 178–85
sampling frame 178
scatter graphs 16–17
scenarios 153
seasonal component of time series 118–19
    adjusted, finding 126
    finding and eliminating 124, 126
    in forecasting 127–9
secondary data 5
segmented sampling 180
self-selection sampling 184
semi-interquartile range 52
The Shard 309
Siegel, Eric 108, 254
significant figures 318–19
simple bar charts 10–11
simple interest 70–1
    formula for 71
simple linear regression 99–101
simplification in algebra 327
simultaneous equations 331–3
    in linear programming 238
skewed distributions 46–52
    Central Limit Theorem in 188
    measurement of skew 47–50
snowball sampling 183
software for project management 305–6
Spearman's coefficient of rank correlation 116–18
spreadsheets
    and correlation 114
    and least squares line 104–5
square roots 324
stable equilibrium in game theory 156
standard class width 20
standard deviation 57–9
    in PERT 307–8
standard error 185–6
    in t distribution 206
standard normal distribution 159–63
stock control, differentiation in 271–3
stock-out costs in inventory control 272
stratified random sampling 180–2
    features 181–2
    steps in 180
structural constraints in linear programming 234–6
    capital constraint line 235

feasible region 235–6
    labour constraint line 234–5
    non-negative constraints 236
Student t distribution 306–10
    critical values 208, 348–9
    t statistic 208
    t tables 208–9
subject of formula 326
substitution in algebra 326
subtraction
    of fractions 316–17
    of negative numbers 315
sum, derivative of 260–1
surveys 6–7

t statistic 208
t tables 208–9
tabular form of data in Chi-squared (χ^2) test
    214
tally charts 6
Tesco 237, 240
theoretical probability 137–8
time profile of money 69
time series data 118
time series in correlation 118–26
    additive or multiplicative model 119–21
    components 118–19
    moving average 121–2
    trend, finding 122–4
    variations, finding 124–6
transposition in algebra 326–7
    rules 326–7
trend in time series
    as component 118
    finding 122–4
    using moving averages 124
turning points in differentiation 258–60
two-tailed hypothesis testing 197–9
    acceptance and rejection regions 198–9
    critical values 201–2
type 1 error in hypothesis tests 196
type 2 error in hypothesis tests 196

unbiased selection in sampling 179
uncertainty 149
unemployment and home ownership 108
unequal-width histograms 19–21
ungrouped data
    arithmetic mean for 40
    dispersion for 58–9
    mean deviation for 53
    median for 42–3
    variance for 55–6

upper class boundaries (UCB) 44
upper quartile 27

variable cost in break-even analysis 223
variable value when probability known 164–5
variance 55–7
   for grouped data 56–7
   in PERT 307–8
   for ungrouped data 55–6

variations in time series, finding 124–6
Venn diagrams 141–2
   area of overlap 141

whole numbers 314–16

Z score (statistic) under normal distribution 159–60
   for one- and two-tailed tests 201–2
   for sample means 185, 186–7